METEOROLOGY
WITH MARINE APPLICATIONS

Crepuscular rays illuminate a merchant marine convoy.

Official U.S. Navy Photograph.

(Frontispiece)

Marvelous are the offices and wonderful is the constitution of the atmosphere. Indeed, I know of no subject more fit for profitable thought on the part of the truth-loving, knowledge-seeking student, be he seaman or landsman, than that afforded by the atmosphere and its offices. Of all parts of the physical machinery, of all the contrivances in the mechanism of the universe, the atmosphere, with its offices and its adaptations, appears to me to be the most wonderful, sublime, and beautiful. (*Maury, The Physical Geography of the Sea.*)

METEOROLOGY
with Marine Applications

BY

WILLIAM L. DONN, Ph.D.

Associate Professor, Department of Geology,
Brooklyn College
Formerly Head of Meteorology Section,
U.S. Merchant Marine Academy
Research Associate,
Columbia University

SECOND EDITION

New York   *Toronto*   *London*
McGRAW-HILL BOOK COMPANY, INC.
1951

METEOROLOGY: WITH MARINE APPLICATIONS

IX

17599

To Tina
MY MOTHER

PREFACE TO THE SECOND EDITION

The modifications in this edition include a complete revision of Chapter 12, *Weather Coding and Notation,* and minor changes and additions in a few places throughout the text.

As of January 1, 1949, the new International Weather Code, both land and marine, replaced the previous code in effect since 1942. The forms of reports from both land and marine stations were also changed considerably. The station model used on maps was revised as a result of the use of modified and new symbols. As a consequence, Chapter 12 has been completely rewritten and includes all changes and new information, together with most of the important supplements as of August, 1950.

Nearly all the new information pertaining to codes and forms was provided through the cooperation of the Offices of The United States Weather Bureau at Battery Park and New York International Airport in New York.

WILLIAM L. DONN.

Brooklyn College,
BROOKLYN, N.Y.,
March, 1951.

PREFACE TO THE FIRST EDITION

During the past 20 years the science of meteorology has progressed with giant strides, but there is still much ground to be covered. Although many excellent books, treating of the modern general and special phases of the subject, have been written, there is a pronounced dearth of such works containing marine applications. Modern emphasis has been placed on aeronautical meteorology, following the lead of the rapid developments in aviation, in which field a knowledge of atmospheric conditions is vital.

Now, meteorology is meteorology. There is actually no marine nor any other kind of meteorology, but rather there are applications of the subject to different fields of endeavor, *i.e.*, marine, aviation, agriculture, forestry, flood control, water supply, etc. In the same way, for example, there is no marine mathematics, although the application of certain phases of mathematics, particularly trigonometry, provides the basis of navigation.

Thus, although there are many previous works in this field, it is felt that the justification for this, a new book, is twofold: (1) It treats of the marine phases of meteorology in addition to the general exposition of the subject; (2) it is written in what is believed and hoped to be a simpler and more readable style than is usually encountered. Thus, the book should be of value to the occasional lay reader, as well as to the mariner and student. Formal academic style has been avoided as much as possible. However, the brevity associated with academic discussion has often required its use where simpler language would have yielded overlong explanations.

Repetition of ideas, facts, and principles will be encountered. This is in accord with the theory that the learning process involves two fundamental processes: repetition and concentration. The book supplies much of the repetition; the reader must supply the concentration, although the explanations given attempt to aid him in this process.

Since visual aids have proved to be of great value in teaching, particularly during the war training programs, a large number of diagrams, charts, maps, and photographs have been incorporated with the text. Many of the maps and photographs appear here for the first time in published form.

For those desiring an even further simplification of treatment, Chap. 4, on Atmospheric Equilibrium, may be entirely omitted without affecting the rest of the text.

WILLIAM L. DONN.

BROOKLYN, N.Y.,
January, 1946.

ACKNOWLEDGMENTS

Lieut. Graham V. Lowe, USNR, of the U.S. Merchant Marine Academy has given invaluable assistance in his very careful and critical reading of most of the manuscript, and in his proofreading of all of the page proofs. I wish to thank Professors Haurwitz and Austin of the Massachusetts Institute of Technology for their permission to reproduce a number of plates from their "Climatology." I also feel indebted to my brother, Bertram Donn, of the Harvard College Observatory, for the enlightening discussions held over some of the more technical portions of the manuscript. My deepest gratitude is offered both to the U.S. Navy Department and to the U.S. Weather Bureau for their kind permission to reproduce a host of photographs, maps, and other illustrations. In addition, certain printed extracts appearing in the text have been obtained from Weather Bureau publications. The tables of weather summaries in the appendix have been compiled mostly from the "Sailing Directions" published by the U.S. Hydrographic Office. Probably greatest of all is my debt to the modern writers and authorities in the field of meteorology. I am fully aware of their effect on this book. Unfortunately, after years of teaching, ideas and techniques gleaned from various sources become incorporated into one's own methods, with such sources being forgotten, or worse, being considered original with oneself. Let me again express my appreciation to the writers and recent pioneers in the field, many of whom provided, indirectly, the foundations of this book.

WILLIAM L. DONN.

CONTENTS

CONTENTS

LIST OF TABLES

METEOROLOGY
WITH MARINE APPLICATIONS

CHAPTER 1

INTRODUCTION AND BASIC PRINCIPLES

Scope and Purpose of the Book

Meteorology is the study of the air and of the changes that take place in the air. Since the daily variations of the different conditions of the air are what are known as "weather," it is with this second phase of the subject that we shall be especially concerned.

One cannot doubt the importance of meteorology to the well-trained mariner. When at sea, his common natural surroundings are the sea and the air. Of the two, it is the air that has the more fundamental relationship to the seaman since the condition of the sea surface is merely a reflection of the prevailing and past conditions of the atmosphere. There is scarcely a seasoned mariner who has not at some time experienced the full fury of the air when out on the open seas.

Obviously, then, a knowledge of the weather and its expected changes will contribute greatly to efficient navigation and seamanship. The officer who can figure the wind, waves, and fog, among other things, will be able to make his runs in the shortest possible time and with the greatest efficiency. He will also know how best to avoid "tangling" with the destructive storms common in the lower latitudes. Clearly, the officer who "knows the weather" will give greater assurance of safety to vessel, passengers, and cargo, which is one of the prime functions of merchant marine officers. This will greatly enhance his personal reputation and his company's as well.

The facts of meteorology are also of great value to the merchant officer in determining the proper care and ventilation of cargo. Vast damage can be caused by overlooking the effect of temperature and humidity of the air on cargo care. Further, merchant vessels are often the only source for the observations on which the pilot charts of the seas are constructed; and the extensive development of ocean airways will depend to a great extent on air observations made by modern officers of merchant vessels.

Since a complete knowledge of weather conditions over a large area depends on observations from many points, they must be taken accurately and correctly to be of any value. We may also note that there exists no other way to obtain continuous records of oceanic air conditions, for the further advancement of the science of meteorology itself, than

3

through the accurate observations made by merchant vessels. For example, the dread hurricane is almost entirely a maritime feature. Relatively little is known of the origin of such storms, there seldom being trained observers at the marine localities where they develop. A better understanding of their origin will yield quicker and more accurate Weather Bureau warnings for the eventual profit of the mariner.

The modern mariner will not become an expert weather forecaster from this general study, for that requires years of specialized training. But he will gain sufficient knowledge concerning his atmospheric environment to be of invaluable aid to him, whether navigating small craft or large.

This book is therefore intended to include such material as will enable the reader

1. To obtain a good understanding of the weather changes and their causes

2. To take weather observations properly and accurately

3. To make local short-period weather predictions based on these and other observations received by radio

4. To relate weather information to the problems of seamanship and navigation.

Functions and Importance of the Atmosphere

We take the atmosphere very much for granted. In so doing, many of its important functions are usually overlooked, just as the forest is often invisible because of the trees. From the biological viewpoint alone, the atmosphere is of tremendous significance. The air—particularly the oxygen component—supports life as we know it. All living organisms, whether advanced or primitive in development, require oxygen for survival. Although the manner of obtaining this gas may vary, the purpose for which it is absorbed is the same. Not only does the atmosphere supply the vital oxygen, but it also provides living things with the equally important *fresh* water. The importance of our atmosphere to biologic existence cannot be doubted.

Geographically, the contours of the earth's surface, with its timeless changes, are the result of that greatest of "sculptors," the atmosphere. From time immemorial the effect of the wind, rain, and running water resulting from rain, has been to modify continuously the relief features of the earth. Flat areas are made more rugged; rugged areas are rounded and flattened through the ceaseless operations of these atmospheric agencies. We have only to regard the moon to be convinced of this effect. That desolate world no longer maintains an atmosphere. As a consequence, the features it exhibits are static and changeless. No molding of the lunar landscape occurs. The shape of our coast lines is under continuous modification through the work of the air. The winds that prevail therein cause waves and currents whose action is to smooth irregular, rugged coastlines and to make more irregular the appearance of those originally straight and uniform.

Much of our great natural wealth is dependent on the conditions of the atmosphere. The accumulation of huge mineral and ore reserves has frequently been the direct result of the amount of water in the air. Where abundant supplies of moisture have existed, great accumulations of economically valuable minerals have been deposited through the chemical actions of rain water soaking into the rock. And conversely, in arid regions, the increased evaporation of ground water leaves behind valuable mineral deposits. Again, from an economic standpoint, international trade could not have flourished nor existed prior to steam power, were it not for the wind that filled the sails for the ancient mariners.

Many of the natural wonders of the world are products of atmospheric agencies. The brilliant colors and weird carvings of the rock mantle, the huge natural bridges, and awe-inspiring canyons and hosts of other features, are the results of the same forces already mentioned. The beauty of the sky itself and the phenomena displayed above us are caused directly by the optical properties of the air. Refraction, diffusion, and dispersion of light within the atmosphere give rise to the colorful sunsets and sunrises, mirages, rainbows, etc. The phenomenon of daylight is merely the diffusion of sunlight by the minute particles that constitute the atmosphere. Were there no air, constant darkness of the sky would prevail, despite the brilliance of the sun.

Lastly, we cannot overlook that very important feature, the continuous changing conditions within the air—the weather—which exerts such a powerful influence on all things, animate and inanimate. Our atmosphere is certainly deserving of a large amount of attention, interest, and study.

Nature of the Atmosphere

Before any attention can be given to the actual weather processes, the nature of the atmosphere itself, in which all our weather occurs, should be at least briefly examined. The air can be considered as a huge shell or envelope of gases surrounding the surface of the earth and extending to a measurable height of over 300 miles. There is, however, no sharp defining limit to the atmosphere; it simply "peters out" more and more slowly with increasing altitude, becoming less and less dense until there is no longer any detectable amount of air left. This decrease of the air with altitude is so rapid that one-half of the whole atmosphere lies within a height of $3\frac{1}{2}$ miles, (or about 18,000 feet); half of what is left lies within the next $3\frac{1}{2}$ miles. In other words, beneath an altitude of

7 miles there exists three-fourths of the entire atmosphere.   This conveys some idea of the extreme rarity or tenuous nature of air at great heights above sea level, even though it does exist in minute measurable amounts as high as 300 miles, and beyond.   The height to which the atmosphere extends has been determined by different indirect methods.   Meteors are luminous only while in the atmosphere, owing to the heat and light of the friction produced by their rapid passage.   One measurement is therefore the result of noting the maximum altitude at which meteors are visible.   The determination of the heights at which the aurora borealis (northern lights) is visible provides another technique.   Another approach is to consider, mathematically, the height at which the density or pressure of the air becomes nil.   Scattering of the sun's rays high in the atmosphere at twilight also gives indications as to its thickness.

We normally do not realize how great is the gaseous medium surrounding us.   Actually, the mass of the atmosphere is 5.6×10^{14} tons.   In later chapters further considerations will be given to the pressure and wind effects of this huge air body.

COMPOSITION.—Of what is the air composed?   It is a mixture of many gases in varying amounts.   The composition of the atmosphere by volume is shown in Table I.

TABLE I.   COMPOSITION OF THE ATMOSPHERE

Per Cent

Fixed components of dry air:
Nitrogen.................................... 78
Oxygen....................................... 21
Argon and other rare gases................... 1
Variable component (moist air):
Water vapor............................... To 4 (of moist air)

The rare gases include mostly argon with very small amounts of xenon, helium, and krypton.   Carbon dioxide also occurs in the atmosphere, but it is limited to about 0.03 per cent.

The water vapor in the air is the most variable part of the air and is therefore not included in the so-called "fixed components" of the atmosphere; it varies at times from a small fraction of 1 per cent up to 4 per cent, for moist air.

In addition to these regular constituents, the air supports several types of material which, although in the air, are nevertheless foreign to it.   Some of these are salt crystals, dust particles, and water droplets.   The air has been defined as a mixture of vapors or gases.   Obviously then, these particles in the air cannot be considered as part of the gaseous atmosphere.   A speck of dust in one's eye is not part of the eye merely because of its presence; just as the speck of dust may have an important effect on one's eye, so do the foreign particles in the atmosphere have a very basic influence on it and the changes therein. This importance will be brought out later.

The effect of water droplets in the air is somewhat more obvious. When the water vapor, which is part of the air, changes its state from a gas to a liquid or solid, the resulting water or ice particles become foreign to the air and provide our clouds, fog, rain, snow, dew, etc. Hence,

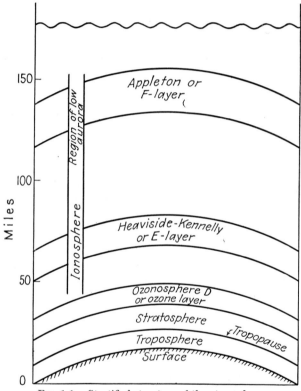

FIG. 1-1.—Stratified structure of the atmosphere.

water has a somewhat dual characteristic in the air, depending on its state, and is also of very fundamental importance in determining weather conditions.

STRUCTURE OF THE ATMOSPHERE.—In addition to its varying composition, the air has a nonuniform structure. That is, it is actually composed of many strata or layers, of which we are interested in only the lowest one. This lowest layer has an average thickness or height of 7 miles, being much thicker at the equator than at the poles, and is known as the "troposphere." Directly overlying the troposphere is the stratosphere, extending to about 20 miles, which is separated from the troposphere by a thin transition zone called the "tropopause."

Above the stratosphere lies the ozonosphere or ozone layer, and the but recently investigated ionosphere. The latter itself is divided into distinct layers separated by wide intervals. They are known, respectively, as the "E" or "Heaviside" layer, and the "F" or "Appleton" layer. Recent investigation indicates the Appleton layer to consist of two distinct strata. It is the electrical properties of these last subdivisions of the ionosphere that permit of long-range radio transmission. Figure 1-1 shows the relative positions of the different strata within the atmosphere.

All the weather features to be studied are common only to the troposphere, for it is in this lower part of the atmosphere that ordinary weather changes occur. Most of the weather phenomena disappear above this zone, explaining one of the reasons for the desirability of airplane flights through the stratosphere.

The basic difference between these two air layers is one of temperature change. As a rule, the temperature in the troposphere decreases steadily with increasing altitude until the tropopause is reached. It then stops declining and remains constant or nearly so with increasing elevation above the tropopause, in the stratosphere. The stratosphere is thus referred to as an isothermal (equal temperature) layer.

Weather Elements

We have noted that the word "weather" refers to the short-period variations in the atmosphere. But just what varies? There are certain phases of the atmosphere on which observations are made, that are subject to constant change, their state at any time determining the state of the weather. These variable factors are

1. Temperature of the air
2. Humidity of the air
3. Horizontal visibility (fog, etc.)
4. Clouds and state of the sky
5. Kind and amount of precipitation
6. Atmospheric pressure
7. Winds

Although other strictly observational features are frequently added to this list, these are the seven basic weather elements that will be studied, together with the factors affecting and related to them. It is principally on these elements that observations and reports are made. The actual observations and reports may be brief or complex depending on the instruments available and the purpose for which they are made. Of the seven elements listed, two are of particular importance in making observations for the purpose of local short-period predictions, when no reports are obtainable. These are the clouds and the wind direction. One of the purposes of this book is to teach the marine observer enough about the processes underlying weather changes to enable him to use his observations to advantage in foretelling weather conditions.

These weather elements are not to be considered as separate entities. On the contrary, they are closely interrelated. Of the seven mentioned, temperature is the most basic and fundamental and the variations of it cause changes in the other weather elements, the results of which we know as "weather."

It is well known that hot air can hold more water vapor than cold air. In many drying processes the blowing of hot air on the object greatly expedites evaporation of moisture. If warm air is cooled sufficiently, the excess water vapor that was present must settle out as liquid water droplets. Thus, temperature changes in the air are the direct cause of humidity variations, which in turn yield clouds, fog, and precipitation.

The temperature variations are also responsible for pressure differences. If a part of the air becomes relatively warmer than the surrounding air, it will expand, become lighter, and tend to rise from the earth. Cold air surrounding the warmer air will be relatively heavy. Consequently, the warm air will have less weight and show less downward pressure than the surrounding cold air, and will therefore (other things being equal) show lower barometer readings.

Now, whenever such a condition arises, there will clearly be a heaping up of air in one locality and a deficiency in a neighboring area. For example, consider an inverted bowl of water: when the bowl is removed, the water will flow outward from the center. Similarly, a flow of air tends to start along the earth's surface from the region of higher pressure (heavier air) to the region of lower pressure (lighter air). This horizontal movement of air is called "wind."

It has now been shown rather briefly that temperature changes cause humidity changes that result in clouds and precipitation, and also that temperature differences cause changes in pressure that result in winds.

The weather elements will be studied in more detail and in the order outlined, during the course. When a knowledge of these elements, the reasons for their changes, and their methods of observation are understood, the structure of storms and hurricanes and some of the principles underlying weather forecasting will be studied.

Heat and Its Transmission

Having mentioned the importance of heat and temperature distribution, let us examine briefly the nature of heat and temperature and the methods of heat transmission. Since continual reference will be made to these basic factors, an elementary review of them is necessary.

NATURE OF HEAT AND TEMPERATURE.—Heat and temperature are closely related terms that have always evaded simple definition. Our senses tell us whether something is hot or cold. But what is "cold"? It is simply a relative absence of heat. Then what is heat? Technically, heat is defined as the total energy of molecular motion within a body. All matter is composed of minute particles called "molecules," which are the smallest particles of a substance that still preserve the properties of the substance. These particles are in different states of motion. The greater the total motion of these molecules, the more heat is contained within the body.

Different sources may increase the heat of a substance. When an object is rubbed or struck, it becomes hotter as a result of friction, or as a result of the transfer of mechanical energy into heat energy. The energy of chemical reactions often results in much heat being produced. And, more important from our point of view, the absorption of solar energy raises the heat content of an object. In each case it is actually the increase of molecular motion of the material that raises the heat.

What is temperature? We may consider it to be a measurement of the amount of heat in a particular body. Actually temperature is a measure of the average or mean motion of the molecules within a substance. But it is temperature that determines the flow of heat from one object to another. Heat will flow only from a body of higher to a body of lower temperature. When one substance is colder than another we really mean that the temperature of the first is lower than the temperature of the second. Remember, temperature is a measurement, or a state; heat is an energy quantity.

PROCESSES OF HEAT TRANSMISSION.—Heat energy is transmitted from place to place by the processes of "radiation," "conduction," and "convection." Each of these three processes has an important function in determining processes affecting weather changes, and will be considered now in some detail.

Radiation.—This is the process of heat transfer in wave form, without the use or necessity of a transmitting medium. For example, all of the insolation received by the earth comes from the sun by radiation in wave form through the emptiness of space between the two bodies. When we stand near a very hot object, the intense heat felt is mostly the result of heat rays radiated by the hot object. By the use of infrared (or heat-sensitive) film in a camera in a pitch-dark room, it is possible to obtain an excellent photograph of an ordinary hot pressing iron merely by the heat rays radiated from the iron.

Conduction.—This is the process of transmitting heat through a medium by contact of the minute particles of which the medium is composed. For instance, if one end of a metal rod is heated, the other end will soon become hot. This is accomplished by conduction, in which the heat energy is passed (or conducted) along the rod from the heated to the cold end by the molecules within the rod. See Fig. 1–2.

Convection.—This is the process of transmitting heat by the actual motion of the heated material. When the air over a radiator is heated, it expands and rises to the ceiling. This motion is evident by the distortion of the light coming through the window and passing through the rising air. Similarly, images seen across an airport runway often waver owing to the disturbance caused by the warmed air rising from the heated runway. In the same way, when water or any liquid is heated, the

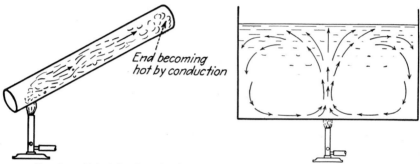

FIG. 1-2.—Principle of conduction. FIG. 1-3.—Typical convection system.

warm liquid at the bottom rises to the top and is replaced by cooler descending water. Gases exhibit convection as a means of heat transfer more so than liquids, and liquids more so than solids. In fact, convection, or the rising and falling of warm and cold air masses, respectively, is one of the most important and fundamental processes in the atmosphere.

The typical convection system is illustrated in Fig. 1–3, where the fluid over the flame becomes overheated and rises as it becomes lighter through expansion. The surrounding colder liquid falls and moves in to replace the rising material.

We can summarize these processes by an analogy. Let us consider that an object is given to the first person in a line of people, with orders to transmit it to the last man in the line. The first man may simply throw the object to the last one, with no one else involved; that would be radiation. Or he may pass it along from one person to the next, which would be conduction; or he may himself walk over and hand it to the last man, which would be similar to convection.

The earth heats the air. This can now be carried a bit further. The earth heats the lower part of the air in contact with it *basically* by the process of conduction. The air is also heated to some extent by radiation, although conduction is the more important process here. Then, the lower air, being overheated in some localities compared to others, may rise and by convection transmit this heat to greater heights. Conduction alone will not transmit heat to any considerable height for air is a good insulator or a very poor conductor of heat.

The heating of the atmosphere is similar to the convection system illustrated above. The flame heats the container by conduction. The heated container in turn heats the lower portion of the fluid by conduction, and when sufficiently heated, this fluid rises. The atmosphere behaves similarly.

Insolation—(the Energy Received from the Sun)

Having discussed the importance of temperature as a weather element, and the significance of heat as a basic weather regulator, we must naturally examine the origin of the heat and the method by which it is received.

The source of the significant heat and light received at the earth's surface is the sun. The name given to all this radiant energy we receive from the sun is "insolation." Paradoxical as it may seem, it is, as we have noted above, not the sun that heats the air, but the earth. The sun heats the earth and the earth in its turn is responsible for heating the overlying air. The air, with the exception of the water vapor, is for the most part almost completely transparent to the sun's rays. Not until the earth has absorbed much of the sun's energy and then transferred this back to the air, does the latter become appreciably warmed.

That such is the case can quickly be seen by noting the time of maximum daily temperatures. The heat from the sun is most intense at noon, nevertheless it is not until well into the afternoon that the air reaches its peak temperature. The reason for this is that the earth absorbs this excess noontime heat and retains it until the afternoon, when it is slowly released to the air. On a larger scale, the hottest part of the year occurs on the average a month after the summer solstice, when the sun has its greatest annual intensity. Further, the air has its highest temperatures near the earth's surface, rather than at higher altitudes which would be the case were it heated by the sun.

DISPOSAL OF INSOLATION.—Since the radiant energy of the sun is so important in the heating of the earth, which then relays this heat to the air, let us give some attention to the methods of disposal of insolation. These processes are "reflection," "absorption," and "transmission."

Reflection.—As a result of reflection, energy falling upon the surface of an object is turned back from this surface. For our purpose, we can consider that no significant change takes place in this energy as a result of reflection.   Thus, if the sun's rays have little effect on the atmosphere on their passage through the air to the earth, why should reflected radiation have any effect on the air?   It doesn't.   But reflection is important in that it lessens the amount of energy the earth would otherwise absorb and utilize in heating the air.

The amount of reflection depends on the color and smoothness of the surface.   The smoother and lighter in color the surface, the better is its reflective ability.   Dark, dull material is a poor reflector, and hence a good absorber of heat.   Obviously then, ocean surfaces will reflect far more insolation than land.   Depending on the state of the sea, the ocean water will reflect from 40 to 50 per cent of all the insolation striking it.   The amount reflected by land varies considerably with locality, owing to the wide variation of the surface composition from place to place.   Some substances will reflect but a few per cent, while others, such as beach sand, will reflect a very large proportion of the sun's rays.

Absorption.—Dark, rough surfaces are the best absorbers of heat. When a substance absorbs solar radiation (consisting of light and heat energy), the nature of this energy is changed almost completely into heat, increasing the heat content of the absorbing medium.   Hence the temperature of any part of the earth's surface rises when insolation is absorbed.

Since land surfaces differ so much as compared to the oceans, it follows that land temperatures will show much greater variation than water temperatures.

An important feature of good absorbers of heat is that they are good radiators of heat—*the better the absorber, the better the radiator.*   Consequently, an object that absorbs heat readily under the sun's influence loses this heat readily after sunset, and will become noticeably colder than other objects that absorbed less heat.   It is a matter of common observation (especially to campers) that stones and stony material remain quite warm all night, after being heated slowly.

Transmission.—This is the process of transfer of insolation after it has been absorbed.   The processes by which heat is transmitted have been explained above under Conduction, Convection, and Radiation.

VARIATION OF INSOLATION AND FACTORS RESPONSIBLE.—The irregular heating of the air gives it different temperatures which cause the other elements to vary.   If the air is heated unevenly and if the earth heats the air, it tends to follow that the earth must be heated unevenly.   *This irregular heating of the earth's surface may be considered as a fundamental cause of weather phenomena.*   In other words, the variation in the absorption of insolation by the earth causes the familiar weather changes. The reason for this irregular absorption can be broken down into two basic causes:

1. The difference in amount of insolation reaching the earth's surface
2. The difference in the amount absorbed by the earth

Note again that only insolation absorbed by the earth and later released has any effect in heating the air. If the light and heat passing through the atmosphere on the way toward the earth are but slightly absorbed, then the light and heat reflected by the earth, undergoing no great change, have similarly very little influence on the temperature of the air.

1. Several factors contribute to the varying amounts of insolation reaching the earth's surface:

a. The most important is the variation of the angle of incidence of the sun's rays, or the varying angle at which the insolation strikes the earth's surface. Since the sun's position in the heavens shifts every day

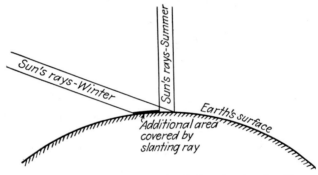

Fig. 1-4.—Seasonal variation of insolation at a given locality.

as a result of its daily and yearly paths, this angle must differ considerably from place to place; and at the same place it must change depending on the time. When the sun's rays strike the earth perpendicularly, their intensity is much greater than when impinging at a lesser angle, since the same beam has a much larger area to cover. Figure 1-4 illustrates this variation at a given place at different times of the year. Figure 1-5 shows this variation at different parts of the earth, at the same time.

b. The thickness of the atmosphere traversed by the sun's rays varies widely, also as a consequence of the variation in the angle of incidence. Solar energy coming in at a low altitude is filtered out to a much greater extent by the air and the foreign particles present, than when approaching from near the zenith. Consider the weakness of the sun at sunset compared to the blazing noontime sun. Figure 1-6 indicates this effect.

c. Foreign particles such as dust and clouds show pronounced variation in the atmosphere with locality and time. The dust in the air over mid-ocean is at a minimum whereas the industrial city atmosphere exhibits a maximum dust count. The dust and water particles are of great importance in filtering out much of the sun's energy by absorption and reflection.

d. The period of insolation is rarely constant at any one place. Aside from protracted periods of cloudiness, which of course obscure the sun, the length of the daylight period shows great seasonal change.

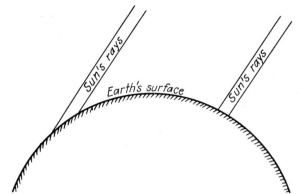

Fig. 1-5.—Variation of insolation over the earth's surface at a given time.

Summer days are twice, (or more, depending on the latitude) the duration of winter days and greatly affect the amount of energy reaching any one area.

2. The second basic factor concerning irregular absorption of insolation by the earth is the result of the differing composition of the earth's surface. Even if the sun's energy were equally received at the earth's

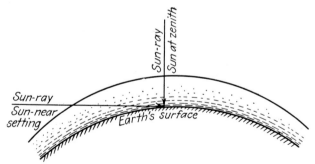

Fig. 1-6.—Comparison of thickness of atmosphere traversed by tangential and vertical rays of the sun.

surface, the great variation in composition of the earth would cause considerable differences in the amount absorbed (which later heats the air). This difference of the earth's composition is of extreme importance in determining weather and climate.

The most notable difference is that between land and water. Of the two, land is the far better absorber of heat.   However, a substance that is a good absorber of heat always tends to lose its absorbed heat as soon as possible.   In the summer, land absorbs insolation at a much greater rate than the oceans, thus giving continental air much higher temperatures than marine air during those months.   But during the winter months the oceans tend to hold on to the heat that they have absorbed, and fall only slightly below the summer temperatures whereas land rapidly loses the heat absorbed during the summer and becomes much colder than the neighboring oceans.

Since the amounts of solar energy received at the earth's surface and the amount absorbed by the earth vary considerably from time to time and from place to place, it is clear that the earth is heated very irregularly, with its consequent effect on the weather.

The Heat Balance of the Atmosphere.—It is interesting and important to note that despite local and relatively short-period heat and temperature changes in the atmosphere, the air as a whole is becoming neither warmer nor colder.   A nice balance exists between the amount of heat gained from the absorption of solar and terrestrial energy, and the amount of heat lost by the atmosphere through radiation and other methods.   This is known as the "heat balance of the atmosphere." Although this principle is of great importance in many theoretical considerations, we will omit further discussion of it here.

CHAPTER 2

HEAT AND TEMPERATURE OF THE AIR

Temperature is a fundamental weather element. In response to the irregular disposal of the sun's energy (insolation) the air temperatures show variations between wide extremes. These variations in turn cause other significant weather changes. The necessity for accurate measurement of this element is quite apparent. We shall consider first the instruments and methods of measuring temperature. From this we shall proceed to the nature of temperature variations, examining the periodic, the horizontal, and the vertical air temperature changes. Then the extremely important temperature variations that result whenever a mass or masses of air engage in vertical motion will be considered.

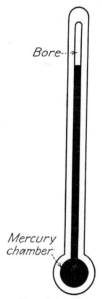

Bore

Mercury chamber

Fig. 2-1.—Principle of construction of thermometers.

Temperature Instruments

THERMOMETERS.—The temperature of an object is measured by a thermometer, which is a sealed glass tube with a very small opening—the bore—running through the center of it from top to bottom. The bore of the tube is greatly enlarged into a bulb-shaped opening within the bottom of the tube, as indicated in Fig. 2-1. The bulb end of the tube is filled with a liquid, usually mercury or alcohol, which rises into the narrow bore. The space above the liquid is a vacuum. When the temperature changes, the liquid within the thermometer expands and rises, or contracts and falls, depending on whether the temperature increases or decreases.

The outer glass surface of the thermometer is etched in the form of a graduated temperature scale. Hence, by reading the height of the upper surface of the liquid in the bore of the thermometer, the existing temperature is obtained.

MAXIMUM THERMOMETERS.—It is often necessary to determine not only the current temperature, but also the highest temperature reached during a given period. For this purpose a type of registering thermometer known as a "maximum thermometer," is used. This is almost identical with the standard thermometer described above, with one exception.   Just above the bulb of the thermometer, the bore pinches together very abruptly for a short space.   This leaves a constriction or narrowing of the bore of the thermometer to a very thin channel, much thinner than the bore in the rest of the tube, as shown in Fig. 2-3*b*.   Then, as the temperature rises, the mercury in the bulb expands.   The force of the expansion is sufficient to force the mercury through the constriction in the tube, causing the liquid to rise higher and higher in the bore above the constriction.   When the temperature reaches its maximum and then starts decreasing, the mercury below the constriction contracts and sinks down into the bulb.   But the extreme narrowness of the constriction prevents the mercury above from falling through under its weight alone.   Consequently the mercury above the constriction remains in the position it took at the highest temperature, and the top of the column of mercury indicates the maximum temperature reached.

Although the mercury thread in the bore also contracts with a fall in temperature, this contraction is so minute that it may be considered negligible.

The clinical thermometer is a common example of the maximum registering type.   To reset the thermometer after it is read, it is generally whirled around rapidly, and the force of whirling or shaking forces the mercury back through the constriction and into the bulb of the thermometer.

MINIMUM THERMOMETERS.—Minimum registering thermometers are used to register the lowest temperatures reached during a given period. The minimum thermometer resembles the regular thermometer in appearance, except that it always contains a liquid of low density such as alcohol, instead of mercury.   In addition within the liquid in the bore of the tube, there is a thin glass rod, shaped somewhat like a dumbbell and called the "index."   This is indicated in Fig. 2-3*a*.   When the temperature decreases, the liquid contracts, and its level falls in the tube. As the liquid descends, its surface, which is in contact with the top of the index, drags the index down the tube with it.   This force of a liquid surface is called "surface tension."

When the temperature starts to rise again, the alcohol flows around the index and rises up the tube, leaving the index at the lowest point to which the alcohol surface descended.   Hence, the upper surface of the glass index marks the lowest or the minimum temperature reached, at the same time that the alcohol surface itself always indicates the current temperature.   Obviously, the minimum thermometer should always be kept in a horizontal position, or the glass index will fall through the liquid to the bottom of the tube.   (If mercury were used, its density would always cause the index to float up to the surface, so that it would not register minimum temperatures.)

To reset the thermometer after reading, the instrument is inverted with the bulb end uppermost, until the index falls to the surface of the alcohol under its own weight; it is then restored to a horizontal position.

Six's Thermometer.—Six's thermometer being so common aboard ship will be explained in detail. This is a combination maximum-minimum thermometer commonly found aboard ship because of its

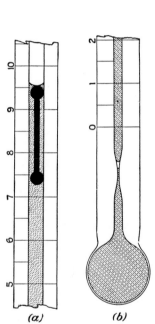

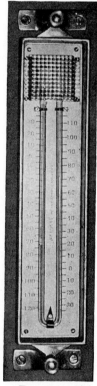

Fig. 2-2.—Standard exposed thermometer and common type of support.

Fig. 2-3.—*a*, Construction of minimum thermometer showing index; *b*, construction of maximum thermometer showing constriction in bore.

Fig. 2-4.—Six's thermometer showing indexes above the dark mercury thread in both arms.

convenience. As shown in Fig. 2-4, the instrument is a U-shaped glass tube with sealed widened ends. The lower portion of the U is filled with mercury. The remainder of the left-hand horn of the U is filled with alcohol, including the widened upper portion. The right-hand side of the U above the mercury is also filled with alcohol except that part of the expanded chamber contains a gas above the alcohol.

Above the surface of the mercury, within the alcohol in both arms of the thermometer, is a colored glass index, containing a thin iron pin in the center. To prevent the index in either arm from falling through the alcohol to the surface of the much denser mercury, a thin, hairlike wire protrudes from the index and presses against the inner glass wall surrounding the bore of the tube. The pressure of this wire keeps the pin suspended in whatever position it is pushed by the mercury surface.

When the temperature increases, the alcohol in the left side, in expanding, forces the mercury and the alcohol column to the right of it into the gas chamber in the upper right bulb of the tube. The gas thereby becomes compressed. As the mercury rises in the right-hand column, its high density causes the glass index above it to be pushed higher and higher in the tube. When the temperature starts decreasing, the alcohol in the left side contracts and the gas therefore expands, forcing all the liquids back toward the left side of the tube. As explained previously, the glass index will remain suspended in the alcohol as the mercury recedes, and its *lower surface* indicates the *maximum* temperature reached.

As the temperature continues to fall, the alcohol in the left-hand arm of the U contracts more and more, allowing the gas in the upper right side to expand further. This expansion of the gas now causes the mercury to be forced around into the left-hand arm of the U, and the more the temperature falls, the higher is the mercury forced in the left arm. The overlying index in this arm is now raised by the rising surface of the mercury.

When the temperature has reached its lowest point and begins to increase again, the mercury is once more forced to the right, leaving the glass index up in the left side of the tube, with its *lower surface* marking the *minimum* temperature reached. It should be seen from this that the side indicating minimum temperatures will have the highest temperature readings on the bottom of the arm of the U and the lowest on top, in contrast to the maximum side of the thermometer which reads from the bottom up, in the normal fashion. The surface of the mercury in both arms of the thermometer will always show the same readings and will indicate the current temperature. The fact that the glass index arms are reset to the mercury surface by means of a magnet explains the reason for the iron core within the glass indexes.

THE THERMOGRAPH.—The last instrument to be considered is the thermograph. This is a purely mechanical device consisting essentially of a metallic element whose curvature varies with the temperature. One end of the curved sensitive element is connected to a long movable lever arm which contains an inked pen at its end. The arm, in turn, rests on a cylindrical drum which rotates by means of a clockwork within, so that it makes one rotation a week. A sheet of graph paper is wrapped around the drum and is divided into days and hours, horizontally, and temperature in degrees, vertically.

Changes in temperature cause variations in curvature of the sensitive metallic element. This variation causes the long pen arm to move up or down, depending on the nature of the temperature change, and to inscribe an inked line on the sheet surrounding the drum. But as it does so, the drum is slowly rotating. Hence a line is traced which indi-

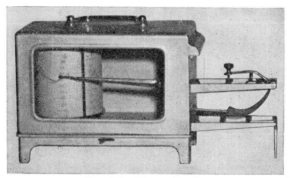

Fig. 2-5.—Thermograph.

cates the temperature at any time during the preceding week, as well as the current temperature.

Thus the thermograph gives a continuous record of the temperature, combining the results of the other instruments. Being mechanical, however, the thermograph may vary from correct readings at intervals, and has to be reset by a thumb screw provided for that purpose, after being compared to an accurate thermometer.

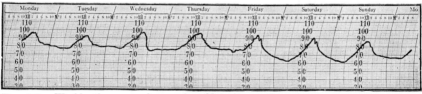

Fig. 2-6.—Weekly thermograph record. (Note hours of maximum and minimum temperatures.)

LOCATION OF TEMPERATURE INSTRUMENTS.—In placing temperature instruments properly to record or register air temperatures accurately, several factors should be taken into consideration:

1. The instruments should be shaded from direct sunlight. The air temperature is desired and not the temperature of the sun rays falling on the instruments. Thermometers should also be sheltered from radiation from walls, bulkheads, or any other source of heat.

2. The instruments should always be outdoors. It is the open-air temperatures that are part of weather observations, and not indoor temperatures. This does not prevent the use of small, well-ventilated shelters for the instruments.

3. Good ventilation is required. If the air is not in motion in the vicinity of the instruments, they will not indicate the true air temperature. Hence, any shelter used for thermometers should allow the air to pass through it without obstruction. For this purpose, such shelters are constructed with louvered sides.

Thermometer Scales

There are two common systems of scales or units used in measuring temperatures: Fahrenheit and centigrade. To compare the two systems

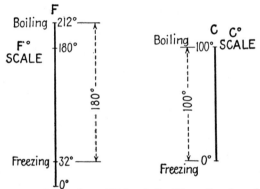

Fig. 2-7.—Comparison of Fahrenheit with centigrade scales.

we note that the boiling point of water is arbitrarily put at 212° on the Fahrenheit (F.) scale, and at 100° on the centigrade (C.) scale. The freezing point of water is put at 32° on the Fahrenheit scale and 0° on the centigrade scale (Fig. 2-7).

Hence, between freezing and boiling points on the Fahrenheit scale there is a range (from 32° to 212°) of 180°. However, from freezing to boiling (0° to 100°) on the centigrade scale, there is a range of 100°. Thus the relationship between the two scales is 180 to 100, or 9 to 5. For every 9°F., we have 5°C.

To convert from Fahrenheit to centigrade it is clear that we must take ⅝ of the Fahrenheit (the larger figure) to obtain the centigrade. But before we take ⅝ of the Fahrenheit figure, we must reduce the freezing points on both to the same level. Thus, if we subtract 32° from the Fahrenheit figure, we shall have the freezing point on both scales starting at zero. Then, ⅝ of the Fahrenheit figure after 32° has been subtracted, will give the centigrade equivalent. Hence,

$$C = (F - 32)\tfrac{5}{9}$$

Conversely, to change from centigrade to Fahrenheit, we first multiply the centigrade figure by $\tfrac{9}{5}$ to change the units to Fahrenheit, and then add 32°, since the Fahrenheit freezing point is 32° above zero. Thus,

$$F = \tfrac{9}{5}C + 32$$

TABLE II. EQUIVALENT TEMPERATURE (CENTIGRADE AND FAHRENHEIT)
C.° = temperature centigrade; F.° = temperature Fahrenheit

C.°	F.°	C.°	F.°	C.°	F.°	C.°	F.°	C.°	F.°
−10	14.0	0	32.0	10	50.0	20	68.0	30	86.0
−9	15.8	1	33.8	11	51.8	21	69.8	31	87.8
−8	17.6	2	35.6	12	53.6	22	71.6	32	89.6
−7	19.4	3	37.4	13	55.4	23	73.4	33	91.4
−6	21.2	4	39.2	14	57.2	24	75.2	34	93.2
−5	23.0	5	41.0	15	59.0	25	77.0	35	95.0
−4	24.8	6	42.8	16	60.8	26	78.8	36	96.8
−3	26.6	7	44.6	17	62.6	27	80.6	37	98.6
−2	28.4	8	46.4	18	64.4	28	82.4	38	100.4
−1	30.2	9	48.2	19	66.2	29	84.2	39	102.2

Periodic Temperature Variations

It is a matter of common observation and knowledge that the air temperature shows periodic variations from high to low peaks. These variations can be differentiated into daily and annual changes. The daily maximum temperatures occur in mid-afternoon, between 1 and 4 P.M. on the average, after the earth transmits to the air the excess noon time insolation. Then, just before sunrise, on the average of 4 to 6 A.M., after the earth and air have been cooling all night, the lowest or minimum temperatures are experienced (see Fig. 2–6).

On a larger scale, the yearly variations follow the daily ones. The end of July, a full month after the summer solstice, shows the highest temperatures, and the end of January shows the lowest. These are mean conditions. During December, when the greatest deficiency in insolation occurs, the earth is transmitting to the air much of the heat received a month earlier. It should be remembered that these annual variations are for the Northern Hemisphere only, the seasons being the reverse in the Southern.

Horizontal Temperature Variation

Having examined the causes of temperature variation and the instruments and systems used to measure temperature, let us inspect the variation in air temperature over the earth's surface. The most notable is the slow decrease in air temperatures going poleward (north or south) from the equator. This is the normal effect of latitude on temperature, as a result of the increasing slant of the sun's rays, as discussed previously.

However, this is a uniform change and, should the earth's surface have been perfectly homogeneous in composition, *i.e.*, all water, then the air temperatures at a given latitude would be pretty much the same, regardless of longitude. But it is quite evident that temperatures along a given parallel of latitude vary widely. This recalls the effect of the irregular composition of the earth's surface on temperature. In the summer season, the land will be definitely warmer than the ocean at the same latitude. Then, in the winter, the land, cooling off much faster than the water, will show much lower temperatures.

Further, in response to the transportation of huge quantities of warm and cold water by ocean currents, the temperature over the oceans themselves is rarely uniform. Only over large ocean areas that have no northward or southward currents will the air temperature be uniform.

To show the horizontal distribution of air temperature most conveniently, isotherms are used. *Isotherms* are lines connecting points of equal temperature. Consequently, if the earth were all uniform in composition, the isotherms would be straight east-west lines, similar to parallels of latitude. The isotherms representing the highest temperatures would be near the equator. But from one isotherm to the next, a change in temperature is indicated. In the hypothetical case under consideration, the isotherms would always be equidistant, for a given temperature change.

Actually, of course, such is not the case. Isotherm distribution on a world map is quite irregular and varies greatly from winter to summer and from hemisphere to hemisphere. For an isotherm to remain on equal temperature points, it must be deflected away from the equator in the winter time when passing from land to ocean, and toward the equator in the summer. The reason for such a bending or deflecting of isotherms can be clearly seen as a result of the discussion above. If we assume that the winter temperature along an east-west line over the land is 30°, then the adjacent ocean will be warmer (in winter). Hence, the isotherm must bend northward to remain on points having a 30° temperature.

Similarly, in the summer, with the oceans colder, the isotherms must deflect southward to discover equivalent warm temperatures. Ocean currents, depending on whether they are cold or warm, may add to or detract from this isotherm deflection. These effects are shown clearly

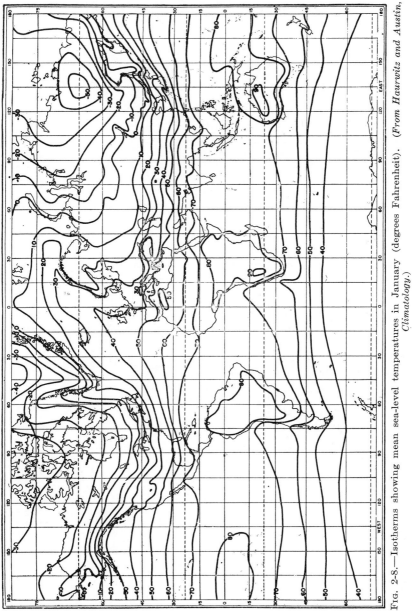

FIG. 2-8.—Isotherms showing mean sea-level temperatures in January (degrees Fahrenheit). *(From Haurwitz and Austin, Climatology.)*

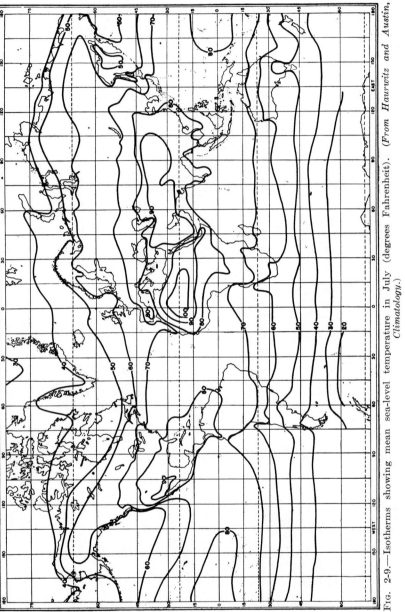

FIG. 2-9.—Isotherms showing mean sea-level temperature in July (degrees Fahrenheit). (*From Haurwitz and Austin, Climatology.*)

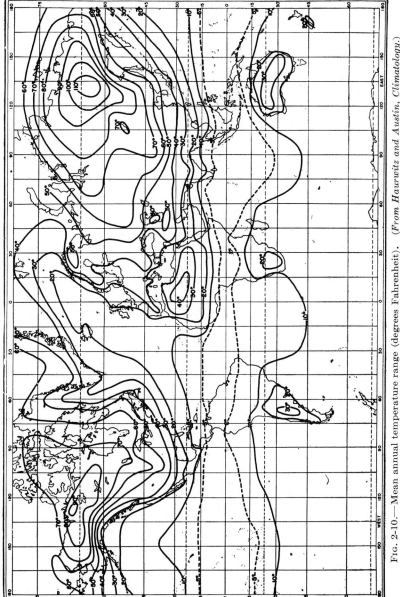

FIG. 2-10.— Mean annual temperature range (degrees Fahrenheit). (*From Haurwitz and Austin, Climatology.*)

on the world isotherm charts for January and July (Figs. 2-8 and 2-9). A line known as the "heat equator" is sometimes drawn connecting places showing the highest average temperatures.

Obviously, the greatest horizontal temperature variation from summer to winter will occur over the largest land mass, which mass will, by virtue of the amount of insolation it absorbs, become extremely warm in summer. Then, since land masses rapidly lose their heat in winter, such a large mass would show a very pronounced temperature decrease. For example Asia becomes very warm in summer and very cold in winter.

Just the opposite condition exists over the southern part of the South Pacific and Atlantic. Here, the large expanse of ocean is undisturbed by land, being nearer to the ideal case than any other part of the earth. In this region the isotherms are straight east-west lines, indicating a gradual and uniform temperature decrease from north to south. The temperature conditions in each of the above regions have a very pronounced effect on the weather and climate of the parts of the earth affected by them. That effect will be considered in a later chapter.

It is always interesting to note some of the global extremes in temperature. The lowest valid temperature ever registered was −93.6°F. at Verkhoyansk, Siberia. The lowest average temperature for one month, was at the same place, being −64°F. Yellowstone Park holds the low record in the United States with a reading of −66°F.

The high temperature mark for the world was recorded in North Africa in Tripoli, where the mercury reached 136°F. Death Valley in the United States follows closely with a record of 134°F.

Vertical Temperature Variation

THE VERTICAL TEMPERATURE GRADIENT—LAPSE RATE.—As one ascends in the atmosphere, steadily decreasing temperatures are encountered. This decrease of temperature with higher altitudes in the air is known as "vertical temperature gradient." There are three essential causes for this decline in temperature. (1) A major source of heat of the air is the earth. Clearly, then, with increasing distance from the source of its heat (the earth), the air temperatures must grow less and less. (2) The density of water vapor decreases with elevation so that less heat can be held in the air and the temperature falls. (3) Temperature changes result from expansion and contraction of air moving with any vertical component of motion (see page 29).

However, although air temperatures decrease vertically, there is nothing constant about the rate at which this temperature drop occurs. In fact, the only constant thing about the vertical temperature gradient is that it varies. As stressed previously, the heating of the earth, and subsequently of the air, varies so widely from time to time and from day to day, that there can be no uniform rate at which the temperature decreases. The only way to determine this rate is to obtain air temperature readings at different elevations by means of balloon or airplane observations.

Lapse Rate.—The actual figures obtained by observations of the vertical temperature decrease or gradient are known as the "lapse rate." As stated, this lapse rate varies through a wide range. But at a given place the different lapse-rate figures that have been observed can be averaged. This average value for the lapse rate is known as the "normal lapse rate." The normal lapse rate was determined after thousands of lapse-rate measurements had been found at various places over the earth, and it has been found that the normal lapse-rate figures all coincided regardless of where the measurements have been made.

Although the lapse rate at a given time and place can be obtained only by observation, the average or normal rate can be given, since it is always the same. The following figures show the average rate of decrease of air temperatures with increasing altitude:

$$1°F. \quad per \quad 300 \text{ feet}$$
$$3.3°F. \quad per \quad 1,000 \text{ feet}$$
$$6°C. \quad per \quad kilometer$$

Notice that the lapse rate refers to temperature conditions existing in a vertical column of air at a given place and time. This air should not be considered as having any vertical motion, either upward or downward.

INVERSIONS.—Occasionally at some altitude, the temperature abruptly increases instead of decreasing. This can occur only if a warm layer of air overlies a colder layer. The temperature will fall with increasing altitude in the cold layer and will rise suddenly as the warm layer is encountered. After a short vertical distance, the temperature in the warmer layer will also continue to fall. The condition in which this abrupt *rise* instead of a *fall* in temperature occurs in the air, is called an "inversion." An inversion may result (1) when the air near the ground cools off faster than the overlying air, because of conduction to the earth which might be cold, (2) from an actual warm air layer passing over a lower cold one, (3) from warming by subsidence or falling, or (4) from turbulence.

Effect of Vertical Air Motion on Temperature

CAUSES OF VERTICAL AIR MOTION.—In addition to horizontal movement of the air, there is often pronounced vertical movement. The amount of air exhibiting this rising or falling motion depends upon the force that initiates the movement. The causes of vertical air motion can be separated into three distinct influences: (1) heating and cooling of isolated parts of the air; (2) topographic uplifting; (3) the effects of "fronts" or cold air wedges.

1. If a portion of the earth's surface becomes highly heated, the overlying air also becomes heated. Upon being heated, air expands, becomes lighter, and tends to rise. Air over a cold surface will become cold, hence heavier than the surrounding warmer air, and will tend to sink. This is, on a much larger scale, the same process that occurs in a room heated by a radiator where the hot air rises in a vertical stream toward the ceiling. Although it is difficult to see these rising and falling air columns, their presence is well known to air travelers, who constantly encounter so-called "bumpy air," or "air pockets," which are nothing more than air columns in vertical motion.

2. The topographic effect is easily shown. Air in motion, approaching a mountain or a ridge, will ascend the windward slopes and descend on the leeward sides of the elevation.

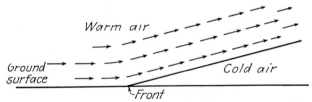

Fig. 2-11.—The flow of warm air over an intruding wedge of cold air.

3. Fronts are the bounding surfaces between different air masses. For example, we can consider a cold-air mass moving southward until it meets a warmer moving mass of air. The line of separation between them is called a "front." However, it is not a vertical boundary between the two, but a sloping one. The cold air, being heavier, will flow in the form of a wedge beneath the warmer air and force the latter up over the cold air, as indicated in Fig. 2-11. Consequently, there will be a continuous mass of warm air rising over the cold beyond the meeting point of the two air masses. Briefly, these are the causes of vertical motion in the air. The extreme importance of the last process will be explained in greater detail later.

Regardless of the influences causing air to rise or fall, once air does so, there occur very profound effects on temperature and consequent weather. *The temperature change in vertically moving air is one of the most fundamental and important processes in the atmosphere.*

RESULTING TEMPARATURE EFFECT, ADIABATIC CHANGES.—We have seen that relatively local masses of air can be forced to rise and fall in the atmosphere as a result of one of the three methods just considered. During this process, the greater part of the atmosphere can be considered more or less calm and motionless as regards vertical movement. This can be compared to the oceans, wherein pronounced currents occur although most of the great quantity of water in the seas remains relatively quiet. Just as the Gulf Stream flows steadily northeastward, apparently independent of the main ocean body, so do small parcels of air move up and down, independent of the main body of air.

Let us consider a mass of air on the earth's surface. Assume that this air is forced upward, either through surface heating, or a mountain obstruction, or a cold-air wedge. As this "isolated" mass of air rises, the pressure on it grows less. As the pressure on the air grows less, it will naturally expand. This principle is very familiar in the case of ordinary gas-filled or hydrogen balloons, which, when released, rise

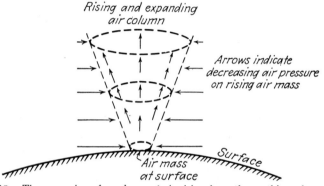

FIG. 2-12.—The expansion of a column of air rising from the earth's surface. (This is purely diagrammatic since the lengths of the horizontal arrows are not proportional to actual pressure decreases.)

in the air and expand continuously until they burst. This process is shown in the Fig. 2-12, where the horizontal arrows indicate the decreasing pressure on a rising air mass. The arrow lengths are proportional to the air pressure and indicate the decrease of pressure with altitude.

Remember that the atmosphere is an ordinary mixture of gases. It is a physical property of all gases that, upon expansion, they become cooler. As a gas expands, it uses up heat energy from within itself to supply the energy necessary for expansion. Clearly, then, if no external source of heat is available, the expanding gas or air must cool. We have previously noted that a rising or falling air mass can be considered as isolated from the rest of the air. Practically no heat can be transmitted to the rising or falling air mass either by the earth or by the surrounding air, for air is well known as a good insulator (or poor conductor) of heat.

An excellent and common example of this process occurs in the ordinary bicycle or automobile tire. When the valve is opened, the compressed air in the tire will rush out very rapidly. As it rushes out, the air expands very rapidly and, consequently, its temperature decreases very rapidly. The resulting cooling is a common observation to all who have handled compressed-air tires.

In the same manner then, rising air grows continuously cooler, and since the surrounding air pressure falls off uniformly, expands uniformly. If the air expands at a uniform rate, it will cool at a uniform and constant rate.

Oppositely, air that is descending will encounter greater and greater pressure from the surrounding air. Thus, the falling air is compressed. Whenever a gas is compressed, the work done on it will cause its temperature to rise. When air is pumped into a tire, the temperature rises noticeably as a result of the compression. When air subsides or sinks in the atmosphere, it will therefore always grow warmer and will do so at the same rate at which rising air cools when rising an equivalent distance.

This change in the temperature of a gas or the air, due only to the change in pressure on the air, is called an "adiabatic change." The rate at which the temperature changes as air rises or falls is called the "adiabatic rate." This rate is constant for ordinary dry air. It does not change. If the original temperature of the air is known and the distance through which it rises or falls is known, then the resulting temperature can be calculated by means of the adiabatic rate. The rate for dry air, known as the "dry adiabatic rate" is

$$1°F. \quad per \quad 185 \text{ feet}$$
$$5.5°F. \quad per \quad 1,000 \text{ feet}$$
$$10°C. \quad per \quad kilometer$$

If a mass of air rises 1,000 feet, whether vertically or at an angle through the effects of ground slopes or cold-air wedges, the mass will cool by 5.5°F. The air rising at an acute angle will not of course cool so rapidly as that rising vertically.

To summarize: As a result of the influence of heating and cooling, of interference of mountains, and of cold-air wedges, relatively small parts of the atmosphere are often forced into vertical motion. *Whenever air rises, it cools* at the adiabatic rate; whenever air falls, it warms at the same rate. This change in temperature has nothing whatsoever to do with the surrounding air conditions, or with the earth. This adiabatic should not be confused with the lapse rate, which refers to the general decrease of temperature with altitude in the large quiet atmosphere. If air is in the process of rising or falling, its temperature is determined by the adiabatic rate. If air has no vertical motion, its temperature at any elevation is determined by the lapse rate. Thus, the adiabatic rate can really be considered as a special and constant case of the lapse rate, applied only to air having vertical motion.

CHAPTER 3

HUMIDITY

Nature of Water Vapor

Humidity refers to the water vapor in the atmosphere. Before we continue with the discussion of it as a weather element, it is essential that a clear understanding of the term "humidity," or atmospheric moisture, be gained. Water is a compound of hydrogen and oxygen in the ratio of two parts of hydrogen to one part of oxygen, yielding the familiar formula H_2O. This compound is practically never broken down in the atmosphere regardless of the state of the water. By "state" is meant the physical condition of a substance. There are three states of matter: solid, liquid, and gas. Water commonly occurs in all three of these forms. As a solid, it is known as ice; as a liquid it is known commonly as water; and in a gaseous condition it is known as water vapor or steam.

The water vapor in the air constitutes atmospheric humidity. Water vapor is colorless, odorless, and tasteless. The white mass of water droplets seen escaping from whistles or stacks, etc., is not steam or water vapor. It is rather a mass of minute water droplets, so small in size that they rapidly evaporate into true vapor. It will be observed, however, that between the exhaust stack and the white cloud of escaping droplets there is always a small clear area just above the exhaust opening. This clear space actually contains the true water vapor. Upon entering the cooler air, this vapor is suddenly chilled and turns to minute liquid droplets. The same effect is observed when one breathes rapidly in cold weather, as the moisture in the breath condenses on meeting the cold air.

Relationship between Temperature and Humidity

We noted earlier that the water content of the air is closely related to the atmospheric temperature conditions. The control that temperature exerts over humidity will now be examined in greater detail.

CAPACITY.—The amount of water vapor that the air can hold at a given time depends mostly on the temperature at that time. We have seen earlier that warm air can hold more moisture than cold air. Hence the ability of the air to hold moisture and the actual humidity of the air will vary as the temperature varies. The quantity of water vapor that a given amount of air can support at a given temperature is often known as the "capacity" of the air. It is clear, then, that the capacity must vary directly with the temperature. This does not mean that the capacity of the air is always reached. We can liken the capacity of the air to a container for rain water. The container may have a capacity to hold a gallon of water. However, it may not be filled at any particular rainfall, just as the capacity of the air may not be reached by the actual amount of water vapor in the air.

SATURATION.—When the air contains all the water vapor it can possibly hold at a given temperature, or when the capacity is reached, the air is said to be "saturated." From the discussion above it appears that there are two methods of accomplishing saturation in the atmosphere: (1) If the temperature, and hence the capacity, remains the same, saturation may be brought about by increasing the amount of water vapor in the air through evaporation from some source. (2) If the temperature should decrease, then the capacity decreases accordingly until the capacity will just equal the actual amount of water vapor in the air, thereby achieving saturation. Of these two methods, the latter, the decrease of temperature, is the more important natural process of saturating the air.

DEW POINT.—If the temperature should continue to fall below the temperature point at which the air became saturated, there will be an excess amount of water vapor present, compared to the capacity of the air at the new lower temperature. Consequently, this excess (represented by the difference between the amount in the air and the new capacity) will change its state to water droplets or ice particles. The temperature at which saturation occurs, or the temperature at which a change from water vapor to liquid water will occur on further cooling, is called the "dew point." The process by which the water vapor changes to liquid water is called "condensation."

The dew-point temperature of the air at any time can be obtained by a simple experiment. If a metallic or thin glass container is filled with water containing lumps of ice, the water will become continuously colder as the ice melts. To ensure uniform water temperatures, the liquid should be stirred. When the water and hence the air in contact with the container are cooled to the dew point, beads of water (sweat) will form on the outer surface of the glass. Thus, if the temperature of the ice water is taken the moment the first droplets of water appear, the thermometer reading will be the dew point of the air.

The dew point of rising air decreases with altitude at the rate of about 1°F. for every 1,000 feet, since the water vapor concentration per unit volume decreases as the air expands.

A great value of this dew-point property of the air is its constancy. For a given quantity of air, there is present a certain amount of water vapor. Saturation of this air will occur if the temperature decreases sufficiently, until the dew point is reached. What determines the temperature at which this occurs is the amount of water vapor in the air. If the amount of water vapor in the air increases, the dew point is increased —is reached at a higher temperature. Should the water content of the air decrease, the dew point temperature is decreased accordingly. As long as the water content of a given quantity of the air remains constant, the dew point of that air will remain practically constant. In a later consideration of weather analysis, the importance of this property will be more easily recognized.

Since the cooling of the air is all important in determining humidity changes, we may note briefly the causes of this temperature decrease. Any one or a combination of the following is effective in reducing the temperature of the air:

1. The air may be cooled adiabatically by rising and expanding.

2. It may be cooled by contact with a cold surface beneath.

3. The mixing of warm and cold air masses will result in a lowering of the temperature of the warmer mass.

4. Radiation by the air itself may result in cooling of the air.

The actual results dependent on the above processes will be considered in a later chapter.

Humidity Measurements

ABSOLUTE HUMIDITY.—So far, we have considered the quantity of water vapor in the air, but only as it is governed by the temperature. One of the methods of expressing the actual water content of the air is to give the absolute humidity, which is the weight of water vapor in a particular volume of air. More specifically, it is the weight of water vapor per unit *volume* of air. The unit volume generally used is either the cubic foot or the cubic meter. Hence if we extract the amount of water vapor in 1 cubic foot of ordinary air and weigh this water, the result expressed in grains per cubic foot would be the absolute humidity. If cubic meters are used, the weight is given in grams.

We can see that the absolute humidity will vary if the air expands or contracts, even though the water vapor itself is constant in amount. Suppose for example, that 10 grains of water vapor exist in 1 cubic foot of air. The absolute humidity is then 10 grains per cubic foot. If this air should for any reason (an increase in temperature) expand and occupy 2 cubic feet, the amount of water vapor left in 1 cubic foot would now be only 5 grains, the absolute humidity equaling the 5 grains measurement, although the water content has actually remained the same.

Table III shows the absolute humidity (grains of water vapor per cubic foot of air) for saturated air at different temperatures and indicates strongly the control exerted by air temperatures over humidity.

TABLE III. ABSOLUTE HUMIDITY VALUES FOR SATURATED AIR

Temperature, °F	Water vapor, grains per cubic foot	Temperature, °F	Water vapor, grains per cubic foot
0	0.479	50	4.108
5	0.613	55	4.891
10	0.780	60	5.800
15	0.988	65	6.852
20	1.244	70	8.066
25	1.558	75	9.460
30	1.942	80	11.056
35	2.375	85	12.878
40	2.863	90	14.951
45	3.436	95	17.305

NOTE: 1 grain = 0.002 ounce or 0.0648 gram.

SPECIFIC HUMIDITY.—This is the more constant property of the air and has come into use in meteorology as a result of the variability of of absolute humidity.   The specific humidity is the weight of water vapor per unit *weight* of moist air, expressed as grams of water vapor per kilogram of air, or as grains of water vapor per pound of air.   Obviously, if we are to extract and weigh the water vapor in a given weight such as a pound of air, regardless of what happens to the temperature and volume of the air, a pound is still a pound and will contain the same mass of air regardless of any volume changes.   We simply include a larger volume of air to obtain a pound, should the air expand between measurements.   Only by an actual variation of the water content of the air will the specific humidity change.   This too is an extremely important property as regards weather analysis.

MIXING RATIO.—This is another fairly constant or conservative property of the air that has come into widespread use.   It is the weight of water vapor per unit weight of dry air and is expressed in units similar to those for specific humidity.   The numerical difference between these properties is very small.

RELATIVE HUMIDITY.—Generally, when humidity is mentioned, it is relative humidity to which reference is made.   Relative humidity is the ratio of the amount of water vapor in the air to the amount the air can hold at that temperature (or the capacity).   This ratio is always expressed as a percentage.

If the air has 40 grains of water vapor per pound and can hold at that temperature 50 grains per pound (the capacity), then the relative humidity is $^{40}\!/_{50}$, or 80 per cent.

The relative humidity is therefore a very important atmospheric property.   "Sticky," "muggy" days are those with a high relative humidity.   Evaporation is very slow since the air is nearly saturated.

It is clear that the relative humidity must change whenever the amount of water vapor in the air changes and whenever the capacity of the air changes. Thus, the relative humidity varies inversely with the temperature. A decrease in temperature causes corresponding capacity decrease. If the capacity decreases, the relative humidity increases as the air is brought nearer the saturation point. When the temperature, hence the capacity, decreases, such that the relative humidity is 100 per

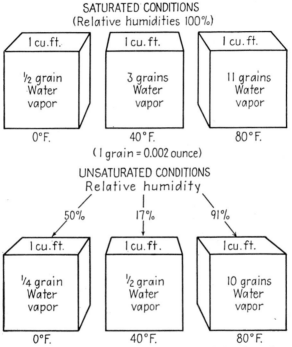

SATURATED CONDITIONS
(Relative humidities 100%)

I cu.ft.	I cu.ft.	I cu.ft.
½ grain Water vapor	3 grains Water vapor	11 grains Water vapor
0°F.	40°F.	80°F.

(I grain = 0.002 ounce)

UNSATURATED CONDITIONS
Relative humidity

50%	17%	91%

I cu.ft.	I cu.ft.	I cu.ft.
¼ grain Water vapor	½ grain Water vapor	10 grains Water vapor
0°F.	40°F.	80°F.

Fig. 3-1.—Relationship between capacity, absolute humidity (actual water content), relative humidity, and temperature.

cent, the air will be saturated, and the temperature at which this humidity is reached is the dew point. Further cooling causes condensation.

Humidity Instruments

The measurement of humidity in the air is known as "hygrometry," and the instruments used fall under the general name of "hygrometers." Many types of hygrometers have been developed for the purpose, but only the common types will be considered.

PSYCHROMETER OR WET- AND DRY-BULB HYGROMETER.—The most common of the humidity instruments is a hygrometer consisting of a support to which are attached two ordinary accurate mercury thermometers. One of the thermometers has a thin layer of muslin wrapped around the bulb, which is kept wet when the instrument is in use.   This is therefore called the "wet-bulb" thermometer and the other the "dry-bulb" thermometer.   The muslin should never be wet with salt water.

The dry-bulb thermometer will show the current air temperature. However, as the moisture in the muslin of the wet bulb evaporates, latent heat is absorbed by the evaporating moisture, causing the mercury

of the wet-bulb thermometer to fall.   The faster the rate of evaporation, the more heat is absorbed from the covered wet bulb, and the lower the wet-bulb reading falls below that of the dry.   Now the rate of evaporation always depends on the degree of saturation of the air, which is relative humidity. Hence the difference in temperature between the wet- and dry-bulb thermometers is a measure of relative humidity.

To ensure proper evaporation from the wet-bulb thermometer, the air surrounding it should be continuously replaced.   Otherwise evaporation would slow down as the stagnant air surrounding the wet bulb becomes saturated.   Therefore the psychrometer should be fanned to replace this air.   Readings of the wet bulb should be taken at intervals of 10 to 20 seconds until two successive readings of the wet bulb show the same temperature.

To avoid fanning, an instrument called the "sling psychrometer" is used.   Here, the whole instrument is whirled rapidly until the lowest wet-bulb reading is obtained.   Another convenient psychrometer allows air to be drawn over the thermometer bulbs by means of hand pressure on a rubber bulb.   This avoids the whirling, which is often difficult to do in confined quarters, such as cargo holds (see Fig. 3-3).

FIG. 3-2.—A type of sling psychrometer. (*Courtesy of Friez Instruments Division of Bendix Aviation Corporation.*)

"Psychrometry" is another name commonly applied to the process of humidity measurement.

From these facts, tables have been developed to obtain both the relative humidity and the dew point of the air (see Tables IV and V).   It is simply necessary to note the dry-bulb reading and the difference between the wet and the dry, known as the "depression" of the wet bulb, to obtain these properties of the air from the tables.

An example indicates how the tables are to be used:

Assume the dry bulb to read 80°F.   Assume the wet bulb after whirling or fanning to read 70°F.   Then the depression of the wet bulb is 10°F.

Looking down the left-hand column of Table IV, we find 80°F. for the dry-bulb reading. Across the top of the table we find the difference of 10°F. This yields a reading of 61 per cent for the relative humidity.

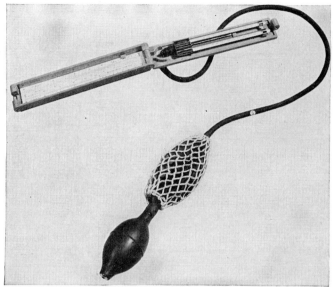

FIG. 3-3.—Hand-aspirated psychrometer. (*Courtesy of Friez Instruments Division of Bendix Aviation Corporation.*)

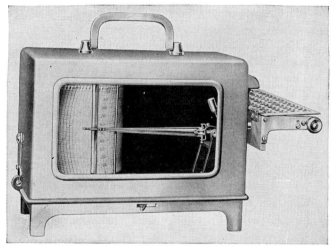

FIG. 3-4.—Hygrograph. (*Courtesy of Friez Instruments Division of Bendix Aviation Corporation.*)

Table V gives dew-point figures using the same dry bulb and depression of the wet-bulb readings. For the figures given above, the dew point is 65°F.

TABLE IV.   RELATIVE HUMIDITY IN PER CENT

Depression of wet-bulb thermometer, °F.

Air temp. °F.	1	2	3	4	5	6	7	8	9	10	11	12	13	14	15	16	17	18	19	20	21	22	23	24	25	26	27	28	29	30	31	32	33	34	35
0	67	33	1																																
5	73	46	20																																
10	78	56	34	13																															
15	82	64	46	29	11																														
20	85	70	55	40	26	12																													
25	87	74	62	49	37	25	13	1																											
30	89	78	67	56	46	36	26	16	6																										
35	91	81	72	63	54	45	36	27	19	10	2																								
40	92	83	75	68	60	52	45	37	29	22	15	7																							
45	93	86	78	71	64	57	51	44	38	31	25	18	12	6																					
50	93	87	80	74	67	61	55	49	43	38	32	27	21	16	10																				
55	94	88	82	76	70	65	59	54	49	43	38	33	28	23	19	5	9	5																	
60	94	89	83	78	73	68	63	58	53	48	43	39	34	30	26	11	17	13	9	5	1														
65	95	90	85	80	75	70	66	61	56	52	48	44	39	35	31	21	24	20	16	12	9	5	2												
70	95	90	86	81	77	72	68	64	59	55	51	48	44	40	36	27	29	25	22	19	15	12	9	6	3										
75	96	91	86	82	78	74	70	66	62	58	54	51	47	44	40	37	34	30	27	24	21	18	15	12	9	7	4	1							
80	96	91	87	83	79	75	72	68	64	61	57	54	50	47	44	41	38	35	32	29	26	23	20	18	15	12	10	7	5	3					
85	96	92	88	84	81	77	73	70	66	63	59	57	53	50	47	44	41	38	36	33	30	27	25	22	20	17	15	13	10	8	6	4	2		
90	96	92	89	85	81	78	74	71	68	65	61	58	55	52	49	47	44	41	39	36	34	31	29	26	24	22	19	17	15	13	11	9	7	5	3
95	96	93	89	86	82	79	76	73	69	66	63	61	58	55	52	50	47	44	42	39	37	34	32	30	28	25	23	21	19	17	15	13	11	10	8
100	96	93	89	86	83	80	77	73	70	68	65	62	59	56	54	51	49	46	44	41	39	37	35	33	30	28	26	24	22	21	19	17	15	13	12
105	97	93	90	87	84	81	78	75	72	69	66	64	61	58	56	53	51	49	46	44	42	40	38	36	34	32	30	28	26	24	22	21	19	17	15
110	97	93	90	87	84	81	78	75	73	70	67	65	62	60	57	55	52	50	48	46	44	42	40	38	36	34	32	30	28	26	25	23	21	20	18
115	97	94	91	88	85	82	79	76	74	71	69	66	64	61	59	57	54	52	50	48	45	44	42	40	38	36	34	33	31	29	28	26	25	23	21
120	97	94	91	88	85	82	80	77	74	72	69	67	65	62	60	58	55	53	51	49	47	45	43	41	40	38	36	34	33	31	29	28	26	25	23
125	97	94	91	88	86	83	80	78	75	73	70	68	66	64	61	59	57	55	53	51	49	47	45	44	42	40	38	37	35	33	32	30	29	27	26
130	97	94	91	89	86	83	81	78	76	73	71	69	67	64	62	60	58	56	54	52	50	48	47	45	43	41	40	38	37	35	33	32	30	29	28

TABLE V. TEMPERATURE OF DEW POINT

Air temp, °F	Vapor pressure	Depression of wet-bulb thermometer, °F																																		
		1	2	3	4	5	6	7	8	9	10	11	12	13	14	15	16	17	18	19	20	21	22	23	24	25	26	27	28	19	30	31	31	33	34	35
0	0.0383	-7	-20																																	
5	0.0491	-1	-9	-24																																
10	0.0631	5	-2	-10	-27																															
15	0.0810	11	6	0	-9	-26																														
20	0.103	16	12	8	2	-7	-21																													
25	0.130	22	19	15	10	5	-3	-15	-51																											
30	0.164	27	25	21	18	14	8	2	-7	-25																										
35	0.203	33	30	28	25	21	17	13	7	0	-11																									
40	0.247	38	35	33	30	28	25	21	18	13	7	-41																								
45	0.298	43	41	38	36	34	31	28	25	22	18	13	7	-1	-14																					
50	0.360	48	46	44	42	40	37	34	32	29	26	22	18	13	8	0	-13																			
55	0.432	53	51	50	48	45	43	41	38	36	33	30	27	24	20	15	9	1	-12	-59																
60	0.517	58	57	55	53	51	49	47	45	43	40	38	35	32	29	25	21	17	11	4	8	-36														
65	0.616	63	62	60	59	57	55	53	51	49	47	45	42	40	37	34	31	27	24	19	14	7	-3	-22												
70	0.732	69	67	65	64	62	61	59	57	55	53	51	49	47	44	42	39	36	33	30	26	22	17	11	2	-11										
75	0.866	74	72	71	69	68	66	64	63	61	59	57	55	54	51	49	47	44	42	39	36	32	29	25	21	15	8	-2	-23							
80	1.022	79	77	76	74	73	72	70	68	67	65	63	62	60	58	56	54	52	50	47	44	42	39	36	32	28	24	20	13	6	-7	-53				
85	1.201	84	82	81	80	78	77	75	74	72	71	69	68	66	64	62	61	59	57	54	52	50	48	45	42	39	36	32	28	24	19	12	3	-12		
90	1.408	89	87	86	85	83	82	81	80	78	76	75	73	72	70	69	67	65	63	61	59	57	55	53	51	48	45	43	39	36	32	28	24	19	11	1
95	1.645	94	93	91	90	89	87	86	85	83	82	80	79	78	76	74	73	71	70	68	66	64	62	60	58	56	54	52	49	46	43	40	37	33	29	24
100	1.916	99	98	96	95	94	93	91	90	89	87	86	85	83	82	80	79	77	76	74	72	71	69	67	65	63	61	59	57	55	52	50	47	44	41	37
105	2.225	104	103	101	100	99	98	96	95	94	93	91	90	89	87	86	84	83	82	80	78	77	75	74	72	70	68	67	65	63	61	58	56	54	51	48
110	2.576	109	108	106	105	104	103	102	100	99	98	97	95	94	93	91	90	89	87	86	84	83	81	80	78	77	75	73	72	70	68	66	64	62	60	57
115	2.975	114	113	112	110	109	108	107	106	104	103	102	101	99	98	97	96	94	93	92	90	89	87	86	84	83	81	80	78	76	75	73	71	69	67	65
120	3.425	119	118	117	115	114	113	112	111	110	108	107	106	105	104	102	101	100	98	97	96	94	93	92	90	89	87	86	84	83	81	80	78	76	75	73
125	3.933	124	123	122	121	119	118	117	116	115	114	112	111	110	109	108	106	105	104	103	101	100	99	97	96	95	93	92	90	89	88	86	84	83	81	80
130	4.504	129	128	127	126	124	123	122	121	120	119	118	116	115	114	113	112	110	109	108	107	106	104	103	102	100	99	98	96	95	94	92	91	89	88	86

HYGROGRAPH.—This instrument makes a continuous record of humidity. The sensitive element is a bundle of ordinary blonde-human hair which expands or contracts in length as the humidity increases or decreases. By means of delicate springs and levers, this change in

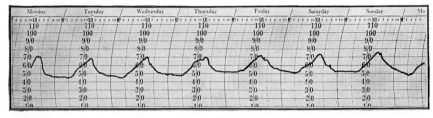

a

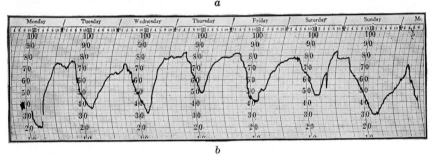

b

FIG. 3-5.—Comparison of thermograph, *a*, and hygrograph, *b*, records for same week. Note the inverse relationship between times of temperature and relative humidity extremes.

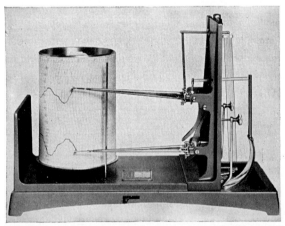

FIG. 3-6.—Hytherograph. (*Courtesy of Friez Instruments Division of Bendix Aviation Corporation.*)

length of the hair is communicated to a long pen arm which inscribes a trace on a revolving drum. In appearance the instrument resembles the thermograph. The graph chart is calibrated vertically in relative humidity from 0 to 100 per cent.

HYTHEROGRAPH.—The hytherograph is commonly observed on merchant ships in connection with Cargocaire units. This instrument is a combination of the thermograph and the hygrograph, the two units being placed in the same case. The chart encircling the revolving drum is divided into two horizontal sections, the upper indicating temperature and the lower showing the relative humidity. The pens attached to the temperature and humidity elements inscribe their traces on the upper and lower sections of the chart, respectively.

Humidity and Cargo Ventilation

To cope with the problem of ventilating cargo holds, a knowledge of humidity and its measurement is of utmost value. Although a full treatment of the subject is given in texts dealing with the handling and stowage of cargo, some of the more essential points involving humidity can be considered here.

Varied climates are encountered by vessels in following different trade routes. Marine air is naturally more humid than continental air in the same latitude owing to the large amounts of water available for evaporation. Consequently, vessels in the tropics encounter air with a very high absolute or specific humidity as a result of the high capacity of the hot tropical air. The air in the higher middle latitudes will have a much lower humidity.

In proceeding from one climate to another of contrasting type, very significant temperature and humidity changes are encountered, which, if not properly anticipated and understood, may seriously affect the cargo. Sweating or condensation of moisture from saturated air is one of the worst evils involved. From our discussion of humidity, it is clear that, if tropical air is admitted to a hold still chilled from a previously visited colder region, the entering air may be cooled rapidly to and below the dew point. The resulting moisture will be deposited directly on the cargo, as well as on the interior surfaces of the hold, and will later drip down onto the cargo.

A vessel loaded in the tropics and steaming to higher latitudes should have the holds ventilated frequently. Otherwise the air there will gradually become chilled and saturated. Since such air contains a naturally large amount of water vapor, it will release large amounts of "sweat" on the cargo and on the cooling bulkheads. If the air is changed very suddenly, a similar effect will result from the rapid mixture of warm and cold air.

The passage of a vessel across warm and cold ocean currents may produce humidity changes similar to those experienced in sailing through marked differences in latitude.

Effect of Water Vapor on Air Temperatures

The water vapor in the air has a profound effect on the temperature of the atmosphere. Although constituting nearly 99 per cent of the air, oxygen and nitrogen are insignificant in their heat-absorption effect. It is here that the water vapor, almost insignificant in amount, shows much of its influence on the atmosphere. Despite its relative scarcity water vapor is the principal absorber of heat in the air. Since nine-tenths of the water vapor lies beneath a height of 5 miles, we can further appreciate why the air near the earth's surface is higher in temperature than the overlying air.

The effect of water vapor in controlling and regulating temperatures can be shown very convincingly. How better can we describe the influence of water vapor on the atmosphere than by contrasting regions where there exist an abundance and a scarcity of water vapor in the air? For this purpose let us consider dry desert air and moist jungle air.

Anyone familiar with deserts has experienced the extreme range in temperature from day to night. Such air is extremely dry. Consequently, during the daytime objects in the desert are heated by the direct rays of the sun. The air itself is found to be quite cool in the shade. At night the heated objects cool rapidly. The air, having little water vapor, absorbs only a slight amount while the sun is shining and, with its disappearance at night, becomes remarkably cold, having little moisture to retain any heat. High mountain air exhibits the same phenomena.

Humid air has a much more uniform temperature, since the water vapor absorbs much heat during the daylight hours and tends to retain it after the sun has set.

Thus temperature and humidity have somewhat reciprocal effects. Irregularities in temperature cause daily variations in humidity but one of the original causes contributing to these temperature irregularities is this compositional change in the amount of atmospheric water vapor, mentioned in Chap. 1.

Evaporation

No discussion of humidity would be complete without a consideration of the process by which the air acquires its water content. "Evaporation" is the process by which water in a liquid state is changed to vapor. The water vapor in the air is obtained by evaporation from the surface waters of the earth. Subsequent condensation and precipitation return this water to the earth, completing a continuous cycle.

However, evaporation does not take place at a constant rate, regardless of the supply of surface water available. There are many factors that retard or promote the rate and amount of evaporation.

FACTORS AFFECTING EVAPORATION. 1. *Temperature.*—The rate of evaporation varies directly with the temperature of the water. As the water temperature increases, the vapor pressure of the water, or the ability of the water particles to fly off into the air, increases rapidly. It is common knowledge that hot water will evaporate—"dry up"— faster than cold water.

2. *Relative Humidity.*—When the air above the water is dry or has a low relative humidity, evaporation will clearly be greater than when air with a high relative humidity overlies the water surface.

3. *Wind.*—Wind is an important aid in evaporation in that it replaces the moist air near the water with dry air. Clearly a minimum wind velocity is required to remove the moist air completely. Any further increase in velocity is of no greater value. Further, over ocean surfaces, the more the vertical gustiness of the wind the greater will be the evaporation. Obviously, simple horizontal air motion will result only in the transposition of moist air above the ocean surface, without the introduction of drier air from aloft.

4. *Composition of Water.*—Evaporation varies inversely with the salinity of the water, proceeding at a greater rate from fresh water than from salt water. Under equivalent conditions, ocean water will evaporate about 5 per cent more slowly than fresh water.

5. *Area of Evaporation.*—Clearly, if two volumes of water are equal, evaporation will be greater for the one having the larger exposed surface.

6. *Atmospheric Pressure.*—The lower the pressure of the air above the water, the greater will be the evaporation. Normally, however, when low atmospheric pressure prevails naturally, other factors are present, such as higher relative humidity, which tend to nullify this factor.

LATENT HEAT OF VAPORIZATION.—Whenever water evaporates, a large amount of heat is absorbed. This heat energy is required for the change of state from liquid to gas. Since this heat is used only to effect the transition to a vapor state and has no effect on the temperature of either the liquid or the vapor, it is known as "latent heat." When water reaches the boiling point, it remains at a temperature of 100°C. (or 212°F.), until all the water has boiled off. The heat absorbed after the liquid reached 100°C. is employed in the change of state, and the resulting steam or water vapor is also at a temperature of 100°C.

We are all familiar with the cooling effect produced by evaporation. Why are we afforded relief in hot humid weather by fanning if more hot air is brought in contact with the skin? Fanning (wind motion) stimulates evaporation. The latent heat absorbed in this process cools the skin. In the same way a porous earthenware water jug remains cool in hot weather owing to the loss of heat from the evaporation at its moist surface. Specifically, the latent heat of vaporization is the heat necessary to change 1 gram of water under normal conditions at 100°C. to 1 gram of vapor at 100°C., and equals 540 calories per gram of water.

It is extremely important to note that when water vapor condenses, this latent heat is liberated, sometimes being known as "latent heat of condensation." Consequently, during condensation in the atmosphere, heat is released. This process tends to warm the air, or rather to slow the cooling that results from other influences.

CHAPTER 4

ATMOSPHERIC EQUILIBRIUM—STABILITY AND INSTABILITY

The importance of vertical air motion was stressed in Chap. 2 on Air Temperatures. Consequently the equilibrium of the atmosphere should be examined since it has an important bearing on vertical air motion. Equilibrium in this connection refers only to mechanical equilibrium and to vertical air motion.

Nature of Equilibrium

The atmosphere would be in a state of equilibrium, *i.e.*, show an absence of vertical air motion, except for the effect of certain special influences. These influences, as considered earlier, are (1) heating, (2) fronts, (3) topographic irregularities. There are two important types of equilibrium: stable and unstable. Air in stable equilibrium, or stable air, is air that, once set in vertical motion, tends to come to rest or, theoretically, to return to its original position. Air in unstable equilibrium, or unstable air, is air that, once set in vertical motion, tends to continue moving from its original position with increasing velocity. The type of equilibrium existing in the atmosphere at a particular time depends upon existing temperature and humidity conditions. Hence, before studying the question of stability and instability, we should give further attention to these conditions.

Vertical Temperature and Humidity Conditions

Since stable and unstable equilibrium of the atmosphere are associated with vertical air motion, the study of the problem involves the examination of *vertical* temperature and humidity conditions. This requires further analysis of the adiabatic and existing lapse rates, whose relationship actually determines stability conditions.

DRY ADIABATIC RATE.—We considered elsewhere the effect of rising or falling air motion on temperatures within the particular moving air mass. In the process of uplift, air always expands, owing to the decrease of pressure from the surrounding atmosphere, and in so doing causes a consequent decrease in temperature. It was noted that this decrease takes place at a constant rate for air that is dry, *i.e.*, unsaturated. Dry air is defined as air with a relative humidity below 100 per cent. We

47

noted that the rate of cooling of ascending dry air is 5.5°F. per 1,000 feet or 1°F. per 185 feet. This is the *dry* adiabatic rate.

SATURATED ADIABATIC RATE.—When air is saturated, having a relative humidity of 100 per cent, adiabatic temperature changes (resulting from the expansion or the contraction of air) occur at a different and somewhat variable rate depending on temperature, pressure and moisture content. Saturated air is also termed "wet" or "moist" air.

Assume that a mass of moist air is set in vertical motion by any of the conditions explained earlier. As the moist air rises, expansion results in cooling, and cooling of saturated air causes condensation. But in the process of condensation, latent heat is always liberated by the condensing water vapor. Consequently, as saturated air rises and cools adiabatically, latent heat is returned to the air as long as condensation continues. The amount of heat liberated depends on the amount of condensation, which may vary. On the average, rising moist air liberates heat at a rate which warms the air by 2.3°F. per 1,000 feet. However, rising air cools normally at a rate of 5.5°F. per 1,000 feet. If saturated, however, the moist air regains 2.3° from condensation and leaves a net cooling effect of 3.2°F. per 1,000 feet. The average rate of cooling for saturated air is thus 3.2°F. per 1,000 feet. The saturated adiabatic rate is sometimes referred to as the moist, or pseudo, adiabatic rate. It is emphasized that this rate may show considerable variation. Subsiding moist air usually warms at the dry adiabatic rate of 5.5°F. per 1,000 ft. unless evaporation of the condensed moisture occurs.

From a consideration of the two rates, it is clear that a mass of air can and does cool according to both the dry and wet adiabatics, along different portions of its path. A parcel of air may be originally dry before uplift begins, regardless of the cause of the uplift. The rising air then cools according to the dry adiabatic rate. If the air rises sufficiently, it will ultimately cool to the dew point and become saturated. Further rising will result in cooling according to the saturated or moist adiabatic rate. Hence, rising moist air within clouds, usually exhibits pseudo or moist adiabatic conditions.

ADIABATIC AND LAPSE RATES COMPARED.—From the values given, we note that the dry adiabatic rate is steeper or greater than the saturated adiabatic or the normal lapse rates. The normal lapse rate is very nearly the same as the moist adiabatic. Remember, however, that the lapse rate varies widely with time and location, being sometimes less than the saturated adiabatic and at other times more than the dry adiabatic. We shall see very shortly just how this erratic behavior of the lapse rate affects atmospheric equilibrium.

The graphic relationship of these three temperature rates often aids in the understanding of them. In Fig. 4-1, altitude is shown on the vertical axis, increasing from sea level upward; temperature is shown on the horizontal axis, increasing to the right. In (*a*), the dry adiabatic has the smallest slope, showing the greatest temperature change with altitude. The adiabatic curve in (*b*) shows the case in which dry air after

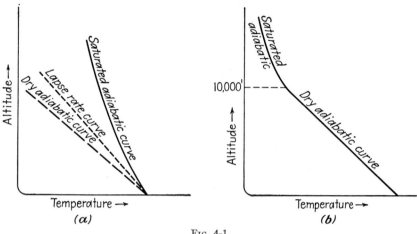

Fig. 4-1.

rising 10,000 feet has become saturated, and then cools as shown by the saturated adiabatic curve. Depending on the time and place of observation, the lapse rate curve may show a widely varying slope.

VARIATIONS OF THE LAPSE RATE.—It is interesting and very important to note that the lapse rate varies not only horizontally in the atmos-

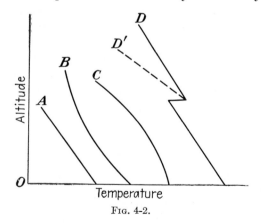

Fig. 4-2.

phere but vertically as well. The graph in Fig. 4-2 shows four possible conditions of the lapse rate. Curve *A* represents a constant lapse rate showing no change with altitude. Curve *B* illustrates a lapse rate that grows smaller with increasing altitude, while curve *C* indicates a lapse

rate that increases with altitude.   Curve *D* illustrates a lapse rate in air
having an abrupt inversion, shown by the sudden temperature increase
at the horizontal part of the curve.   Note that the lapse rate in the overlying warm air mass may be entirely different, as indicated by the branch
curve *D'*.   These lapse-rate variations have a pronounced effect on the
stability conditions now to be studied.

Stability and Instability

At any particular time the relationship between the adiabatic rate
and the existing lapse rate determines whether or not the air will be stable.
Let us now examine the different possibilities.

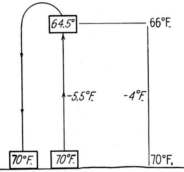

Fig. 4-3.—Stability in the case of forced uplift of air such as might occur when air is forced
over mountains.

Stable Air.—Assume that the surface air is at a temperature of
70°F., with a lapse rate of 4°F. per 1,000 feet existing.   Imagine that a
parcel of this 70° air is forced into vertical ascent as shown in Fig. 4-3.
After 1,000 feet of uplift, the rising air cools to 64.5°F., while the surrounding quiet air, cooling at the vertical lapse rate, cools to only 66°F.
Thus the rising air is colder than the adjacent air at the same level
and must sink downward, until its *temperature,* and hence its *density,*
equal that of the air at some lower level.   Where is this level?   Obviously, it is back at the ground, where the upward motion originated and
where the temperatures and densities are the same.   Theoretically, this
parcel of air would never start to rise at all, for the slightest ascent
would cause it to become colder and heavier than the surrounding air.
Such air, with adiabatic and existing lapse rate relations such as to cause
a resistance to vertical displacement, is said to be "stable."   Notice that
the real or existing lapse rate in this case is the lower of the two rates.

Consider another case.   On a warm summer day, with the surface
air at 80°F., a parcel of air becomes relatively overheated for some
reason, gains additional energy, and reaches 90°F.   Assume the lapse

rate to be 3.5°F. per 1,000 feet on this occasion. Clearly the warmer air will rise and expand, thereby cooling adiabatically, while the surrounding quiet air cools at the current lapse rate of 3.5°F. per 1,000 feet. Thus the rising air will cool faster than the surrounding air, for the lapse rate is here also less than the adiabatic rate. At some level the ascending air will therefore overcome the 10° initial difference and will then cease to rise.

This is illustrated in Fig. 4-4. Note that the temperature difference between the rising and the adjacent quiet air grows steadily less, until it is nil at 5,000 feet.

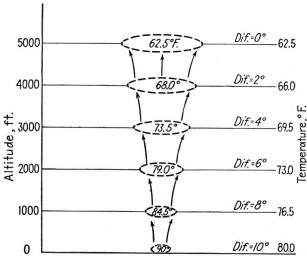

Fig. 4-4.—Restoration of equilibrium in air when vertical motion is initiated by surface temperature differences and when stable lapse-rate conditions prevail.

This case illustrates again the behavior of the atmosphere when stable equilibrium conditions prevail. Even though a local air parcel rises from its original position as a result of receiving an energy increase as its temperature rises, this air again reaches a state of stable equilibrium at a new level. As we shall see, this would not occur if the atmosphere were in an unstable equilibrium state.

From these cases we conclude that whenever the *lapse rate* is *less* than the *adiabatic rate*, the air is stable. Air that is displaced vertically for mechanical reasons (fronts or mountains) tends to resist displacement or return to its original position. Air that is displaced through temperature differences soon reaches the temperature of the surrounding air at some new level and comes to rest.

UNSTABLE AIR.—We can illustrate unstable air conditions in the same manner as above. As a first case, we assume the lapse rate to be greater than the adiabatic (Fig. 4-5) being 7°F. per 1,000 feet, with the surface air temperatures still at 70°. Suppose we now permit a parcel of the 70° air to rise and thus cool adiabatically. But the lapse rate is here greater than the adiabatic rate, causing the surrounding air to become increasingly colder with reference to the rising air at increasingly higher levels. Consequently, the rising air becomes relatively warmer at each new level, accelerating its upward velocity.

Let us also consider the case in which an initial temperature difference exists, with a parcel of air warming to 90°F., 5° more than the adjacent air. The lapse rate is again 7°F. per 1,000 feet. Note that in this case the rising air temperatures do not overtake those of the surrounding atmosphere. Rather, the difference at each level becomes increasingly greater, causing the ascending air to become relatively still warmer than

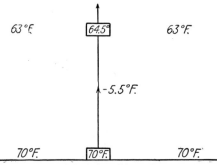

FIG. 4-5.—Instability in the case of forced uplift such as may occur over mountains.

the surrounding air. This causes an acceleration of the velocity of the rising air (Fig. 4-6). Here again is an example of instability in the atmosphere, caused simply by the fact that the lapse rate is greater than the adiabatic rate. Thus, air is unstable whenever the *lapse rate* is *greater* than the *adiabatic rate*. In this case rising or falling air always shows a greater temperature difference than the adjacent quiet air at any new level, and thereby its own rate of motion is accelerated.

So far we have considered the lapse rate to remain constant. However, we observed above that this is often not the case, especially when inversions exist, with the introduction of an entirely new mass of air at some altitude. It is clear, therefore, that air may be stable at its lower levels and become unstable at some higher altitude where the lapse rate may increase sufficiently to exceed the adiabatic. Or the reverse may be true, with unstable air at low altitudes becoming stable at higher levels owing to a decrease in the lapse rate.

CONDITIONAL INSTABILITY.—To complete our discussion of stability we should also consider the results when air is saturated, with the moist or saturated adiabatic rate prevailing, instead of the dry, as examined above. The average saturated adiabatic is closely 3.2°F. per 1,000 feet. In the example above for stable air, we considered the lapse rate to be 4°F. per 1,000 feet, or less than the dry adiabatic of 5.5°F. per 1,000 feet. This relationship yielded stable air. But for saturated air, the lapse rate now *exceeds* the adiabatic rate, hence this air is unstable. The reader should prove this to himself by developing an example similar to those used to illustrate stability and instability above.

Whenever the existing *lapse rate* lies *between* the values for the *wet* and the *dry adiabatics*, whether or not the air is stable, depends on whether the air is dry or saturated. *The air is then said to be conditionally unstable.*

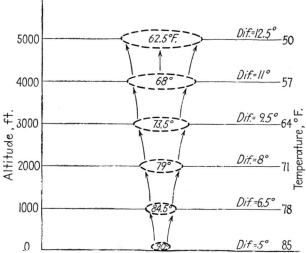

Fig. 4-6.—Loss of equilibrium in air when vertical motion is initiated by surface temperature differences and when unstable lapse-rate conditions prevail.

If the air is initially dry, it is then stable, but should the air for any reason become saturated, it will immediately assume an unstable condition.

A column of rising air may be stable and unstable at different elevations as a result of condensation after sufficient uplift and cooling.

In Fig. 4-7 the ascending air column is stable up to 2,000 feet, for its temperature is slowly overtaking the surrounding air temperature. But at 2,000 feet the air has cooled to its dew point, with condensation forming a cloud as the air rises above this level. The air now cools at the saturated adiabatic, which is here exceeded by the lapse rate, resulting in the moist air becoming unstable above 2,000 feet. This is clearly shown by the increasing temperature differences between rising and surrounding air at corresponding levels.

It is evident that whenever the lapse rate is less than the moist adiabatic the air must be stable under all conditions, since dry air with its high adiabatic rate will certainly be stable, as will moist air also, whose lower adiabatic rate will still be higher than the lapse rate. Such air is said to be "absolutely stable."

When the lapse rate exceeds even the dry adiabatic, the air is said to be "absolutely unstable," for instability will exist regardless of the humidity condition of the air.

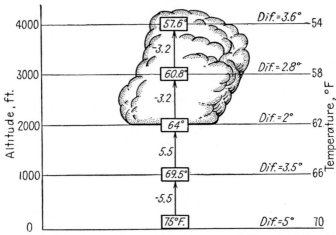

FIG. 4-7.—Conditional instability in an air column where stability exists below the original dew-point level (2,000 feet) and instability above.

SUMMARY.—Let us summarize the conditions affecting equilibrium in the atmosphere:

In general:

> *Stability.* Lapse rate is less than the adiabatic rate, or $LR < AR$
> *Instability.* Lapse rate exceeds the adiabatic rate, or $LR > AR$

In particular:

> *Neutral Stability.* Lapse rate equals dry adiabatic rate for dry air and wet adiabatic for moist air, $LR = AR$
> *Conditional Instability.* Lapse rate lies in between values of wet and dry adiabatic rates, or $LR \genfrac{}{}{0pt}{}{> SAR}{< DAR}$
> *Absolute Stability.* Lapse rate is less than the saturated adiabatic, or $LR < SAR$
> *Absolute Instability.* Lapse rate exceeds the dry adiabatic, or $LR > DAR$

We can also illustrate graphically the actual examples considered earlier.

1. Figure 4-8 shows the stability example considered previously. The coordinates of the point of intersection of the adiabatic and lapse-

rate curves give the altitude and the final temperature at which the rising air comes to rest.

2. Figure 4-9 illustrates the case of instability, wherein the curves

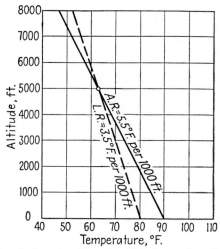

FIG. 4-8.—Graphic solution of problem in which dry surface air at 90°F. (rising and cooling at the dry adiabatic rate as a result of initial 10-degree temperature difference) reaches new position of equilibrium at 5,000 feet at 62.5°F. when the lapse rate is 3.5°F. per 1,000 feet.

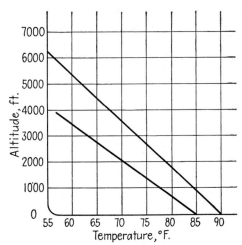

FIG. 4-9.—Loss of equilibrium due to instability when the lapse rate is greater than the adiabatic rate as shown by the divergence of lapse-rate curve (left), from adiabatic curve (right).

representing the adiabatic and the lapse rates separate continuously with increasing altitude.

3. The example of conditional instability is shown graphically in

Fig. 4-10.   The dry adiabatic curve below 2,000 feet approaches the lapse-rate curve, showing stability below that altitude.   Above 2,000 feet, the saturated adiabatic curve now separates from the lapse rate, showing instability.

The importance of equilibrium and stability factors of the atmosphere cannot be overlooked in explaining and interpreting many of the

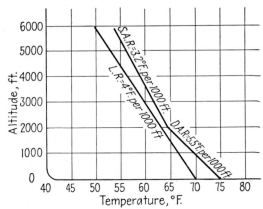

Fig. 4-10.—Conditional instability with saturation occurring in a rising air column at 2,000 feet.

weather phenomena.   Note well that stability and instability refer to equilibrium conditions of the air.   Thus, air may be in a very unstable state of equilibrium and yet be perfectly free of vertical motion.   The unstable equilibrium conditions do not become manifest until vertical motion is initiated.   Similarly, the state of stable equilibrium does not preclude the existence of vertical motion.   But, should such motion be initiated by any of the factors considered heretofore, it would tend to diminish and the air would come to rest or return to its original position.

CHAPTER 5

ᶜ ᴕNDENSATION AND PRECIPITATION

ᴵn continuing our examination of the behavior of atmospheric moisture, let us note again the ceaseless humidity cycle. The vast expanse of oceans is the main source for the moisture evaporated into the atmosphere. This condition is as old as the atmosphere and the oceans themselves. Yet there has been no significant diminution of the volume of the seas nor increase in the water vapor of the air. How do we account for this remarkable balance between the waters of the air and the oceans?

By the processes of condensation and precipitation, huge quantities or water are returned to the seas, either directly or from streams that convey this water to the oceans. In addition to the rain, snow, etc., that fall directly on the sea surface, thousands of rivers pour their contents into the sea. The mighty Amazon, for instance, contributes so great a share that fresh water is experienced in the Atlantic 200 miles beyond its mouth! But with all this, the ocean volume is not significantly increased for the cycle of evaporation, condensation, and precipitation is continuous and will be so as long as the sun exists to supply the heat energy necessary for the operation of this tremendous atmospheric machine.

We have previously considered one phase of this cycle—the process of evaporation and the nature and behavior of water while in the atmosphere. This was considered in relation to the all-important humidity regulator—temperature. We followed the variations in humidity until the air was saturated or the dew-point temperature was attained. In continuing our study of the cycle, we shall examine the processes and forms of condensation and then of precipitation.

Conditions of Condensation

Condensation has been defined earlier as the process in which water vapor is changed to liquid water. It should be noted that when this process occurs at subfreezing temperatures, the vapor often turns directly into the solid form—ice—with no intervening liquid stage. Technically, the transition from vapor to solid is known as "sublimation," but we shall use the term "condensation" to cover either situation for they are both a part of the same major process.

In order for condensation to occur within the atmosphere, certain conditions must be satisfied:

1. SUFFICIENT AMOUNT OF WATER VAPOR.—There must be enough water vapor in the air to allow for condensation. It is the water vapor in the air that condenses; hence, no water vapor, no condensation.

2. COOLING.—If sufficient moisture exists, the air must be cooled below the original dew point before condensation will occur. Of the two methods of saturating the air (cooling and increasing the water content), we have noted that the cooling is considerably more important.

3. NUCLEI OF CONDENSATION.—All the water droplets condensing in the air above the earth's surface form around microscopic or sub-microscopic solid particles. Whenever moisture is cooled below the original dew point, it must have something to provide this center or nucleus on which it can condense. These minute solid particles must be somewhat water absorbent—hygroscopic—to be suitable condensation centers. If the air were absolutely free of such particles, there would be practically no natural condensation, regardless of the first two conditions. These hygroscopic nuclei are mostly minute crystals of salt commonly found in sea water.

Thus, all three conditions are necessary: water vapor; cooling or temperature decrease; and minute hygroscopic particles, or nucleuses of condensation. Of these factors the temperature is the most variable. Normally, sufficient water vapor and hygroscopic particles exist in the air to provide for some condensation. If the temperature drops sufficiently, condensation will nearly always result. If no falling temperatures occur or are expected, condensation is unlikely.

Forms of Condensation

The forms assumed by condensed moisture in nature are varied and often beautiful in appearance. Depending upon differing conditions under which cooling occurs, the resulting condensation types may be classified under the common headings of dew, frost, clouds, and fog.

DEW.—Dew is familiar to everyone. Leaves and blades of grass covered with sparkling beads of water droplets are almost normal morning features of the spring, summer, or autumn landscape. The formation of dew (sometimes called snakespit) is readily explained. On clear, calm evenings, the earth will cool rapidly by the process of radiation and become colder than the air resting on the surface. Consequently, this surface air will cool by contact with the colder earth beneath. As this process continues after the sun has set, the air will become cooler and cooler until the dew point is reached. It should be carefully understood that this all takes place in a very thin layer of air in contact with the earth, perhaps a mere few inches. This cooling of the air in contact with the earth is a conduction process and is restricted to a thin layer, since the air is, as explained previously, a very poor conductor of heat.

On further cooling below the dew point, the excess water vapor in the air will condense. Dark objects such as vegetation always cool the fastest, for it will be remembered that dark objects are good absorbers of heat and good absorbers are always good radiators and lose their heat rapidly when the source is removed. Thus the moisture will condense directly on the cold dark surfaces, whether they be of natural or artificial origin.

Consequently, what is commonly known as "sweating" of pipes, cargo, or hulls is actually the formation of dew. It is obvious that *clear* and *calm* conditions must prevail. Clouds act as blankets and greatly reduce the cooling of the earth by radiation, and hence, also, the subsequent cooling of the air. Windy nights prevent the warm air from remaining in contact with the earth or cold objects long enough to cool sufficiently, even if clear skies prevail. Both clear skies and calm air are necessary conditions for dew formation.

Frost.—Frost is *not* frozen dew. The conditions of formation of dew and frost are practically identical, with one exception. Dew forms when condensation occurs on cold objects above the freezing point; frost forms when condensation takes place below freezing temperatures. Under such conditions the moisture changes from the vapor state directly into the solid or ice state, skipping the liquid condition entirely. A similar but reverse phenomenon occurs with dry ice, where the solid carbon dioxide evaporates directly into a gas, with no liquid forming.

Clouds.—Clouds are so important a topic in weather description and analysis that they will be treated separately in Chap. 6. Briefly, however, clouds form when the air at higher altitudes is cooled to the dew point, yielding water droplets which condense around the nucleuses of condensation. Nearly all clouds form as a result of air that has cooled adiabatically: *i.e.*, air that has risen, expanded, and consequently cooled. When air rises sufficiently, it will cool to the dew point. Continued uplift of the air above this level results in clouds.

Rising air currents tend to keep the clouds from falling, since the droplets composing the clouds are very small and light. Many a cloud often does fall, but as its base falls to an altitude where the air temperature is above the dew point, the small droplets readily evaporate. If the clouds form at sufficiently high altitudes, the temperatures are below freezing and, as in the case of frost, the condensation often yields ice crystals, with no water-droplet stage. Thus high clouds are composed not of water but of ice crystals.

Fog.—Fog is one of the common forms of condensation that occur when the air near the earth's surface falls below the original dew-point temperature. Physically, there is very little difference between a fog and a cloud. They are both composed of minute water droplets suspended in the air. Fog, however, forms in the air near the earth's surface whereas clouds are features of much higher altitudes. Essentially, then, the difference between fog and clouds is one of method and place of formation rather than of structure or appearance.

Clouds form when the air cools adiabatically through rising and expanding. *Fog* forms through cooling of the air by contact with colder material, or on occasions through saturation of the air by increasing the water content. Frequently a continuous gradation exists from thick fogs into low-lying clouds, there being no definite distinction in appearance. The type of fog that forms depends on existing conditions and falls into four recognized categories: "radiation fog," "advection fog," "frontal fog," and "upslope fog."

In general, then, if surface air (the air near the earth's surface) is close to and is approaching the dew point (as determined by the psychrometer), fog formation can be anticipated. If the temperature should be increasing after the fog has formed, the dispersal of the fog may be expected. The thickness of the fog depends on various factors of humidity, temperature, wind, nucleuses, etc.

Radiation Fog.—Radiation fogs are simply explained and are of less importance than the other types. They form under the same conditions, though further advanced, that formed dew and frost. On clear nights, with very slight wind, the earth and consequently the air above it will cool rapidly. If the air is cooled to a greater depth than the slight layer necessary for dew and reaches its dew point, the resulting condensation will form not only on the ground but also on the nucleuses of condensation in the air. This yields minute droplets suspended in the air which constitute fog. Since the cooling of the air depends on the earth beneath cooling rapidly by radiation, it is known as "radiation fog."

Obviously, there will always be dew or frost when a radiation fog forms. Since clear nights are always necessary, radiation fog, in addition to dew or frost, usually indicates fair weather for 12 hours at least. A slight wind is necessary in order to stir the cold air in contact with the ground and scatter it sufficiently so that fog forms. Further, the fog forms first and is thickest in the low areas or depressions since cool, relatively heavy air flows to the lowest points. Thus, radiation fog is sometimes known as "ground fog" owing to this tendency to "hug" the ground.

Harbors, especially those surrounded by forested hills, are often shrouded in radiation fog during the night and early morning. Then, as the sun comes up over the horizon the fog is said to "lift" or "burn off." Here again we have an excellent example of the earth's influence in heating the air. The fog is not simply blown away and does not actually rise. Rather, it evaporates back into the air as the latter is warmed.

But does it evaporate from the top down? On the contrary, the rising sun warms the earth, which then warms the surface air first. Hence the fog evaporates from the bottom up, or lifts. The last remnant of a thick radiation fog may therefore look like a low white cloud extending outward from the hilltops or other high spots.

In certain areas where inversions are frequent, the cold, heavier air is trapped beneath a lid of overlying warm air. Consequently during nights favorable to radiation, pronounced cooling occurs in this cold air layer which may have considerable thickness and yield thick, high fogs that dispel slowly even after the sun rises.

Advection Fog.—It will be recalled that convection refers to the transportation of air in a vertical direction, the warm air rising and the cold air falling. *Advection* refers to air in horizontal motion. Thus, advection fogs are those which result from air being cooled following horizontal movement.

There are essentially two processes responsible for the production of this type of fog:

1. Cold air may, as a result of its horizontal motion, pass across a warmer sea surface and at the same time mix with the warmer air prevailing there.

2. Warm moist air may blow across a cold surface and become chilled by contact and by mixing with the cold air associated with the cold surface beneath.

In the first case, the warm vapors evaporating from the water will immediately condense and form a very shallow "steam fog." This is encountered very frequently when cold air blows across a warm ocean current, such as the Gulf Stream. As a consequence, the water vapor rising from the warm current and meeting the cold air appears to give the water a steaming or smoking appearance as it condenses. This feature is also very prevalent over the northern portion of the warm Japan Current. In general, the waters in the Arctic areas are warmer than their continental surroundings in the winter. Here again the passage of cold air across the warm waters will cause this advection fog to form, giving rise to the name "arctic smoke" owing to its appearance.

The second type of advection fog, in which warm, humid air passes across a cold surface, is by far the most important kind of marine fog encountered. It has been estimated that about four-fifths of all maritime fogs owe their origin to this process. To a great extent, their occurrence depends on a definite contrast between air and water temperatures. Further, the development of these fogs is greatly aided by the presence of ocean currents whose waters differ markedly in temperature. Then, if the winds are such as to transport the air of the warm current across the cold sea, the warm humid air will be chilled by contact with the cold sea surface and by some mixing with the colder air.

Clearly then, fog will develop in these instances over the cold surface and, when the wind direction changes so that the warm air no longer meets the cold current, the fog will be dispelled.

Usually, a wind force of about 4 to 15 miles an hour is required for the proper development of this type of fog. If the wind is less, the fog will form but will be limited to a very shallow layer of the surface air, the effect of the above wind being to disseminate the fog to a greater thickness of air. Too strong a wind will lift the fog to form a low overcast condition.

Fig. 5-1.—Advection fog bank. (*Courtesy of Humphreys, U.S. Weather Bureau.*)

Typical examples of this important kind of fog are very common. The warm Gulf Stream flowing to the northeast encounters the cold southward flowing Labrador Current east of Newfoundland in the vicinity of the Grand Banks. There is an abrupt change in temperature across the line of separation of these currents which is common not only to the water but to the air above as well. Whenever the wind is southerly to easterly, large quantities of warm humid air cross this temperature break, with the consequent thick fog formation so common to the Grand Banks and Newfoundland waters. This forms with a frequency of 1 out of 3 days in winter months, but is more common in summer, with an occurrence of 2 out of 3 days.

Further eastward, the passage of the warm Gulf air across the colder British Isles in winter time produces some of the thickest fogs to be encountered, including the famous "pea-soup fogs" of England.

The air traveling toward the northeast with the Japan Current in the North Pacific forms frequent and dense fogs on encountering the cold air and water flowing south through the Bering Straits. The thick, common fog predominating over the Aleutians owes its origin to this same condition. Warm moist air is often blown on to the coast of California by the prevailing westerly winds in that area, which have picked up much moisture from the Pacific. When meeting the cold shore currents off California, or on striking the chilled coast itself in winter time, the well-known California fog develops.

Precipitation and Frontal Fogs.—There is one other method of fog production that deserves our consideration. Actually, this type forms not so much by cooling as by saturation through increasing the water content. We have already considered the importance of a cold-air wedge in forcing warm air to rise. The line of meeting of the warm and the cold air was defined as a "front." As the warm air rises over the cold wedge, it cools adiabatically, and ultimately clouds will form *in the*

Fig. 5-2.—The formation of frontal fog.

warmer air. The cold-air wedge itself may be very humid and near the dew point. Should the clouds in the warm air yield rain, this rain will partly evaporate in falling through the humid but yet unsaturated cold air beneath. Ultimately saturation of the cold air will result, and any added water vapor, or temperature change, or a combination of the two, will cause a fog to form in the cold air which may extend from the ground up to the layer of clouds in the warmer air. Although a more or less continuous mass of condensed water droplets will then exist, from fog to clouds, there will still be a definite distinction as regards method of formation.

Upslope Fog.—This form of fog develops when relatively humid air ascends a gradually sloping plain. In the course of this motion, adiabatic cooling causes a slow decrease in the air temperature. Ultimately, the dew point may be reached, whereupon an extensive fog layer usually forms. Fog of this type is a rather common occurrence in the interior plains of the United States. It is particularly frequent when humid south or southeast winds, originating in the Gulf of Mexico, follow the contour of the gently rising plains west of the Mississippi, which reach an altitude of more than 2,000 feet.

Commonly in the winter, a combination of upslope and advection fog occurs in this area as a result of the cold land surface beneath the warm air approaching from the Gulf. Such conditions may yield thick and persistent fog.

Fogs are usually classified according to their effect on visibility. These conditions are given in Table VI.

TABLE VI.—FOG-VISIBILITY TABLE

	Objects not Visible at
Dense fog	50 yards
Thick fog	200 yards
Fog	500 yards
Moderate fog	½ nautical mile
Thin fog	1 nautical mile

Forms of Precipitation

For purposes of definition we may consider precipitation to be any condensed atmospheric moisture that falls to the earth's surface. Hence, no precipitation will occur unless the primary process of condensation takes place first. Whether or not we apply the term "precipitation" depends on whether or not the water particles fall to the ground.

All forms of precipitation, regardless of appearance, are often termed collectively as "hydrometeors." The U.S. Weather Bureau has classified these hydrometeors into about 50 specific types, of which only the more common will be examined here.

RAIN.—Rain is obviously the most familiar example of precipitation. It is so common that in ordinary conversation it usually replaces the more general word. Although the definition of rain is simple, the explanation of its origin is complex. Briefly, rain is precipitation in the form of liquid drops. Clouds are the source of rain, yet all or most clouds do not yield any precipitation. The moisture particles composing most clouds are so small that they remain suspended in the atmosphere, buoyed up by even relatively light air currents existing at cloud levels. Further, if the cloud does sink, evaporation of the minute water droplets occurs almost as fast as they descend below the dew point or condensation level. Thus, clouds are normally in a stable condition and tend to "float" in the air.

When the cloud droplets grow in size and become heavy enough to fall through the previously supporting atmosphere, rain occurs. Why this happens with some clouds and not with others has long been a perplexing problem which is not yet completely understood. It is believed at present, and generally borne out by observation, that rain clouds require the association of ice crystals with the water droplets within the cloud. When this combination is present, the physical processes within the cloud permit the growth of moisture particles to the size of raindrops.

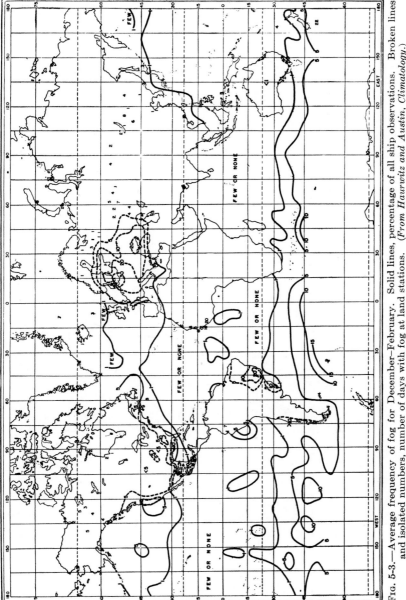

FIG. 5-3.—Average frequency of fog for December–February. Solid lines, percentage of all ship observations. Broken lines and isolated numbers, number of days with fog at land stations. (From Haurwitz and Austin, Climatology.)

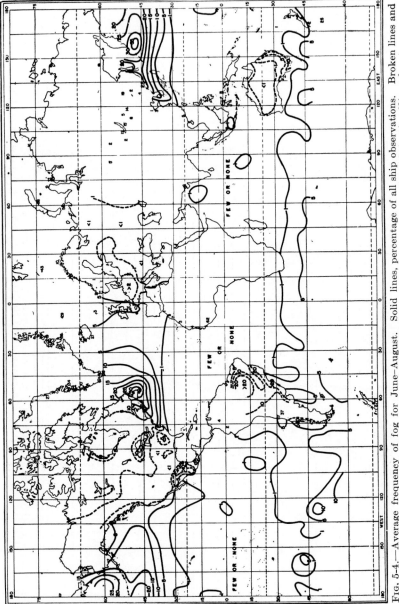

Fig. 5-4.—Average frequency of fog for June–August. Solid lines, percentage of all ship observations. Broken lines and isolated numbers, number of days with fog at land stations. (*From Haurwitz and Austin, Climatology.*)

Regardless of the size of the drops in the cloud, their size upon reaching the ground surface depends on two main factors: (1) the amount of evaporation undergone by the drop in its descent and (2) the effect of the friction of the air on the falling drop. In relatively quiet air, friction imposes a limiting size on raindrops, the effect being to shatter them if they grow too large. Should the air in the precipitation zone also be descending (which exists in certain parts of thunderstorms), drops of maximum size may occur.

Fig. 5-5.—Some types of snow crystals. (*Courtesy of U.S. Weather Bureau.*)

Clearly, the state of the air has a pronounced influence on the velocity of fall of rain, as well. Thus, both the size of raindrops and the intensity of the rainfall show considerable variation. In general, the conditions responsible for heavy rains (as will be studied later) are of relatively brief duration, whereas light and moderate rainfalls are usually associated with widespread weather patterns, of much longer duration. Thus the duration of rain is, in general, inversely proportional to its intensity.

Rain of very light intensity, composed of fine droplets barely reaching the ground, is called "drizzle." If the droplets completely evaporate before reaching the ground, we refer to the condition as "mist."

Snow.—When condensation occurs in rising air that has cooled to subfreezing temperatures, typical hexagonal ice crystals tend to form, instead of liquid droplets.   It will be remembered that condensation at the earth's surface yields frost when the dew point is below 32°F. Snow crystals may exist in isolated form or may coalesce to form snow flakes of varying sizes and shapes.   As a result of the union of hexagonal ice crystals, beautiful snowflake patterns in a tremendous variety occur. It is possible, and often common, for the lower section of a cloud to

Fig. 5-6.—Results of ice storm and freezing rain, New York, January, 1943.   (*Courtesy of Robidean Studios, U.S. Weather Bureau.*)

consist of water droplets, while the upper portion, above the freezing level, consists of snowflakes.

Sleet.—Sleet is true frozen rain.   If the water drops falling from the clouds encounter a layer of air with freezing temperature, they solidify into small, hard, clear ice pellets.   Sleet thus indicates a temperature inversion even though it may be a very slight one.   The temperature in the clouds may be very close to freezing and, if the air below the clouds is somewhat colder, sleet may result.

Hail.—Hail is a product of the violent convection found in a thunderstorm (discussed in Chap. 6) and occurs only in connection with a thunderstorm.   In the thundercloud the strong vertical air swirls the raindrops above and below the freezing level.   As a result, the drop freezes when it is carried to a height above the freezing line and grows by the accumulation of snow and water at the different levels. Consequently, when a hailstone is cut apart, it shows a series of concentric shells formed by the successive passages above and below the freezing level.

GLAZE.—When rain falls on objects or on the ground having sub-freezing temperatures, it freezes into a sheet or coating of ice, known as "glaze" or freezing rain. If this coating becomes thick, it often has a destructive effect owing to its heavy weight.

RIME.—Rime is a freezing fog. It forms as a thick frosty deposit when objects with subfreezing temperatures encounter a fog. In such a case the minute fog droplets freeze and adhere to the cold surface. Rime is thicker on the windward sides of objects, particularly when forming on hulls, masts, or bulkheads of vessels sailing through fog in cold weather. It also occurs on leading edges of airplanes flying through certain types of clouds.

Measurement of Precipitation

It is equally important to determine the amount of precipitation, as well as the kind and duration. Nearly all the measurable precipitation occurs as rain or snow, depending on the latitude and the season. A rather simple instrument, known as the "rain and snow gauge," is employed in their quantitative measurement.

RAIN GAUGE.—The common type of rain gauge is illustrated in Fig. 5-8. A is the receiver; B is the overflow compartment; C is the inner measuring tube; d is the sleeve of the funnel-shaped receiver, A, and fits over the measuring tube, C.

The gauge is supported in a vertical position by means of a tripod or other suitable stand. The area of the receiver, A, is ten times the area of the measuring tube. Therefore as water collects in the inner tube, C, its height is exaggerated tenfold, permitting more precise measurement of the rainfall. Since the inner tube is usually 20 inches high, it actually can contain only 2 inches of rain water. The depth of precipitation is determined by inserting a special hardwood measuring stick through the receiving funnel, A, and into the measuring tube. When withdrawn, the moist portion of the stick shows the depth of water within the tube. The measuring stick is so calibrated as to allow for the vertical exaggeration of the gauge. Thus, 10 inches on the stick is marked as 1 inch; 1 inch is marked as $\frac{1}{10}$ inch, and $\frac{1}{10}$ inch is marked as $\frac{1}{100}$ inch. After measurement, the water within the gauge is poured out. Should more than 2 inches of rain occur between observations, the excess water drains into the overflow tube. After the water in the inner tube is measured and disposed of, the excess in the larger container

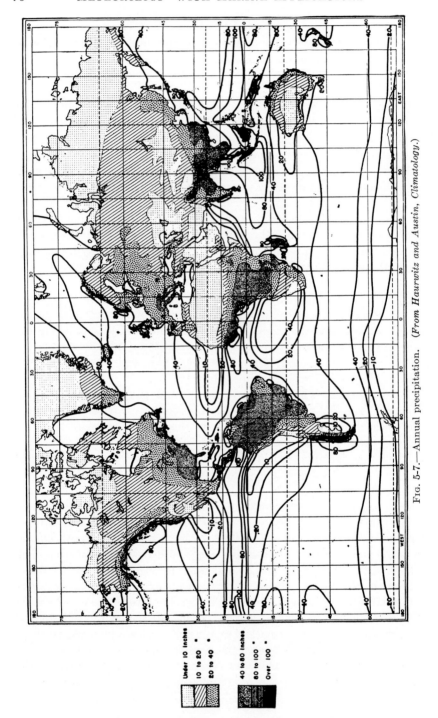

Fig. 5-7.—Annual precipitation.   (*From Haurwitz and Austin, Climatology.*)

Under 10 inches
10 to 20 "
20 to 40 "

40 to 80 inches
80 to 100 "
Over 100 "

should be poured carefully into the measuring tube and measured in the regular manner.   The sum of these two values is the total precipitation in the interval between observations.

The gauge obviously should be so situated as to give the most valid indication of the actual amount of precipitation.   No obstructions should be near it.   It should be placed where the least wind eddies may occur.   If mounted on some elevated surface, it should be as close to the center as possible.

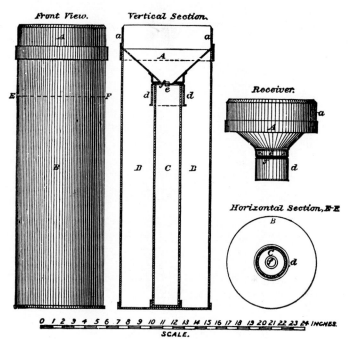

FIG. 5-8.—Rain gauge.

MEASURING THE DEPTH OF SNOW.—It is well known that a mass of snow has a much greater volume than an equivalent mass of water.   On the average, 10 inches of snow equals 1 inch of rain, or an average ratio exists between snow and rain, of 10 to 1.   However, this ratio varies considerably depending on the condition of the snow.   Consequently it is preferable to express the depth of snow according to the depth of rain it represents.

If the actual snow depth is also desired, care should be taken to measure this where uniform, level snow surfaces exist and not in drifts.

To determine the water equivalent of snow, the snow collected in the overflow container, *without the use of the inner tube* or *receiving funnel,* is simply melted and then poured into the measuring tube to be measured as rain. A better method consists of adding a known quantity of warm water to the overflow container, to melt the snow collected therein. The difference between the water added and the resulting melted snow,

Fig. 5-9.—Outer view of one type of recording rain gauge. (*Courtesy of Friez Instruments Division of Bendix Aviation Corporation.*)

as measured by pouring into the measuring tube, represents the water equivalent of the existing snow depth.

Somewhat more complicated automatic recording gauges are in use in the more elaborate weather observation stations. Note Fig. 5-9.

CHAPTER 6

CLOUDS AND THUNDERSTORMS

The varying cloud forms are among the greatest beauties of nature. At times they exhibit the most delicate of appearances, when composed of thin, feathery, curling wisps; or they may present a dappled sky formed of numberless individual scalelike or woolpack masses. At other times the clouds build up in towering majestic masses, with huge billowing domes extending upward thousands of feet.

To the poet and the artist, clouds are mere things of beauty. To the weather-wise officer they are one of the most important of the local weather features. Remember that all clouds are formed of minute water droplets, or ice crystals a few thousandths of an inch across, that actually float or remain suspended in the atmosphere at varying distances above the ground. So small are these particles that the slightest movement of the air is usually sufficient to keep them aloft. Precipitation results only when these particles increase greatly in size.

Clouds indicate the prevailing and past conditions in the air and, more important, the probable future atmospheric conditions. It is consequently very essential to be able to recognize the existing cloud types and to understand their relationship to the other atmospheric processes affecting weather.

We shall therefore examine first the observational features of clouds and conditions of the sky, and then relate these to the conditions causing their formation.

Amount of Cloudiness

Normally the amount of cloudiness is either stated in the number of tenths of the sky obscured by clouds or described verbally. The use of specific decimal fractions to indicate cloud coverage will of course give a more specific indication of this amount. The decimal point is usually omitted when writing numerical designations. Thus 7 indicates that seven-tenths of the sky is covered.

If described verbally, two sets of descriptive terms are often used. These are given in Table VII.

The term "overcast with breaks" is used for a sky more than nine-tenths covered but with slivers of clear sky showing through.

CEILING.—The term "ceiling," although common mainly to aviation, is so familiar that we shall consider it briefly. Ceiling is defined

73

TABLE VII. STATES OF THE SKY

Designation		Amount of cloudiness
Clear	Clear	Less than 1 tenth, or 1
Scattered	Partly cloudy	1 to 5 tenths inclusive, or 1 to 5
Broken	Cloudy	6 to 9 tenths inclusive, or 6 to 9
Overcast	Overcast	More than 9 tenths, or more than 9

as the height above the ground at which the cloud cover appears broken or overcast. Thus, if less than six-tenths of the sky is covered, the ceiling is considered "unlimited," regardless of the cloud heights. If broken or overcast conditions exist, but above 20,000 feet, the ceiling is "unlimited." A cloud ceiling above 10,000 feet is called "high," but is reported in weather messages as "unlimited."

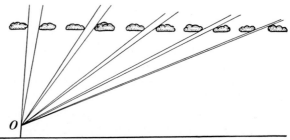

FIG. 6-1.—Perspective effect causing clouds to appear more closely together when near the horizon.

It is a matter of common observation that clouds always appear thicker, darker, and closer together toward the horizon, than overhead. This is merely an illusion and not a coincidence for any particular observer.

If breaks exist between clouds, the angular opening between the clouds appears to close up when seen at a distance. This perspective effect is seen in Fig. 6-1. The clouds may appear darker since several clouds, or a greater thickness of cloud, may be in the observer's line of sight near the horizon, allowing less light to penetrate.

MEASUREMENT OF CEILING.—A knowledge of the height of the cloud ceiling is often of great value. This factor can be determined quite readily whether it be day or night. In the daytime the ceiling height is found by releasing balloons that have been inflated so as to have a known rate of ascent, usually 400 feet per minute. After release, the balloon is kept under observation until it rises and disappears into the cloud base. The time consumed from release to disappearance, multiplied by 400, gives the height of the cloud base in feet.

At night, this height is determined by means of a "ceiling light." This is a powerful projection lamp, usually arranged to shine vertically upward. The observer stands at some known distance from the light and measures the elevation angle at which the light beam is reflected by the cloud base. The angle of elevation may be determined by means of the clinometer, a simple device used for measuring vertical angles, or a sextant, or any other instrument capable of measuring elevation angles. Knowing this angle and the base line of the observer, one can calculate by simple trigonometry the ceiling height. If this base line is constant

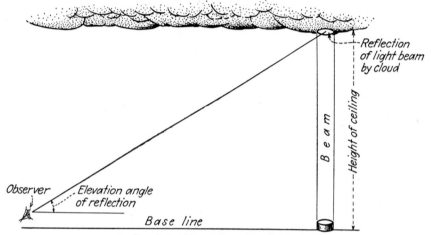

FIG. 6-2.—Use of the ceiling light.

for such measurements and only the angle varies, a table yielding the required height may be used (Fig. 6-2). The "ceilometer," consisting of an ultraviolet beam and a photoelectric scanner, is often used for daytime measurements.

Aboard ship, the ceiling light may be at one end of the vessel, with the observer at the other end. The length of the ship will then be the base line.

Cloud Classification

When clouds are first examined with a view toward recognition, they may well appear to be confused chaotic masses streaming across the sky in more or less disorder. However, most of this confusion vanishes once the cloud classification is understood and the description of the common forms is known. Frequently more than one type of cloud is present in the sky, but when the existence of two or more types is recognized, the identification of each is greatly simplified.

In accordance with an international meteorological agreement all clouds are classified according to two factors: their form and their height.

BASIC CLOUD FORMS.—Three basic cloud forms are recognized: "cirrus," "cumulus," and "stratus." All the other standard types are either these pure forms or modifications and combinations of them at different elevations, where varying air and moisture conditions are responsible for their form. Much more water vapor is available at lower than at higher levels. Clearly then, the higher a cloud, the thinner it will usually be; the lower the cloud, the denser and darker will it appear.

If a basic cloud form (with the exception of cirrus) occurs above its normal level, the cloud will be thin and the prefix "alto" precedes the name. If any cloud is associated with precipitation, the word "nimbus" (Latin for "rain") is introduced in combination with the name.

Cirrus.—This form embraces very high, thin, separated, or detached clouds that develop delicate patches or long extended fibers, frequently with a feathery appearance and always white in color.

Cumulus.—This form always exhibits flat-based individual cloud masses, with a pronounced vertical doming, and frequently a cauliflower-like structure.

Stratus.—This form implies an extended sheet or layerlike cloud covering all or large portions of the sky. This stratus type is usually a continuous cloud deck and may show minor rifts, but no definite individual cloud units.

HEIGHT CATEGORIES.—By height, clouds are classified according to three principal categories and a fourth, corollary division:

1. *High Clouds.*—Mean levels of cloud bases are always above 20,000 feet.

2. *Middle Clouds.*—Mean levels of cloud bases are always between 20,000 and 7,000 feet.

3. *Low Clouds.*—Mean levels of cloud bases are always below 7,000 feet.

4. *Low Clouds with Vertical Development.*—Cloud bases are below 7,000 feet but often tower upward into the middle- or high-cloud level.

INTERNATIONAL CLOUD CLASSIFICATION.—Table VIII shows the 10 standard cloud forms arranged in accordance with the heights at which they occur. Note that there exists a continuous cloud series, starting with the high cirrostratus, and extending through altostratus to stratus and nimbostratus in the low category. The significance of this series in particular will be stressed in this and in later chapters.

Cloud Descriptions

Let us consider a brief description of the foregoing cloud types. This, together with good cloud photographs, should aid measurably in cloud identification. The U.S. Weather Bureau, Circular S, "Codes for Cloud Forms and States of the Sky," will prove very profitable for the earnest cloud observer.

TABLE VIII. CLOUD CLASSIFICATION.

High clouds, above 20,000 ft.	Middle clouds, 20,000 to 7,000 ft.	Low clouds, below 7,000 ft.	Vertical development clouds (low clouds with vertical development)
Cirrus Cirrostratus Cirrocumulus	Altostratus Altocumulus	Stratus Nimbostratus Stratocumulus	Cumulus Cumulonimbus

HIGH CLOUDS.—*Cirrus* (*Ci*).—Cirrus are about the highest of all the clouds, usually forming above 30,000 feet. They are detached, delicate, white cloud units appearing in all seasons. Often they are feathery, fibrous, or tufted in appearance, indicating the well-known mare's-tails. Owing to their great height and the consequent low temperatures prevailing there, cirrus clouds are composed of thin crystals or needles of ice and not droplets of water.

Cirrostratus (*Cs*).—These clouds form typically as a thin whitish veil or sheet, often covering all or a good portion of the sky. They may be very thin, giving the sky a slight milky white or veiled appearance, or they may form a definite white sheet. Cirrostratus clouds are responsible for the halos often occurring about the sun or moon. In fact, the presence of such features usually indicates the presence of cirrostratus. The very thin appearance of these clouds indicates the great height at which they commonly occur, which is the same as for cirrus. Hence these, too, are formed of ice spicules or needles.

Cirrocumulus (*Cc*).—These clouds form as small flaky or scaly globular masses covering small or large portions of the sky. They are nearly always white and occasionally show slight shadows. The delicate groups of cirrocumulus often appear to be rippled in appearance, or they may be arranged in bands crossing the sky. It is this banded arrangement of the delicate white cirrocumulus packs that has resulted in the application of "mackerel sky" to these clouds. They are the rarest of the cloud types, often forming from the degeneration of original cirrus or cirrostratus clouds with which they must be associated in the sky. Being at heights equivalent to the other high clouds they are also usually formed of ice.

MIDDLE CLOUDS. *Altostratus* (*As*).—Altostratus clouds are uniform bluish or grayish-white cloud sheets, covering all or large portions of the sky and sometimes occurring in uniform broad bands. The sun may be totally obscured or may shine through in a weak, "watery" condition. The typical watery sun is characteristic of altostratus. Very frequently there is a complete or nearly complete absence of shadows associated with this weak sun, for the general illumination of the clouds is sufficient to offset the shadows cast by the weakened sun. Just how thick these clouds are depends on the height at which they form. If very high, they may grade into cirrostratus. The lower they form, the heavier and denser they become. Altostratus yield a large percentage of precipitation, particularly in the middle and high latitudes.

Altocumulus (*Ac*).—These clouds form as eliptical globular units occurring individually or in groups. When in groups, altocumulus may form as confused, and more or less closely grouped, masses or in definite bands, with clear sky alternating. The altocumulus may have gray shadows on their under surfaces when thickly developed. Individual altocumulus clouds are frequently elongated elliptical or lenticular units distinguishable from the cumulus (to be studied later) by their height and absence of vertical doming. The wavy or parallel bands of altocumulus, mentioned above, are particularly characteristic of this cloud type. The well-known "sheep clouds" or woolpack clouds are examples of high globular altocumulus groups.

Low Clouds. *Stratus* (*St*).—This is a uniform gray cloud sheet or layer. Stratus clouds have no particular form or structure and usually completely cover the sky. The uniform cloud sheet may sometimes appear partly broken into elongated patches. The stratus sheet is normally thicker and darker than the higher altostratus which may be overlying. It is often difficult or impossible to distinguish low stratus formations from high fog, for an almost continuous graduation exists. Thus, warm, humid air, flowing across cooler regions, may yield very thick advection fogs. During the day, much of the lower portion of the fog may evaporate and leave a high fog or stratus above the ground. Stratus clouds frequently become broken and wind-blown, being more or less formless ragged patches which are then called "fractostratus."

Nimbostratus (*Ns*).—Nimbostratus are thick, dark-gray shapeless cloud sheets with irregular broken clouds beneath and surrounding them. They are the common associates of steady precipitation, whether rain or snow. Nimbostratus have usually been considered as the source of the precipitation. Recent observations indicate that nimbostratus are the product of precipitation, formed by condensation in the saturated zone beneath altostratus, which actually yield the precipitation. The lower surface of the nimbostratus is often wind-torn and broken, releasing small ragged dark cloud shreds that are blown rapidly by the wind. These are known as "scud" clouds, which also may be classified as fractostratus.

Stratocumulus (*Sc*).—These form large heavy rolls or elongated globular masses arranged in long, gray parallel bands that usually cover all or most of the sky. They grade in appearance from definite cloud rolls that are simply close together, to a more or less continuous sheet broken into irregular parallel bands. They often form from the flattening of cumulus clouds which may be arranged in bands, or may develop as a continuation of altocumulus occurring at low altitudes. In this latter case, the stratocumulus will appear darker, lower, and heavier than the related altocumulus.

VERTICAL DEVELOPMENT CLOUDS. *Cumulus* (*Cu*).—Cumulus clouds are the majestic billowing white clouds so prominent in the summertime. However, they may occur at any season. These clouds are typically flat-based with a pronounced vertical thickness, which extends upward as a domed, or cauliflower, or turreted mass. Cumulus are for the most part fair-weather clouds. Frequently after a storm has passed a continuous train of small flat cumulus, with relatively small vertical doming exhibited, will float across the sky from west to east. Their flat bottoms, if extended toward each other, form a nearly perfect plane surface—the dew-point level. Irregular wind-torn patches of cumulus, formed by wind action on larger cumulus clouds, are called "fractocumulus."

Cumulonimbus (*Cb*).—Cumulonimbus arise from cumulus that have developed into tremendous towering clouds with a vertical range, from base to top, of 2 to 5 miles. When grown to this height, such clouds form the well-known thunderstorms, the cloud itself being called a "thunderhead." Such clouds are marked by the turrets which are ever changing in form and shape as the cloud builds up higher and higher. In the well-developed thunderhead or cumulonimbus the top becomes flattened and drawn out in the direction of motion resulting in the anvil shape or top.

Conditions of Cloud Formation

Nearly all clouds are the products of temperature and humidity changes in rising and adiabatically cooling air. The resulting cloud forms depend on the method whereby the air is set in vertical motion and on the height at which the air cools to the dew point. We noted earlier that air may be forced to ascend in response to

1. Local heating, or direct convection
2. The effect of topography
3. The effect of fronts or cold-air wedges

Surface heating results in air rising vertically from the heated surface, usually over a rather limited area. The effect of topography is shown mostly only in the case of slopes with pronounced steepness, and also results in steeply rising air.

The third method usually produces a sheet or layer of air rising from the surface at a small angle, over the cold wedge of air, and therefore cooling more slowly. Frequently (as will be studied later), these cold wedges of air may become very steep and give again nearly vertical uplift to the warm air.

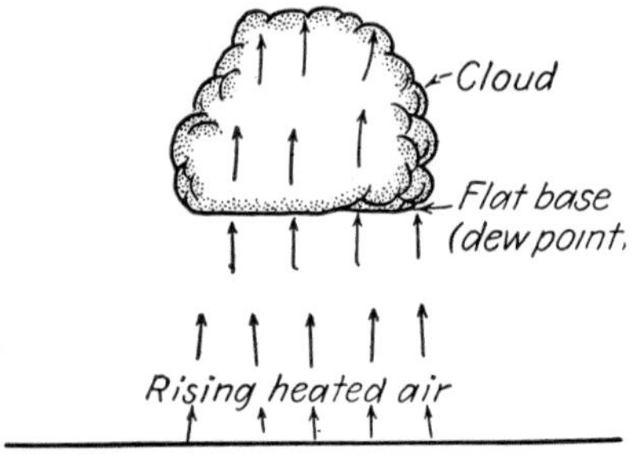

EFFECT OF VERTICALLY RISING AIR COLUMNS.—Whenever air is brought into vertical motion, in response to any of the foregoing causes, the temperature will decrease at the adiabatic rate. Such motion is usually restricted to independent columns of air, which may be widely scattered or relatively close. In any case the temperature throughout such air columns is the same horizontally. Consequently the dew point of these rising air bodies will be reached at the same level and produce clouds having flat, even bases, all at the same elevation. The vertical thickness of the cloud depends upon the height to which the air continued to rise above the dew-point level, and the available moisture supply.

FIG. 6-3.—Production of cumulus cloud by isolated, heated, rising air column.

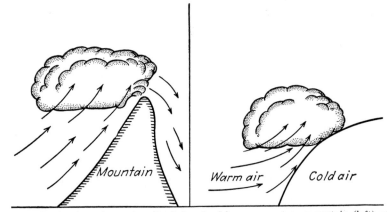

FIG. 6-4.—Production of cumulus clouds by air rising over a steep mountain (left) and a steeply sloping cold-air wedge (right).

Clearly this process will be responsible for the formation of cumulus clouds and, with very exaggerated uplift, cumulonimbus clouds.

The height of a cumulus base may be very easily calculated from a formula derived by means of the adiabatic rate and dew-point decrease for rising air. This formula is

$$H = \frac{T - DP}{4.5} \times 1,000$$

where H is the height of the cloud base, T is the air temperature at the ground (from observation). DP is the dew point at the ground (from observation). If Fahrenheit temperature units are used, the results will be in feet. Approximately the same results are obtained from the formula

$$H = 222(T - DP) \text{ ft.}$$

Cumulus clouds will therefore form in locally isolated air columns or in adjacent columns along a steeply sloping mountain range or cold-air wedge.

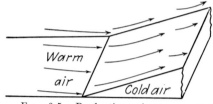

Fig. 6-5.—Production of an extended sheet of rising warm air by a gently sloping cold-air wedge.

EFFECT OF FRONTS ON RISING AIR.—Whenever warm air meets a cold air mass, the cold air, it will be recalled, wedges beneath the warm. Note that the warm-air layer overlying the cold, may have a considerable horizontal extent. As the sheet of warm air rises over the sloping upper surface of the colder air, the temperature decreases adiabatically, causing cloud condensation to begin at the dew-point level and continuing as the air rises still farther. This process occurs more or less uniformly throughout the sheet of warm air and produces a cloud blanket of the stratus type.

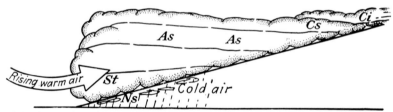

Fig. 6-6.—Formation of the stratus cloud sequence by air rising over gently sloping cold-air wedge.

The cloud deck thus formed in the warm air will be thickest nearest the ground or bottom of the slope, for more moisture is available at lower altitudes; also, the lower clouds will here be covered by middle and high clouds directly above.

The cross section in Fig. 6-6 indicates this process, showing the formation of the stratus cloud sequence.

It is clear that clouds must become thinner and generally lighter in color the higher the air ascends. Then far up near the head of this warm rising sheet the clouds will be scattered and detached, occurring at great heights. These are the cirrus clouds. Following the cirrus the main cloud mass is encountered. The thinnest and highest portion of this sheet will of course be the cirrostratus. Then, descending the wedge, the series passes into the thicker altostratus with its "watery" sun, and stratus, with associated precipitation and nimbostratus.

The significance of an approaching cloud sequence of this type, with the cirrus and cirrostratus appearing first, is therefore very often a good indicator of the approaching rain, snow, and general bad weather. This cloud picture will later be related to the weather pattern as a whole and its significance then will become still greater.

BANDED CLOUD FORMS.—It has been pointed out that cirrocumulus and the more common altocumulus frequently form as parallel bands with alternating clear sky. From what has been studied so far, we know that the air must be rising to produce the clouds and consequently

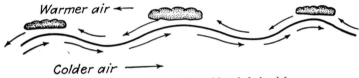

FIG. 6-7.—Method of formation of banded cloud forms.

falling where the clear bands prevail. Since these cloud bands are high and relatively thin, it is evident that they cannot be produced by continuous, alternating walls of air rising and falling from the earth's surface, as in the case of the true cumulus.

They are rather the result of two air streams, one flowing above the other and in differing directions. Consequently the surface between the two air sheets will become rippled in directions more or less perpendicular to the direction of motion.

Hence cloud bands may form in crests of the ripples where the air is rising but will be evaporated in the troughs. Depending on conditions of height, temperature, humidity, and amount of motion, the clouds will be variously developed as alto- or cirrocumulus.

Thunderstorms

Thunderstorms and their associated phenomena are among the most violent displays of nature. They are the product of steeply uprushing columns of air forming cumulus clouds at first, which continue to develop vertically until they tower in billowing masses miles above their bases, forming the cumulonimbus, or thunderhead.

TYPES OF THUNDERSTORMS.—Thunderstorms require for their formation vertically rising air, rushing upward for tens of thousands of feet. The necessary impetus for this condition, as discussed above, may be provided by (1) pronounced local heating, (2) windward slopes of steep mountains, or (3) steeply sloping cold-air wedges. Thunderstorms are classified according to the method of origin.

1. *Air-mass Thunderstorms.*—These include storms resulting from the first two of the above causes. Strong local heating resulting in convection usually produces isolated storms within a single air mass and are known variously as "local" or "convection" storms. "Orographic" or mountain storms result from a pronounced uplift of air on the windward sides of steep mountains.

Local thunderstorms of marine origin are most frequent in the early morning hours. On a clear night the air temperature may fall considerably at high levels, while the sea itself, as explained earlier, retains the

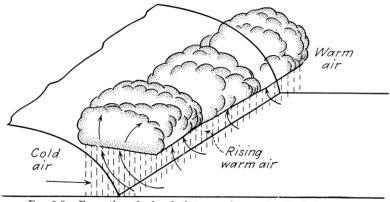

Fig. 6-8.—Formation of a band of storms along a steeply sloping front.

heat of the day for long periods. Consequently, the air adjacent to the sea remains warm. During the night the temperature contrast between warm sea-level air and high-altitude air becomes more pronounced, developing a high lapse rate, necessary to all thunderstorms. Finally, any surface temperature inequality causes a local rising air column to form, culminating in a storm.

Over land, local thunderstorms are most common in the late afternoon, when the effect of solar heating of the land surface is greatest.

2. *Frontal Storms.*—These disturbances occur when the warm air of one air mass rises over the underrunning steep boundary of a colder air mass, forming huge cumulonimbus clouds along the length of this cold-air boundary. Frontal thunderstorms thus occur as a long belt or band of storms moving progressively across country, with the forward movement of the cold-air mass.

3. Many thunderstorms result from a third process. The lapse rate may be increased through the advection (horizontal movement) of

warm air near the ground, and (or) cold air at high levels.   The presence of a steep lapse rate is conducive to the production of rising air columns which may culminate in thunderstorm formation.   Some "trigger action" is still required to initiate the vertical air motion.

THUNDERCLOUD (CUMULONIMBUS).—The thundercloud is a complete atmospheric powerhouse in itself.   The powerful updrafts and downdrafts of air; the local whirls within the cloud, giving the boiling cauliflower appearance to the extremities of the cloud; the heavy downpour of rain and hail; the terrific electric discharges with associated thunder, all contribute to the violence manifested by this "engine" within the air. At the ground level we experience only the fringe of the true storm

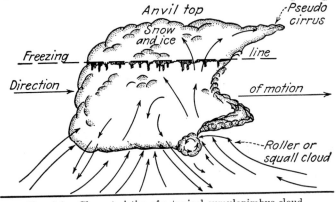

FIG. 6-9.—Characteristics of a typical cumulonimbus cloud.

conditions.   It is the airman who is really aware of the significance of such a storm.

Regardless of the method of formation most thunderclouds are pretty much alike in structure.   They are all tremendously overgrown cumulus clouds often developing a length of 60 miles and a width of 20 miles with vertical dimensions of from $2\frac{1}{2}$ to 5 miles.   The greater the vertical development, the more violent the thunderstorm.   However, the lower two-thirds of the thundercloud, below the freezing line, is always the most dangerous to aviation.

The altitude to which thunderstorms develop is closely governed by the height of the freezing level above the surface.   It follows from this that the maximum height of such storms must depend on the latitude and season.   Observation shows that cumulonimbus clouds have a maximum development in low latitudes and a minimum in high latitudes with an intermediate growth in middle latitudes in conformance with the descent of the freezing level from equator to poles.   Similarly, they reach to a much greater height in summer than in winter.   Since, as we noted, the greater the vertical development, the more violent the storm, low-latitude and summer thunderstorms must, under otherwise equivalent conditions, be more violent than high-latitude and winter storms, respectively. The chief features of a typical thunderstorm are shown in Fig. 6-9. Most storms tend to move with the general flow of air and weather from west to east. Thus the eastern half is usually the forward part. It will be seen in Fig. 6-9 that the air in front of the storm is rushing

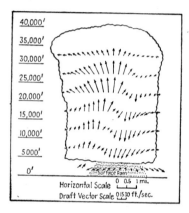
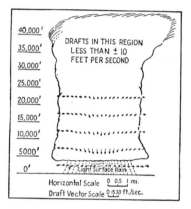

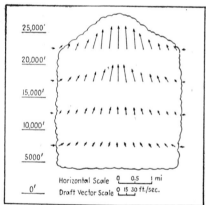

Fig. 6.10.—Three stages in the development of a thunderstorm from original cumulus. *(After Byers and Braham.)*

nearly vertically upward and, just to the rear, downward. This produces the rapidly rotating roller cloud extending the width of the storm cloud, just below and in the forward part of the cloud. This roller or squall cloud is the most violent part of the storm. The air within it frequently attains velocities from 50 to 100 miles an hour. It is marked as a long rolling black cloud with an ominous whitish-gray front as the storm approaches. The sudden gusts and wind shifts attending the passage of this part of the storm are particularly dangerous to sailing vessels.

Following the passage of the roller cloud the heavy showers of the storm set in and are characteristic of the whole central area of the storm. The raindrops often grow to great size since they are falling with a mass of down-rushing air and are not broken apart by friction with the air. However, throughout most of the cloud the water droplets are continuously torn apart by friction of the air. The positive and negative charges become segregated in different parts of the cloud until the potential difference is so great as to produce the terrific discharge known as "lightning." This discharge may take place from cloud to earth or from cloud to cloud, and the sudden expansion and immediate contraction of the heated air along the path of the lightning discharge results in the sudden explosive sound known as "thunder." The original thunder clap may echo and reecho from various cloud surfaces, yielding the familiar rolling peals of thunder.

Sheet lightning is simply the general illumination of the sky produced by a lightning streak obscured by clouds or below the horizon.

Frequently in thundery weather at sea, a great voltage or potential difference is built up between a ship and the air or clouds above. This concentration of static electricity on the vessel tends to leap from all the pointed objects such as the ends of masts and spars. A purplish or bluish spray of light results, called "St. Elmo's fire." Balls of lightning have been observed rolling along the masts and rigging of ships and disappearing with a sudden explosion.

Within the cloud itself the raindrops are often swirled above and below the freezing line, thus forming hail with its concentric shells of ice.

When the cloud has reached its upper vertical limit, it tends to flatten and spread out in the direction of motion developing the flat *anvil top*. At this altitude the cloud is composed of ice. It has the appearance of cirrus as the material is blown by the winds prevailing at this height. This formation is known as the "pseudo cirrus" (false cirrus).

CLOUD ILLUSTRATIONS

Fig. 6-11.—Cirrus. (*Courtesy of Ellerman, U.S. Weather Bureau.*)

FIG. 6-13.—Cirrus bands. (*Courtesy of Davis, U.S. Weather Bureau.*)

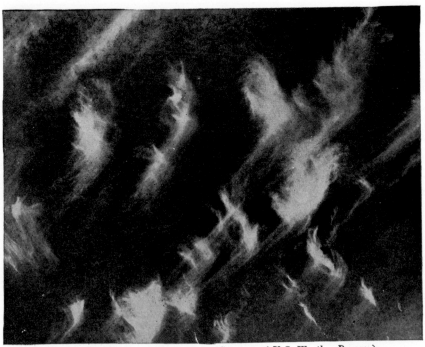

FIG. 6-14.—Cirrus—Mares tails. (*Courtesy of U.S. Weather Bureau.*)

Fig. 6-15.—Tufted cirrus. (*Courtesy of Johnson, U.S. Weather Bureau.*)

Fig. 6-16.—High cirrus illuminated by rising sun. Dawn patrol over Iceland—1 A.M. (*Official U.S. Navy Photograph.*)

FIG. 6-17.—Cirrostratus, terminating in cirrus filaments.   (*Courtesy of Weed, U.S. Weather Bureau.*)

FIG. 6-18.—Cirrocumulus—degenerating from cirrostratus, also visible. (*Courtesy of U.S. Army Photographic Section, U.S. Weather Bureau.*)

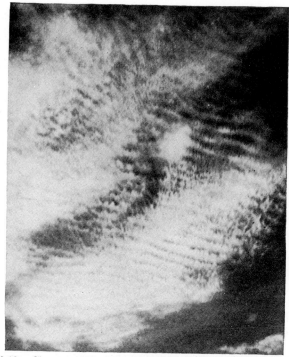

Fig. 6-19.—Cirrocumulus. (*Courtesy of Barnard, U.S. Weather Bureau.*)

Fig. 6-20.—Cirrostratus. (*Courtesy of U. S. Weather Bureau.*)

FIG. 6-21.—Altocumulus bands.   (*Courtesy of U.S. Weather Bureau.*)

FIG. 6-22.—Altocumulus groups with some thicker, lower stratocumulus in right background, Kings Point, N.Y.   (*Photograph by Motowski.*)

Fig. 6-23.—Altocumulus arranged in heterogeneous masses, taken from carrier deck. (*Official U.S. Navy Photograph.*)

Fig. 6-24.—Altostratus sheet overlying swelling cumulus clouds. (*Official U.S. Navy Photograph.*)

FIG. 6-25.—Altostratus, showing watery sun with cumulus and fractocumulus beneath. (*Official U.S. Navy Photograph.*)

FIG. 6-26.—Lenticular altocumulus.   (*Courtesy of Tamehill, U.S. Weather Bureau.*)

Fig. 6-27.—Thick altostratus with some altocumulus at a lower level. (*Courtesy of U.S. Weather Bureau.*)

Fig. 6-28.—Low stratus moving over a small rocky island. (*Courtesy of U.S. Weather Bureau.*)

FIG. 6-29.—Stratocumulus rolls.   (*Courtesy of Davis, U.S. Weather Bureau.*)

FIG. 6-30.—Broken stratocumulus.   (*Courtesy of U.S. Weather Bureau.*)

Fig. 6-31.—Low cumulus and fractocumulus seen in evening with illuminated bands of cirrus visible at high levels. (*Official U.S. Navy Photograph.*)

FIG. 6-32.—Cumulus clouds—Levanter cloud—hovering over Gibraltar. (*Courtesy of Great Britain Meteorology Office, U.S. Weather Bureau.*)

FIG. 6-33.—Typical cumulus and fractocumulus of fair weather. (*Courtesy of U.S. Weather Bureau.*)

Fig. 6-34.—Mammato cumulus clouds, which often precede and may follow severe thunderstorm or tornado conditions. (*Courtesy of U.S. Weather Bureau.*)

Fig. 6-35.—Cumulus overlain by thin cirrostratus veil. (*Official U.S. Navy Photograph.*)

FIG. 6-36.—Fractocumulus showing pronounced wind streaming.   (*Official U.S. Navy Photograph.*)

FIG. 6-37.—Cumulus and fractocumulus at sunset.

FIG. 6-38.—Cumulus clouds at low level overlain by high-level cirrus. (*Official U.S. Navy Photograph.*)

FIG. 6-39.—Patches of low cumulus with uniform veil of cirrostratus above. (*Courtesy of U.S. Weather Bureau.*)

FIG. 6-40.—Cumulus with cirrus and cirrostratus above.   (*Official U.S. Navy Photograph.*)

Fig. 6-41.—Cumulonimbus; east of Pensacola, Fla., showing precipitation beneath central portion of cloud. (*Courtesy of U.S. Weather Bureau.*)

Fig. 6-42.—Low-hanging portion of cumulonimbus cloud hovers over carrier force. (*Official U.S. Navy Photograph.*)

Fig. 6-43.—Thunderstorm at sea, with heavy precipitation beneath forward half of cumulonimbus cloud. (*Official U.S. Navy Photograph.*)

Fig. 6-44.—Nose of a thunderstorm advancing along a line of frontal storms. (*Courtesy of H. L. Crutchen, U.S. Weather Bureau.*)

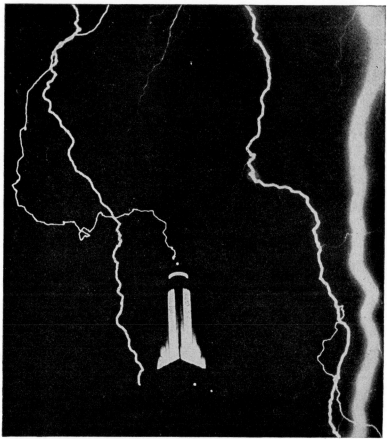

FIG. 6-45.—Lightning striking the Empire State Building, New York, N.Y. (*Courtesy of Gary, U.S. Weather Bureau.*)

CHAPTER 7

ATMOSPHERIC PRESSURE

Nature of Atmospheric Pressure

The atmosphere extends to hundreds of miles above the earth's surface, being held in place by the attraction of gravity. Thus the atmosphere weighs heavily on the earth's surface. But we speak of atmospheric pressure, not weight. In accordance with a physical law (Pascal's Principle), the pressure at any point within an enclosed fluid (gas or liquid) is transmitted equally in all directions. The destructive effect of a depth charge depends upon this same principle. Hence, at any point in the atmosphere the pressure exerted by the overlying air is transmitted not only downward, but in every other possible direction as well. Since weight refers to a downward force and pressure to a force in any direction, the term atmospheric pressure is used.

There are certain other fundamental physical properties of gases that are also applicable to the air. They consist essentially of temperature-pressure-volume relationships and are known as the "gas laws." They refer mainly to relatively dry air, since they are not strictly obeyed by water vapor.

BOYLE'S LAW.—This law explains the pressure-volume relationship of gases. Assume that we have a given volume of gas in a cylinder, with an attached piston. Then as pressure is exerted by driving in the piston, the volume of the gas decreases. But remember that compression of a gas causes it to warm adiabatically, and warm air tends to expand.

Hence, Boyle's Law states that at a *constant temperature* the volume of a gas varies inversely as the pressure on it, or simply

$$V \alpha \frac{1}{p}$$

Thus if we double the pressure of a given mass of gas, the volume decreases by one-half; if we triple the pressure, the volume decreases to one-third, and so on. We can state this relationship by saying that the product of the original pressure and volume, PV, is equal to the product of the new pressure and volume $2P \times \frac{1}{2}V$, which equals $3P \times \frac{1}{3}V$, and so on; or

$$PV = P_1V_1 = P_2V_2 = P_3V_3 = \cdots$$

106

As a result, regardless of the pressure change on a given volume of gas, the product of the pressure and the resulting volume change is always the same—as long as the temperature is unchanged. Algebraically, we say

$$PV = K \text{ (constant)}$$

LAWS OF CHARLES AND GAY-LUSSAC.—These laws govern the temperature-pressure and the temperature-volume relationships.

1. If the temperature of a gas is increased, without permitting the volume to change, there will be a proportional increase in the pressure of the gas. Or at constant volume, the pressure of a gas varies directly with the temperature. Using the centigrade scale, it is found that for each increase or decrease by 1°C., the pressure of a gas shows a corresponding increase or decrease of $\frac{1}{273}$ of its pressure at 0°C. The pressure at 1°C. will be $\frac{1}{273}$ more than the pressure at 0°C.

In general then, at constant volume, the pressure of a gas at any temperature can be found as follows:

$$P_t = P_0 + (\tfrac{1}{273}P_0)t$$

or factoring,

$$P_t = P_0(1 + \tfrac{1}{273}t)$$

where P_t is pressure at any temperature, P_0 is the pressure at 0°C., and T is the temperature.

2. In the same way, if the temperature increases, the volume of a gas also increases in direct proportion, provided that now the pressure is kept constant. Again, the change in volume per °C. is equal to $\frac{1}{273}$ of the volume of the gas at 0°C.

Thus, if V_0 is the volume at 0°C. and V_t is the volume at any temperature,

$$V_t = V_0(1 + \tfrac{1}{273}t)$$

As a consequence of the above, we note that at 273°C., if the volume is constant, the pressure of a gas will be doubled; and if the pressure is kept constant, the volume will be doubled.

NORMAL ATMOSPHERIC PRESSURE.—Under specified normal conditions, a given area will have a certain weight of air resting on it. This is spoken of as "normal atmospheric pressure." Arbitrarily the area taken is 1 square inch. The normal conditions are set at mean sea level, at 45° latitude at a standard temperature. Under such conditions a column of air 1 square inch in cross section, extending to the top of the atmosphere, will exert a force of 14.7 pounds. Hence normal air pressure is 14.7 pounds per square inch.

Pressure Variations

As in the case of temperature, atmospheric pressure also exhibits important variations, vertically, horizontally, and periodically.

VERTICAL PRESSURE GRADIENT.—The air is a mixture of gases. Gases are compressible. Thus the air near the earth's surface is much heavier or denser than the air above. This accounts for the rapid decrease in density with altitude, as pointed out in Chap. 1. Actually the pressure in the lower portion of the atmosphere decreases by one-thirtieth of its previous value for each 900-foot increase in altitude. At 900 feet above sea level the pressure would thus be one-thirtieth less than at sea level. At 1,800 feet the pressure would be one-thirtieth less than at 900 feet, and so on.

HORIZONTAL PRESSURE VARIATIONS.—We have already noted that the air is heated very irregularly as a consequence of the irregular heating of the earth. This provides the basis for variations in pressure, since warmer air will be lighter than adjacent cooler air. At any given place on the earth's surface the pressure may therefore be above or below the normal pressure. These pressure differences over the earth are closely associated with, and responsible for, the weather changes in the air and will be studied in further detail in this and in later chapters. One of the most important features of the horizontal variations is the fact that they are not stationary but move generally eastward, carrying with them their associated weather changes.

PERIODIC PRESSURE VARIATIONS.—The atmosphere is not a static body. It is a dynamic medium. At a given station the pressure changes continuously as areas of higher or lower pressure approach.

It has been observed that a periodic pressure change occurs daily. The air pressure shows two high and two low points each day, the pressure peaks occurring at 10 A.M. and 10 P.M., while the low points are midway between, or at 4 P.M. and 4 A.M.

For reasons to be explained later this gradual daily pressure variation is generally overshadowed by other, greater changes in the middle latitudes. However, in the tropics and subtropics the daily change is characteristic.

Pressure Instruments

As previously noted, atmospheric pressure varies from place to place, and from time to time at the same place. To understand and interpret weather conditions it is necessary to measure this pressure and its changes. The standard instruments for this purpose are the "mercurial barometer," the "aneroid barometer," and the " barograph."

MERCURIAL BAROMETER.—The principle of the mercurial barometer is very simple. Basically it consists of a long hollow glass tube from which the air is evacuated. This tube is placed with its open end down, immersed in a receptacle called a "cistern," which is filled with mercury. The pressure of the outside air then forces the mercury in the cistern upward into the vacuum chamber within the tube. The mercury will rise until its weight in the tube just balances the weight or pressure of the air on an area of the mercury in the cistern just equal to the interior cross-sectional area of the tube. Thus if the tube area is 1 square inch and the air pressure is normal, the mercury will rise until its weight within the tube is 14.7 pounds, for normal pressure is 14.7 pounds per square inch. As the atmospheric pressure changes, the height of the mercury will fluctuate accordingly.

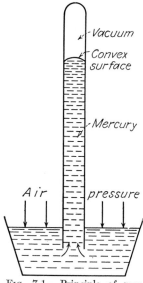

Regardless of the area of the tube the mercury will always rise to the same height at a given time. If the tube is narrow, as it commonly is, the mercury within simply balances the air pressure on a smaller area in the cistern. Under normal pressure conditions the mercury will rise to height of 29.92 inches in the barometer tube. Conventionally, atmospheric pressure is expressed not in pounds, but according to the height of mercury in the barometer tube. Thus normal pressure is said to be "29.92 inches."

If the barometer is calibrated in inches, there will be a fixed scale near the top of the barometer tube divided into inches and tenths of inches. A sliding vernier scale, much the same as that on a sextant, permits readings

FIG. 7-1.—Principle of mercurial barometer.

to a tenth of the smallest fixed scale division, or to a hundredth of an inch.

When in a narrow tube, mercury always exhibits a curved or convex surface as a result of surface tension. As the top of the curve represents the actual mercury height, readings are taken for the uppermost part of the curving mercury surface.

Marine mercurial barometers have been devised for use on shipboard, which minimize agitation of the mercury caused by movements of the vessel. They are also mounted suspended in gimbals in order to remain as nearly vertical as possible. When not in use the barometer is locked in a protecting wooden case.

CORRECTIONS TO MERCURIAL BAROMETRIC READINGS.—For one to attempt to foretell weather conditions, it is normally necessary to observe only the *change* in pressure and not so much the actual reading. For local interpretation whether the "glass" is rising or falling is of more importance than the reading. However, when data are sent to a central station, it is important to transmit pressure readings, as these are needed for general weather analysis. If barometer readings are to be sent from many points to a central station, these readings must show true differences in atmospheric pressure and not differences resulting from

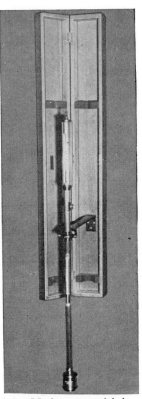

Fig. 7-2.—Fortin-type standard mercurial barometer. (*Courtesy of U.S. Weather Bureau.*)

Fig. 7-3.—Marine mercurial barometer shown in position for use.

varied circumstances under which the readings are taken. In other words, all readings must be reduced to normal conditions of sea level, latitude, and temperature. Accordingly the following corrections are necessary after the barometer is read: altitude correction, temperature correction, latitude or gravity correction, and instrument correction.

1. *Altitude Correction.*—Unless a barometer is located at sea level it will naturally show a lower reading than at that level, since pressure

decreases with altitude. All barometer readings should be reduced to mean sea level by *adding* the proper correction for altitude. Normal pressure is approximately 30 inches. At 900 feet it would be one-thirtieth less or approximately 29 inches. A barometer on a ship's bridge 30 feet above sea level would thus have a correction of 0.03 inch. Since the barometer is read to a hundredth of an inch, this is a significant difference. Note that this correction is always positive. Complete corrections are given in Table IX.

TABLE IX.   REDUCTION OF BAROMETRIC READING TO MEAN SEA LEVEL
(Reading, 30 in.   The correction is always to be added)

Height, ft.	Temperature of air (dry bulb), °F.									
	0°	10°	20°	30°	40°	50°	60°	70°	80°	90°
5	0.01	0.01	0.01	0.01	0.01	0.01	0.01			
10	0.01	0.01	0.01	0.01	0.01	0.01	0.01	0.01	0.01	0.01
15	0.02	0.02	0.02	0.02	0.02	0.02	0.02	0.02	0.02	0.02
20	0.02	0.02	0.02	0.02	0.02	0.02	0.02	0.02	0.02	0.02
25	0.03	0.03	0.03	0.03	0.03	0.03	0.03	0.03	0.03	0.03
30	0.04	0.04	0.04	0.04	0.03	0.03	0.03	0.03	0.03	0.03
35	0.04	0.04	0.04	0.04	0.04	0.04	0.04	0.04	0.04	0.04
40	0.05	0.05	0.05	0.05	0.04	0.04	0.04	0.04	0.04	0.04
45	0.06	0.05	0.05	0.05	0.05	0.05	0.05	0.05	0.05	0.05
50	0.06	0.06	0.06	0.06	0.06	0.06	0.05	0.05	0.05	0.05
55	0.07	0.07	0.06	0.06	0.06	0.06	0.06	0.06	0.06	0.06
60	0.07	0.07	0.07	0.07	0.07	0.07	0.06	0.06	0.06	0.06
65	0.08	0.08	0.08	0.08	0.07	0.07	0.07	0.07	0.07	0.07
70	0.09	0.08	0.08	0.08	0.08	0.08	0.08	0.07	0.07	0.07
75	0.09	0.09	0.09	0.09	0.08	0.08	0.08	0.08	0.08	0.08
80	0.10	0.10	0.09	0.09	0.09	0.09	0.09	0.08	0.08	0.08
85	0.10	0.10	0.10	0.10	0.10	0.10	0.09	0.09	0.09	0.09
90	0.11	0.11	0.11	0.10	0.10	0.10	0.10	0.10	0.09	0.09
95	0.12	0.11	0.11	0.11	0.11	0.11	0.10	0.10	0.10	0.10
100	0.12	0.12	0.12	0.12	0.11	0.11	0.11	0.11	0.10	0.10

2. *Temperature Correction.*—The mercury in a barometer will expand or contract just as in a thermometer. Thus an arbitrary reference level must be taken; for the mercurial barometer this is 32°F. or 0°C. Hence, when the temperature is above freezing, the mercury stands too high in the tube, and the correction is negative and must be subtracted to lower the reading of the mercury column to normal. If below freezing, the correction is added in order to raise the reading of the now contracted mercury column to normal. At freezing, the correction is zero. All

TABLE X.   CORRECTION OF MERCURIAL BAROMETER FOR TEMPERATURE (ENGLISH MEASURES)

Add

Tempera-ture, °F.	Observed reading, in.					Tempera-ture, °F.	Observed reading, in.				
	28.5	29.0	29.5	30.0	30.5		28.5	29.0	29.5	30.0	30.5
0	0.07	0.08	0.08	0.08	0.08	16	0.03	0.03	0.03	0.03	0.04
1	0.07	0.07	0.07	0.08	0.08	17	0.03	0.03	0.03	0.03	0.03
2	0.07	0.07	0.07	0.07	0.07	18	0.03	0.03	0.03	0.03	0.03
3	0.07	0.07	0.07	0.07	0.07	19	0.02	0.02	0.03	0.03	0.03
4	0.06	0.06	0.07	0.07	0.07	20	0.02	0.02	0.02	0.02	0.02
5	0.06	0.06	0.06	0.06	0.07	21	0.02	0.02	0.02	0.02	0.02
6	0.06	0.06	0.06	0.06	0.06	22	0.02	0.02	0.02	0.02	0.02
7	0.06	0.06	0.06	0.06	0.06	23	0.02	0.02	0.02	0.02	0.02
8	0.05	0.05	0.06	0.06	0.06	24	0.01	0.01	0.01	0.01	0.01
9	0.05	0.05	0.05	0.05	0.05	25	0.01	0.01	0.01	0.01	0.01
10	0.05	0.05	0.05	0.05	0.05	26	0.01	0.01	0.01	0.01	0.01
11	0.05	0.05	0.05	0.05	0.05	27					
12	0.04	0.04	0.04	0.04	0.05	28					
13	0.04	0.04	0.04	0.04	0.04	29					
14	0.04	0.04	0.04	0.04	0.04	30					
15	0.04	0.04	0.04	0.04	0.04						

Subtract

	28.5	29.0	29.5	30.0	30.5		28.5	29.0	29.5	30.0	30.5
31	0.01	0.01	0.01	0.01	0.01	66	0.10	0.10	0.10	0.10	0.10
32	0.01	0.01	0.01	0.01	0.01	67	0.10	0.10	0.10	0.10	0.11
33	0.01	0.01	0.01	0.01	0.01	68	0.10	0.10	0.10	0.11	0.11
34	0.01	0.01	0.01	0.02	0.02	69	0.10	0.11	0.11	0.11	0.11
35	0.02	0.02	0.02	0.02	0.02	70	0.11	0.11	0.11	0.11	0.11
36	0.02	0.02	0.02	0.02	0.02	71	0.11	0.11	0.11	0.12	0.12
37	0.02	0.02	0.02	0.02	0.02	72	0.11	0.11	0.12	0.12	0.12
38	0.02	0.02	0.02	0.03	0.03	73	0.11	0.12	0.12	0.12	0.12
39	0.03	0.03	0.03	0.03	0.03	74	0.12	0.12	0.12	0.12	0.12
40	0.03	0.03	0.03	0.03	0.03	75	0.12	0.12	0.12	0.13	0.13
41	0.03	0.03	0.03	0.03	0.03	76	0.12	0.12	0.13	0.13	0.13
42	0.04	0.04	0.04	0.04	0.04	77	0.12	0.13	0.13	0.13	0.13
43	0.04	0.04	0.04	0.04	0.04	78	0.13	0.13	0.13	0.13	0.14
44	0.04	0.04	0.04	0.04	0.04	79	0.13	0.13	0.14	0.14	0.14
45	0.04	0.04	0.04	0.04	0.04	80	0.13	0.14	0.14	0.14	0.14
46	0.04	0.05	0.05	0.05	0.05	81	0.14	0.14	0.14	0.14	0.14
47	0.05	0.05	0.05	0.05	0.05	82	0.14	0.14	0.14	0.14	0.15
48	0.05	0.05	0.05	0.05	0.05	83	0.14	0.14	0.14	0.15	0.15
49	0.05	0.05	0.05	0.06	0.06	84	0.14	0.14	0.15	0.15	0.15
50	0.06	0.06	0.06	0.06	0.06	85	0.15	0.15	0.15	0.15	0.16
51	0.06	0.06	0.06	0.06	0.06	86	0.15	0.15	0.15	0.16	0.16
52	0.06	0.06	0.06	0.06	0.06	87	0.15	0.15	0.16	0.16	0.16
53	0.06	0.06	0.06	0.07	0.07	88	0.15	0.16	0.16	0.16	0.16
54	0.06	0.07	0.07	0.07	0.07	89	0.16	0.16	0.16	0.16	0.17
55	0.07	0.07	0.07	0.07	0.07	90	0.16	0.16	0.16	0.17	0.17
56	0.07	0.07	0.07	0.07	0.08	91	0.16	0.16	0.17	0.17	0.17
57	0.07	0.08	0.08	0.08	0.08	92	0.16	0.17	0.17	0.17	0.18
58	0.08	0.08	0.08	0.08	0.08	93	0.17	0.17	0.17	0.17	0.18
59	0.08	0.08	0.08	0.08	0.08	94	0.17	0.17	0.17	0.18	0.18
60	0.08	0.08	0.08	0.08	0.09	95	0.17	0.17	0.18	0.18	0.18
61	0.08	0.08	0.09	0.09	0.09	96	0.17	0.18	0.18	0.18	0.19
62	0.09	0.09	0.09	0.09	0.09	97	0.18	0.18	0.18	0.18	0.19
63	0.09	0.09	0.09	0.09	0.10	98	0.18	0.18	0.18	0.19	0.19
64	0.09	0.09	0.10	0.10	0.10	99	0.18	0.18	0.19	0.19	0.19
65	0.09	0.10	0.10	0.10	0.10	100	0.18	0.19	0.19	0.19	0.20

mercurial barometers have an attached thermometer to indicate the temperature. The correction for any temperature can be found in Table X.

3. *Latitude or Gravity Correction.*—Since the earth is flattened at the poles and bulges at the equator, there will be a greater pull on a mercury column near the poles and a lesser pull at the equator. This correction is therefore positive above 45° latitude, negative below, and zero at 45°. These correction figures are found in Table XI.

TABLE XI. REDUCTION OF THE MERCURIAL BAROMETER TO STANDARD GRAVITY (45°) (30 IN.)

Lat.,°	Corr., in.	Lat.,°	Corr., in.	Lat.,°	Corr., in.	Lat.,°	Corr., in.
0	−0.08	25	−0.05	45	0.00	70	+0.06
5	−.08	30	−.04	50	+.01	75	+.07
10	−.08	35	−.03	55	+.03	80	+.08
15	−.07	40	−.01	60	+.04	85	+.08
20	−.06	45	0.00	65	+.05	90	+.08

4. *Instrument Correction.*—This varies with the particular instrument and is found by comparison with a standard barometer. The U.S. Weather Bureau will make such comparisons.

The following example is given, the corrections being those found in the tables. A barometer on a ship's bridge is 35 feet above sea level; temperature, 90°F.; latitude, 10°N. or S.

	Inches
Barometer as read..	29.97
Altitude (sea level) correction.................. +0.04	
Temperature correction....................... −0.17	
Latitude or gravity correction................ −0.08	
Instrument correction........................ +0.03	
Total correction........................... −0.18 inches	
Corrected barometer reading..........................	29.79

ANEROID BAROMETER.—The aneroid barometer is a mechanical device which registers pressure. Briefly, it contains a cylindrical vacuum chamber with corrugated tops and sides known as a "sylphon chamber." A strong spring within the chamber prevents it from collapsing under the air pressure. Clearly, as the outside pressure changes, the chamber will either expand or contract. By means of an intricate system of levers and pulleys this change is magnified and conveyed to a pointer. The pointer swings around a dial that is calibrated in the same units as in a mercurial barometer. The whole is enclosed in a protective brass case with a glass window. A movable indicator can be set over the barometer needle to show the change in pressure since the last reading.

Owing to the tendency of the mechanical parts to stick, this instrument should be tapped prior to each reading and should be read with the eye directly in front of the needle pointer to avoid parallax error.

The aneroid is met with much more frequently than is the mercurial, owing to its compactness and ease of mounting and reading. However of the two, the mercurial is the standard instrument, being more reliable and accurate.

CORRECTIONS APPLIED TO ANEROID READINGS.—The aneroid has essentially two corrections: an altitude correction, which is similar to

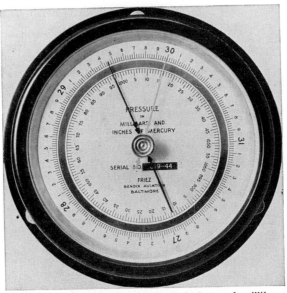

FIG. 7-4.—Aneroid barometer with scales in both inches and millibars. (*Courtesy of Friez Instruments Division of Bendix Aviation Corporation.*)

that of the mercurial, and an instrument correction. All good aneroids are compensated for temperature and obviously show no gravity effect. Should the instrument error become too large, the pointer can be reset after comparison by means of a setscrew on the back of the case. Such barometers should be checked every 3 months. This can be done by taking the barometer to the nearest U.S. Weather Bureau office or, if not convenient, by sending to the Bureau a series of readings on special Weather Bureau cards. The necessary correction will be returned by mail.

BAROGRAPH.—The barograph is simply a recording aneroid barometer. The effect of changes of atmospheric pressure on the vacuum chamber is communicated to a long pen arm which exaggerates this movement. The pen rests on a rotating drum similar to that of the

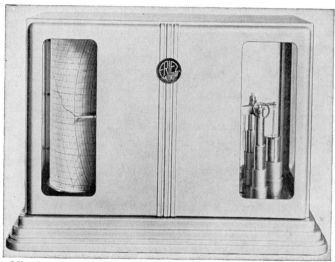

FIG. 7-5.—Microbarograph. (*Courtesy of Friez Instruments Division of Bendix Aviation Corporation.*)

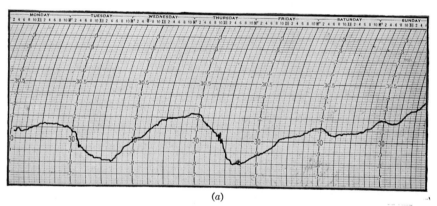

(a)

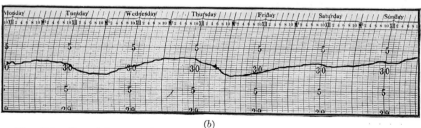

(b)

FIG. 7-6.—Comparison of microbarogram (a) with barogram (b) for the same week, showing the vertical exaggeration of the former. The chart shows passage of two lows with rising pressures at the close of the week. The irregularity of the barograph tracing on Thursday evening marks the abrupt minor pressure fluctuations attending the passage of a severe thunderstorm.

thermograph and yields a continuous trace on the coordinate paper surrounding the drum. This sheet is calibrated vertically in pressure units and horizontally in time, with a line for every 2 hours. The barograph requires the same corrections as the aneroid: altitude and instrument corrections. A setscrew permits adjustment of the barograph to standard pressure after comparison with a more accurate instrument.

An especially sensitive barograph has been developed which permits pressure readings directly to a one-hundredth of an inch. This is known as a "microbarograph."

Units for Measuring Pressure

There are several different systems of units or scales in more or less common use for measuring pressure. These are inches, millibars, and millimeters.

For years American instruments have used the inch as the standard unit of pressure measurement. This stems originally from the height to which mercury rises in the glass barometer tube, or the height of the "glass." We have already noted that 29.92 inches is the normal height under normal pressure. Thus the pressure is simply stated in terms of inches, which are divided into tenths and hundredths.

However the inch is but a unit of length and does not directly convey the amount of force or pressure that the air exerts. Consequently a new system has been developed and has come into widespread meteorological use, replacing the inch as the standard, although that unit is still common.

The new unit is the "millibar." A bar is a definite unit of force conveying to the weather man a definite amount of pressure. Since fluctuations in atmospheric pressure are very small in amount compared to the force represented by a bar, it would be necessary to use decimal fractions to express pressure and changes in pressure Therefore millibars (thousandths of a bar) are used, there being 1,000 millibars in one bar. These units are abbreviated mb.

One bar is a pressure of 1,000,000 dynes per square centimeter. It will be remembered that a dyne is the metric unit of force necessary to give a mass of one gram an acceleration of one centimeter per second. Therefore, when expressing atmospheric pressure in millibars, we are using true pressure units.

Normal atmospheric pressure is 1,013.2 millibars. This is the same as 29.92 inches. Thus, 1 inch is equivalent to 33.86 millibars; 0.1 inch is equivalent to 3.39 millibars; and 3 millibars equals 0.09 inch. It will be seen later why these particular comparisons are made. Complete comparisons are shown in Table XII, but they can always be computed from the information above.

TABLE XII. CONVERSION OF INCHES TO MILLIBARS

In.	Mb.	In.	Mb.	In.	Mb.
27.32	925	28.64	970	29.97	1,015
27.34	926	28.67	971	30.00	1,016
27.37	927	28.70	972	30.03	1,017
27.40	928	28.73	973	30.06	1,018
27.43	929	28.76	974	30.09	1,019
27.46	930	28.79	975	30.12	1,020
27.49	931	28.82	976	30.15	1,021
27.52	932	28.85	977	30.18	1,022
27.55	933	28.88	978	30.21	1,023
27.58	934	28.91	979	30.24	1,024
27.61	935	28.94	980	30.27	1,025
27.64	936	28.97	981	30.30	1,026
27.67	937	29.00	982	30.33	1,027
27.70	938	29.03	983	30.36	1,028
27.73	939	29.06	984	30.39	1,029
27.76	940	29.09	985	30.42	1,030
27.79	941	29.12	986	30.45	1,031
27.82	942	29.15	987	30.47	1,032
27.85	943	29.18	988	30.50	1,033
27.88	944	29.21	989	30.53	1,034
27.91	945	29.23	990	30.56	1,035
27.94	946	29.26	991	30.59	1,036
27.96	947	29.29	992	30.62	1,037
27.99	948	29.32	993	30.65	1,038
28.02	949	29.35	994	30.68	1,039
28.05	950	29.38	995	30.71	1,040
28.08	951	29.41	996	30.74	1,041
28.11	952	29.44	997	30.77	1,042
28.14	953	29.47	998	30.80	1,043
28.17	954	29.50	999	30.83	1,044
28.20	955	29.53	1,000	30.86	1,045
28.23	956	29.56	1,001	30.89	1,046
28.26	957	29.59	1,002	30.92	1,047
28.29	958	29.62	1,003	30.95	1,048
28.32	959	29.65	1,004	30.98	1,049
28.35	960	29.68	1,005	31.01	1,050
28.38	961	29.71	1,006	31.04	1,051
28.41	962	29.74	1,007	31.07	1,052
28.44	963	29.77	1,008	31.10	1,053
28.47	964	29.80	1,009	31.13	1,054
28.50	965	29.83	1,010	31.15	1,055
28.53	966	29.85	1,011	31.18	1,056
28.56	967	29.88	1,012	31.21	1,057
28.58	968	29.91	1,013	31.24	1,058
28.61	969	29.94	1,014	31.27	1,059

TABLE XIII. CONVERSION OF MILLIMETERS TO MILLIBARS

Mm.	Mb.	Mm.	Mb.	Mm.	Mb.
696	927.9	726	967.9	756	1,007.9
697	929.3	727	969.3	757	1,009.3
698	930.6	728	970.6	758	1,010.6
699	931.9	729	971.9	759	1,011.9
700	933.3	730	973.3	760	1,013.3
701	934.6	731	974.6	761	1,014.6
702	935.9	732	975.9	762	1,015.9
703	937.3	733	977.3	763	1,017.2
704	938.6	734	978.6	764	1,018.6
705	939.9	735	979.9	765	1,019.9
706	941.3	736	981.3	766	1,021.2
707	942.6	737	982.6	767	1,022.6
708	943.9	738	983.9	768	1,023.9
709	945.3	739	985.3	769	1,025.2
710	946.6	740	986.6	770	1,026.6
711	947.9	741	987.9	771	1,027.9
712	949.3	742	989.3	772	1,029.2
713	950.6	743	990.6	773	1,030.6
714	951.9	744	991.9	774	1,031.9
715	953.3	745	993.3	775	1,033.2
716	954.6	746	994.6	776	1,034.6
717	955.9	747	995.9	777	1,035.9
718	957.3	748	997.3	778	1,037.2
719	958.6	749	998.6	779	1,038.6
720	959.9	750	999.9	780	1,039.9
721	961.3	751	1,001.3	781	1,041.2
722	962.2	752	1,002.6	782	1,042.6
723	963.6	753	1,003.9	783	1,043.9
724	965.3	754	1,005.3	784	1,045.2
725	966.6	755	1,006.6	785	1,046.6

Millimeters are usually found only on the instruments aboard European vessels that use the metric system, a millimeter being a thousandth of a meter. Since there are 25.4 millimeters in an inch, normal pressure in millimeters is very close to 760 (see Table XIII).

PRESSURE TENDENCY.—The pressure tendency is the net change in pressure for the preceding 3 hours. Since we have already mentioned that, for local interpretation, the change in pressure is of great importance, the significance of the pressure tendency with any observation should be clear.

Isobars and the Pressure Gradient

We have said that weather conditions are closely related to, and to a great extent dependent upon, atmospheric pressure variations over the earth's surface. The atmosphere may be considered as a huge ocean of gases resting on the earth. But, as pointed out earlier, this air ocean does not rest uniformly on the earth. Consequently, to understand and interpret weather conditions, a knowledge of the distribution of atmospheric pressure is necessary. This is best accomplished by representing pressure distribution over the earth's surface diagrammatically. For this purpose, "isobars" are used.

ISOBARS.—Isobars are lines drawn through points of equal pressure. The values of air pressure are obtained by the use of barometers at local

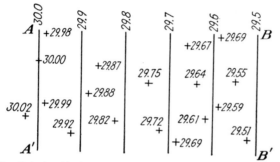

FIG. 7-7.—Relationship between isobars and actual pressure observations.

observation stations on land and from ships at sea. The corrected pressure readings, reduced to sea level, are entered on maps, and points on the map showing the same pressure readings are connected with lines, isobars. Obviously all points on a map with the same pressure cannot be so joined, as an infinite number of lines would result. Hence isobars are drawn for points showing integral tenths of an inch, *i.e.*, points on successive isobars may have readings of 29.7, 29.8, 29.9 inches, etc.

If pressure readings are shown in millibars, the isobars are labeled in those units and are drawn through points whose pressure readings are divisible by 3. Thus successive isobars might be drawn through points having readings of 1,008, 1,011, 1,014 millibars, etc. Occasionally isobars are drawn for every 4 millibars on marine weather maps, owing to the relative scarcity of ship reports. On U.S. Weather Bureau weather maps, millibars have replaced inches in designating the pressure.

Let us consider a simple example of the representation of atmospheric pressure distribution by means of isobars. Assume, as in Fig. 7-7, that the pressure at *A* and *A'*, two points on our map, show a pressure of 30 inches, while points *B* and *B'* show a pressure of 29.5 inches. An examination of the figure shows the pressure to be equal along north-south lines. However, very few of the readings are in integral tenths of an inch. Thus the position of the isobars must be approximated. The 30-inch isobar is drawn between A and A', estimating its position from the figures given. In the same way the 29.9-, 29.8-, 29.7-, 29.6-, and the 29.5-inch isobars are drawn, the last from B to B'.

RELATION BETWEEN ISOBARS AND THE PRESSURE GRADIENT.—If isobars are lines of equal pressure, then adjacent isobars indicate a change in pressure from one isobar to the next. In the case above a continuous pressure change exists between the lines AA' and BB', for the pressure over this distance falls from 30 to 29.5 inches. This change in pressure with horizontal distance is known as the "pressure gradient." To see more clearly the meaning of the pressure gradient let us consider its

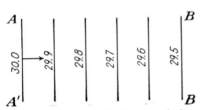

FIG. 7-8.—Relationship between isobars and the direction of the pressure gradient.

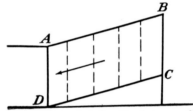

FIG. 7-9.—Relationship between the direction of slope of a surface and lines of equal altitude on the surface.

relationship to the isobars as regards (1) direction of the gradient and (2) the steepness of the gradient, or the amount of change of pressure.

1. *Directional Relationship of Isobars and the Pressure Gradient.*—The pressure gradient is measured along the line of greatest pressure change. This is shown in Fig. 7-8. From A to B there is a pressure change of 0.5 inch. The same pressure change exists between A and B', or between A and any other point on the 29.5 isobar. Clearly the gradient should be measured over the shortest distance between isobars or in a direction perpendicular to them. This is indicated by the arrow.

Let us compare the pressure gradient to a sloping surface. Actually, the term is borrowed from the surveyor and refers to a slope of the ground surface (Fig. 7-9). The gradient of the surface $ABCD$ is measured directly down its slope. In the same way then, the pressure gradient is measured directly down the pressure change. The dotted lines in the figure represent lines of equal altitude on the sloping surface. Just as the gradient here is perpendicular to the line of equal altitude, so the pressure gradient is perpendicular to lines of equal pressure (isobars).

2. *Steepness of Pressure Gradient.*—Borrowing another surveyor's term, we note that the amount of pressure change between two points is described as "steepness" of the pressure gradient. In Fig. 7-10, the

first surface slopes up to 50 feet while the second slopes up to 100 feet over the same horizontal distance. If we draw lines of equal altitude on the surfaces with a vertical interval of 10 feet between them, it is clear that these lines drawn on the surface must be much closer together,

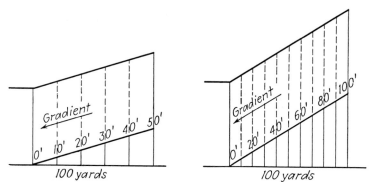

FIG. 7-10.—Effect of change in slope of a surface on the spacing and number of lines of equal altitude.

and also be more numerous in the second case. This is the steeper gradient.

Similarly in the case of atmospheric pressure, the steeper the pressure gradient between the points, the more numerous, and more closely

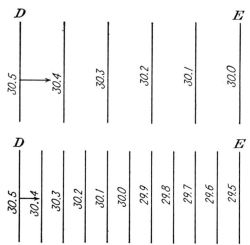

FIG. 7-11.—Effect of change in pressure gradient on the spacing and number of isobars.

spaced will be the isobars. Isobars relatively far apart show a very slight pressure difference or gradient. Thus the gradient between *D* and *E* is 0.5 inch in the first case and 1 inch in the second (Fig. 7-11). Hence the number of isobars is doubled, and they are much closer. A barometer carried over the horizontal distance *DE* would fall twice as fast in the second as in the first case.

TYPES AND FORMS OF ISOBARS.—If an isobar is extended sufficiently, it must always close up on itself and become a continuous curved line. However, in depicting atmospheric pressure distribution, isobars may assume various shapes and patterns for any particular part of their length. This is particularly true in the middle latitudes, between 30° and 60°, where continuous horizontal pressure variations occur. Some typical forms are shown in Fig. 7-12.

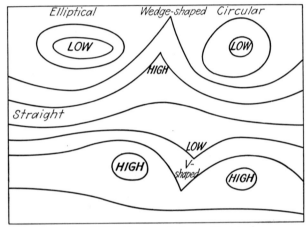

FIG. 7-12.—Common isobar patterns.

High- and Low-pressure Areas

In the middle latitudes isobars display characteristic shapes indicating relatively large areas of alternately high and low pressure. These areas as shown by isobars are rudely circular or elliptical in shape and usually cover tens of thousands of square miles. A particular pressure configuration, whether high or low, may cover a few states or one-half of the entire country. Figure 7-13 shows a typical middle latitude pressure pattern as indicated by isobars which are labeled in millibars.

In Fig. 7-13 the lower pressure is within the 999 isobar but never reaches 996 or another isobar would be drawn. The word "low" is simply written within the last isobar, and the whole is known as a "low-pressure area," or "low," or "depression."

The highest pressure is within the 1,017 isobar, and that whole area is known as a "high-pressure area" or "high." It should be emphasized that there is no particular point where the low ends and the high begins. There is rather a continuous increase in pressure from the center of the low to the center of the high, and then a steady decrease to the next low, and so on.

The highs and lows are not always equally well developed. One may be much stronger than the other, and their circular or elliptical shapes may be considerably distorted at times. Thus, two well-developed low-pressure areas may exist on a map adjacent to each other, in which case they are separated by a narrow *ridge* of higher pressure (Fig. 7-14). The reverse may be true, with two strong highs separated

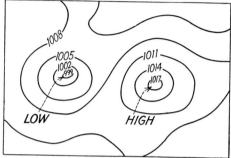

Fig. 7-13.—A common middle latitude pressure pattern showing a low and a high.

by a narrow *trough* of low pressure. Whatever the case, the uniformity or irregularity of the pressure gradient will be indicated by the shape and spacing of the isobars, as explained earlier.

A continuous series of highs and lows exists in the atmosphere of the middle latitudes, which may be likened to water waves whose crests and troughs follow each other continuously. In the same way these low- and high-pressure areas (waves) move continuously through the

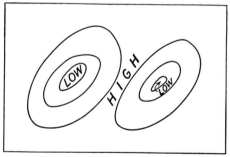

Fig. 7-14.—Areas of low pressure separated by a ridge of high pressure.

atmosphere of the middle latitudes, more or less in the direction of the earth's rotation, or approximately west to east. The passing of the highs and lows is responsible for the weather changes experienced in these latitudes.

The rise or fall in a particular barometer is now seen to herald approaching highs or lows. We know roughly from experience that a falling barometer indicates bad and a rising indicates fair or clearing weather. Therefore a low is an area of bad weather generally, and a high is one of fair weather. The actual weather relationship of lows and highs will be examined in more detail later, but we have already learned enough to form at least a rough picture of the process.

An area of low pressure represents an area having less air above it than an adjacent high-pressure area. Clearly then, the air in a low must be rising continuously to maintain the pressure. Whenever air rises, it expands and cools. If this process is carried far enough, the cooling will produce clouds and consequent rainstorms. These then are the prevailing conditions within a low.

High-pressure areas, having heavier air than surrounding lows, are characterized by falling air which warms adiabatically as it falls. Thus the relative humidity decreases as the falling air warms, yielding relatively dry air and fair weather within the high.

The waves of low and high pressure in the air dissipate with altitude. Their effect is often not recognized above 4 miles and may disappear at lower levels. It is now evident why the daily periodic pressure variation of the lower latitudes is so rarely noticeable in middle and high latitudes. The passage of lows and highs usually masks the daily variation sufficiently to make it unrecognizable.

We have by no means completed our study of highs and lows. On the contrary, in later chapters we shall return and analyze them more thoroughly, owing to their association with and effect on weather changes.

Isallobars

Isallobars are lines of equal pressure tendency or equal pressure change. The analysis of pressure tendency at many stations is very helpful in weather analysis in general and is an aid in forecasting the movement of certain atmospheric elements.

CHAPTER 8

WINDS—OBSERVATION AND THEORY

When differences in atmospheric pressure develop over the earth's surface, air is set in motion. We mentioned briefly in Chap. 1 that winds are the result of pressure differences, which in turn arise from basic irregularities in the heating of the air. A strong interrelationship exists among temperature, pressure, and wind which will manifest itself further in our study of the origin and nature of the winds of the earth.

Basic Wind Features

"Wind" is air in horizontal or nearly horizontal motion. One of the strongest indications of the presence of a relatively thick atmosphere is in the effects of such motion.

In distinction to wind, vertically moving air columns are called "air currents." The so-called "air pockets," so well known to aviators, are not voids in the atmosphere but merely descending air currents. Combinations of rising and falling air currents yield "bumpy" air.

Winds are named in accordance with the direction *from* which they blow. Thus a wind blowing from the northwest is termed a "northwest" wind, etc.

SURFACE WIND MOTION.—Air in motion at or near the earth's surface does not move freely. On the contrary it has a very irregular motion, blowing in series of puffs or gusts along the surface. This unsteady wind motion is known as "turbulence." Near the ground this turbulence is principally a result of friction between the air and the earth's surface, which produces eddies in the air together with the familiar lulls and gusts. Convection from local surface-temperature differences also influences the air motion.

Clearly, the effect of eddies, causing turbulence in the surface winds, varies directly with the irregularity of the ground surface. Since any irregularity produces eddying, turbulent wind motion is much greater for hilly, forested areas than for smooth level ground. In surface air, turbulence is least over the open sea, where friction is reduced to a minimum. Hence, for equivalent conditions, winds are steadier and have higher velocities over sea than over land areas.

It is also important to note that the effect of turbulence increases with velocity. Since the result of wind eddies is to change momentarily

125

both the direction and the velocity of the wind, it follows that the higher the *original* velocity, the more rapid and abrupt will these changes be.

WIND MOTION ABOVE THE SURFACE.—Altitude has a very pronounced effect on wind motion. First, the velocity increases rapidly with altitude as the effect of friction with the ground disappears. This condition continues on the average up to a height of approximately 1,500 feet. Above this level the wind velocity may still continue to increase, or may at times decrease or remain relatively steady. Even at a height of some 30 feet above the ground the wind velocity is double that at 1 foot. The highest sustained wind velocity ever recorded was 210 miles an hour at the observatory on top of Mount Washington in New Hampshire. Of course higher velocities do exist in particular storm conditions but these have been only estimated, never directly recorded.

Second, the effect of altitude is to reduce turbulence. The free air above the earth's surface is subjected to much less eddy action as a

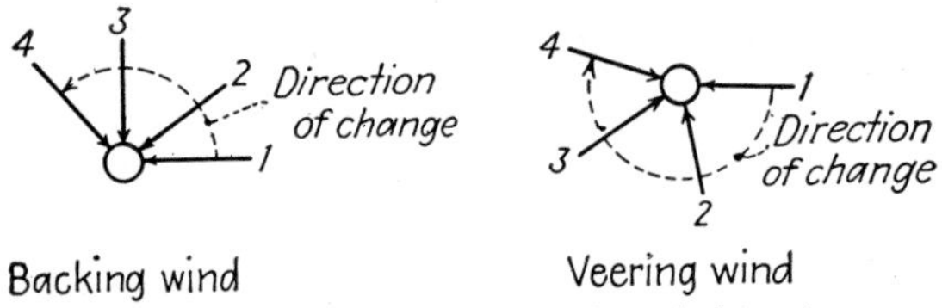

Backing wind   Veering wind

FIG. 8-1.—Backing and veering wind motion.

result of ground friction. High mountains naturally cause such behavior in their vicinities, but their effect is limited in extent. However, turbulence does develop in the upper air owing to the presence of convectional air columns and to the effect of air streams, one above the other, flowing in different directions.

SHIFTING WINDS.—We have noted that the wind direction may be quite variable for short periods as a result of eddy action, although the main mass of air itself may be coming steadily from a given direction. This variable gusty quality of winds should not be confused with the true shifting of winds. A *wind shift* is a steady progressive change in direction. The causes of such shifting will be studied in detail later. At the moment we shall concentrate on the observational phase only.

A wind may shift in either a clockwise or a counterclockwise manner. Thus, a wind whose direction changes from east, through south, to west, has shifted clockwise through the compass; such a shifting wind is called a "veering" wind, or is said to "veer."

A wind that shifts in a counterclockwise manner is said to "back," and is termed a "backing" wind.

Note that the wind is not blowing in a circular manner whether clockwise or counterclockwise. The *directions* of the shifting wind

Fig. 8-2.—Wind direction transmitter—Selsyn type. (*Courtesy of Friez Instruments Division of Bendix Aviation Corporation.*)

describe this circular motion. This is illustrated in Fig. 8-1. The terms "veering" or "backing" therefore indicate immediately the compass points through which the wind direction has changed, without actual mention being made of these points; *i.e.*, a wind backing from west to southeast must pass through all the intervening directions.

Wind Observations and Measurement

Wind direction and velocity can be measured and recorded accurately by means of instruments, or they may be obtained through estimation from certain observations. The means that are used naturally depend on the equipment available and the purpose for which the observations are taken. In placing wind instruments, care should be taken that no

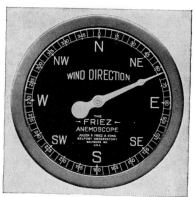

Fig. 8-3.—Wind-direction indicator —Selsyn type. (*Courtesy of Friez Instruments Division of Bendix Aviation Corporation.*)

wind obstructions are near them. Otherwise the influence of eddies described above will yield false readings.

WIND DIRECTION.—Instrumentally, wind direction is most commonly indicated by the familiar "wind vane," of which there are several types. The vane always points *into* the wind. Wind vanes are usually constructed so that the fluctuations in wind direction are communicated instantaneously to some form of indicator or automatic recorder, by means of proper electrical connections.

FIG. 8-4.—Pilot balloon being released from the flight deck of an aircraft carrier.   (*Official U.S. Navy Photograph.*)

The wind sock, a typical airport device to show the wind direction, always flies *with* the wind.

To determine the wind direction and speed in the upper air, pilot balloons are utilized. When inflated properly, they have a known rate of ascent. Observations on a balloon are then made at 1-minute intervals with a "theodolite," which measures the angular horizontal drift of the balloon and also its angle of elevation. Since the drift of a balloon equals the wind speed at the particular elevation, it is a simple matter to compute

these values from the observed data.   A lantern attached to a pilot
balloon provides for nocturnal observations.   A knowledge of upper air
conditions is of great importance in modern weather analysis.   Pilot
balloon observations are therefore very valuable.

From fixed or stationary positions, determination of the wind direction by ordinary observation is usually fairly simple.   Any object that
is bent or swayed or blown by the wind may serve as a useful direction
indicator.   Thus, smoke, flags, or pennants are normally reliable wind
guides.

On a moving vessel, wind direction is best indicated by the surface
of the sea.   The wind will clearly be perpendicular to the crest line

Fɪɢ. 8-5.—Keuffel and Esser shipboard theodolite.   (*Courtesy of U.S. Weather Bureau.*)

of the ripples, waves, or whitecaps.   The direction of the spume blowing
from the white caps will coincide with the wind direction.   Care should
be taken not to confuse waves with any prevailing swell.   Swells are
long undulating waves which are produced by winds at a distant source
and which have since outrun the storm that caused them.   They bear no
particular relationship to local winds.

Clouds are excellent guides to the wind direction prevailing in the
upper free air.   Low clouds usually conform in their motion to the surface
winds, with some variation to be explained later.   The higher clouds,
however, may be under the influence of an entirely different air stream.

Wɪɴᴅ Vᴇʟᴏᴄɪᴛʏ.—Usually wind velocity can be determined quite
accurately by means of the "anemometer."   The common cup-type anemometer consists essentially of three or more hemispherical cups extending

on horizontal arms from a vertical shaft or spindle. The higher the wind velocity, the faster will the cups rotate the movable spindle. By means of a magnetogenerator arrangement, or a gear system with proper electrical contacts, this spinning motion is translated to show on remote instruments the wind force in miles per hour. This equipment may indicate the instantaneous velocity directly by means of dials or buzzers, or it may record instantaneous or average velocities on a graph, for reference purposes.

Fig. 8-6.—Anemometer with buzzer-type wind-velocity indicator—usually remote from the anemometer. (*Courtesy of U.S. Weather Bureau.*)

There are several types of wind transmitting and indicating systems, all of which are completely described in various government manuals on the subject.

When no instruments are available, wind velocity cannot be determined so easily. A moving mass of air, or wind, has a certain effect on objects in its path. The stronger the wind, the greater the force exerted. Once the relation between wind force and its effect is carefully determined, future estimates of wind velocity may be made by noting the reactions of obstacles to the wind. Obviously, determinations to within a mile an hour cannot be obtained by this rough method.

The pressure or force exerted by a wind is proportional to the square of the velocity of the wind. Thus

$$F \propto V^2$$

or

$$F = KV^2$$

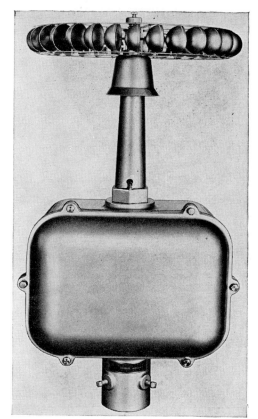

FIG. 8-7.—Wind-velocity transmitter—Selsyn type. (*Courtesy of Friez Instruments Division of Bendix Aviation Corporation.*)

FIG. 8-8.—Wind-velocity indicator—Selsyn type. (*Courtesy of Friez Instruments Division of Bendix Aviation Corporation.*)

FIG. 8-9.—Wind direction and velocity recorder used with Selsyn-type transmitting instruments. (*Courtesy of Friez Instruments Division of Bendix Aviation Corporation.*)

TABLE XIV. TABLE OF COMPARATIVE WIND-VELOCITY TERMINOLOGY

Beaufort force	Velocity		Seaman's description of wind	U.S. Weather Bureau terminology
	M.p.h.	Knots		
0	1	1	Calm	Light
1	1–3	1–3	Light air	Light
2	4–7	4–6	Light breeze	Light
3	8–12	7–10	Gentle breeze	Gentle
4	13–18	11–16	Moderate breeze	Moderate
5	19–24	17–21	Fresh breeze	Fresh
6	25–31	22–27	Strong breeze	Strong
7	32–38	28–33	Moderate gale	Strong
8	39–46	34–40	Fresh gale	Gale
9	47–54	41–47	Strong gale	Gale
10	55–63	48–55	Whole gale	Whole gale
11	64–75	56–65	Storm	Whole gale
12	Above 75	Above 65	Hurricane	Hurricane

If the force is to be found in pounds per square foot, then the velocity should be in miles (statute) per hour. The constant K then equals 0.004. For this formula to hold without correction, the surface exposed to the wind must be perpendicular to the path.

Note that the effect of the wind on any exposed object is determined actually by the direct impact of the air on the windward side, together with the resulting suction on the leeward side.

In the early part of the nineteenth century, Admiral Beaufort of the Royal Navy developed the well-known scale of wind velocity that

Fig. 8-10.—Radiosonde. This instrument, which is carried aloft by a balloon, automatically transmits radio messages of temperature, pressure, and humidity conditions aloft. (*Courtesy of Friez Instruments Division of Bendix Aviation Corporation.*)

bears his name. The Beaufort system employs a series of numbers from 0 to 12, each number standing for a wind velocity between certain limits in miles per hour. Table XIV shows the relationship between the Beaufort scale and the force in miles per hour. This is followed by a brief wind description for land stations (see Table XV). Criteria for determining the Beaufort force at *sea* are given in Table XVI.

Table XVI of sea and wind relations is to be used only on the open sea; *it is not applicable to inland or restricted waters*. Clearly, the effect of the wind on the sea depends in addition to its velocity, on the "fetch," or distance it has blown over the water. Also, the motion of currents

TABLE XV

Beaufort Force	Specifications for Use on Fixed Objects
0	Calm; smoke rises vertically
1	Direction of wind shown by smoke drift, but not by wind vanes
2	Wind felt on face; leaves rustle; ordinary vane moved by wind
3	Leaves and small twigs in constant motion; wind extends light flag
4	Raises dust and loose paper; small branches are moved
5	Small trees in leaf begin to sway; crested wavelets form on inland waters
6	Large branches in motion; whistling heard in telegraph wires; umbrellas used with difficulty
7	Whole trees in motion; inconvenience felt in walking against wind
8	Breaks twigs off trees; generally impedes progress
9	Slight structural damage occurs (chimney pots and slate removed)
10	Seldom experienced inland; trees uprooted; considerable structural damage occurs
11	Very rarely experienced; accompanied by widespread damage
12	Maximum wind damage—hurricane violence

TABLE XVI

Beaufort Force	Description of Corresponding Sea
0	Dead calm, sea surface glassy or mirrorlike; wind has no relation to swell that may be present
1	Sea surface is rippled in patches
2	Sea surface completely rippled; miniature waves about 1 ft. high; horizon line much sharper than with force 1
3	Small waves 2 to 3 ft. high with scattered whitecaps beginning to form
4	Waves about 5 ft. high with numerous whitecaps spotting the surface
5	Waves up to 8 ft. high with prominent white wave crests; spray begins to be blown from the crests
6	10- to 12-ft. waves with numerous streaks of spray blowing from foamy crests
7	16-ft. waves with white foam being whipped out in the direction of the wind gusts
8	Extremely rough, violent sea with 20- to 25-ft. waves; dense foamy streaks show wind direction
9	25- to 30-ft. waves; sea begins to roll as heavy streaks of foam and spray are seen on all sides
10	30- to 40-ft. waves; sea is covered with white foam; visibility is affected by blown spray; ship is shocked by force of waves
11	35 to 45-ft. waves; air is full of spray; small and medium ships hidden in deep troughs of waves; breaking rollers and high wind cause damage to deck fittings
12	Waves 45 ft. or higher; hurricane wind; towering waves will seriously damage ships if force 12 continues for long

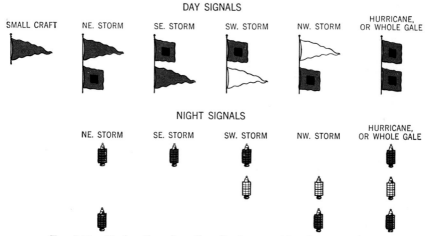

SMALL CRAFT NE. STORM SE. STORM SW. STORM NW. STORM HURRICANE, OR WHOLE GALE

NIGHT SIGNALS

NE. STORM SE. STORM SW. STORM NW. STORM HURRICANE, OR WHOLE GALE

Fig. 8-11.—Explanation of small craft, storm, and hurricane warnings.

The Small Craft Warning.—A red pennant indicates that moderately strong winds that will interfere with the safe operation of small craft are expected. No night display of small craft warnings is made.

The Northeast Storm Warning.—A red pennant *above* a square red flag with black center displayed by day, or two red lanterns, one above the other, displayed by night, indicates the approach of a storm of marked violence with winds beginning from the *northeast*.

The Southeast Storm Warning.—A red pennant *below* a square red flag with black center displayed by day, or one red lantern displayed by night, indicates the approach of a storm of marked violence with winds beginning from the *southeast*.

The Southwest Storm Warning.—A white pennant *below* a square red flag with black center displayed by day, or a white lantern *below* a red lantern displayed by night, indicates the approach of a storm of marked violence with winds beginning from the *southwest*.

The Northwest Storm Warning.—A white pennant *above* a square red flag with black center displayed by day, or a white lantern *above* a red lantern displayed by night, indicates the approach of a storm of marked violence with winds beginning from the *northwest*.

Hurricane, or Whole Gale Warning.—Two square flags, red with black centers, one above the other, displayed by day, or two red lanterns, with a white lantern between, displayed by night, indicate the approach of a tropical hurricane or of one of the extremely severe and dangerous storms which occasionally occur.

adds to or detracts from the wind effects. If the current opposes the wind, the sea surface indicates a higher velocity than exists. If the current runs with the wind, a lower velocity is apparent. Thus white-caps are produced when a tidal current of 3 or 4 knots, opposing a wind with a force of but 2, would indicate a force of 3.

Wind Representation.—Winds may be described by the compass direction and velocity in miles per hour or in Beaufort force, or they may be shown diagram-matically as on weather maps and pilot charts. On

Fig. 8-12.

either of these maps the wind is indicated by an arrow which flies with the wind, thereby indicating the direction. The number and length of the tails or barbs on the arrows indicate the Beaufort force of the wind.

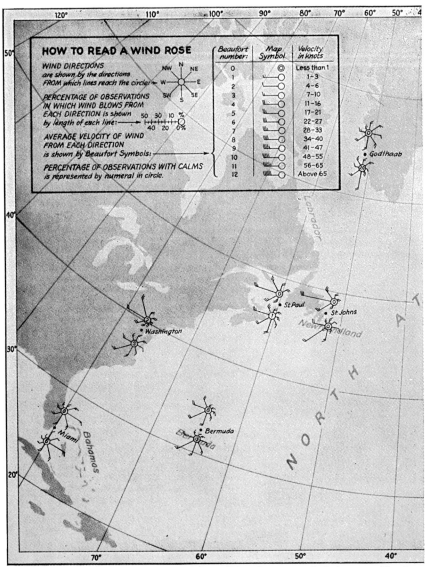

FIG. 8-13.—Representation of average wind conditions by means of wind roses.   (*Courtesy of U.S. Navy.*)

Each half barb stands for a Beaufort force of 1.   Hence Fig. 8-12 shows a southeast wind of force 5.   The small circle at the head of the arrow represents the station at which the observation is made.

To show the average wind conditions in a given locality the wind rose, illustrated in Fig. 8-13, is used.   The lengths of the radiating lines are proportional to the frequency with which the winds blow from the different compass directions.

On pilot charts, 16 directions are shown. "The length of the arrow, measured from the outside of the circle, gives the percentage of the total number of observations in which the wind has blown from or near the given point. The number of barbs or feathers attached shows the average Beaufort force for that direction. In this case the barbs are

FIG. 8-14.—The Storm Breaks. Navy ships ride out the record-breaking gale that at times reached a velocity of more than 100 miles per hour off the coast of Iceland in January, 1942. (*Official U.S. Navy Photograph.*)

drawn on either side of the arrow with each barb representing a force of 1. The number within the circle indicates the percentage of days in which calms existed."

True and Apparent Wind Relationship

The wind experienced on a ship under way is the result of two variable components: the wind created by the ship's motion and the true wind. The resultant wind is called the "apparent wind." Clearly, the direction and velocity of this apparent wind, as experienced on the deck of a vessel, depends on the force and direction of the true wind and that of the wind caused by the forward motion of the ship. For convenience, the latter wind, which results from the vessel's headway, will hereafter be referred to as the "ship's wind."

The apparent wind, being the resultant of these forces, must always lie *between* the true and the ship's wind, except when the true wind is dead ahead or dead astern. Thus, if the velocity and direction of the true and ship's winds are known and plotted to scale on a chart, the apparent wind can be determined by completing the typical diagram of parallelogram of vectors. This is indicated in Fig. 8-15. SW stands for ship's wind, TW for true wind, and AW for apparent wind.

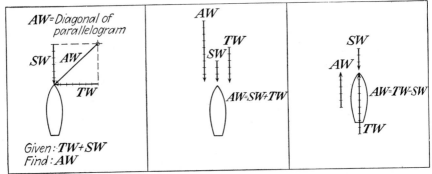

Fig. 8-15.—Determination of apparent wind when the true wind and the ship's wind are known.

It is the *true* and not the apparent wind which is of significance for weather purposes. When conditions of visibility make observation of the sea's surface difficult or impossible, the true wind may be determined by this relationship. The direction and force of the ship's wind are easily determined from the course and speed of the vessel. The apparent wind force and direction can be estimated by observation, or

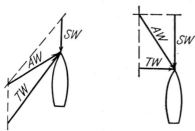

Fig. 8-16.—Determination of the true wind when the apparent and ship's wind are known.

measured accurately if instruments are aboard. With this known, the true wind can be obtained by application of the diagram method described. Some cases are considered in Fig. 8-16. The true wind, TW, is found by drawing a line connecting the tails of the arrows representing the apparent wind, AW, and the ship's wind, SW. The length and direction of this line represent the true wind direction and velocity. For clarity in the diagram, the opposite side of the parallelogram is labeled TW.

Any number of other possibilities exist and may be worked by this method. Many generalities may also be drawn:

1. The true wind direction is always farther from the bow than the apparent wind direction.

2. When the apparent wind is abaft the beam, the true wind is stronger and farther aft than the apparent wind.

TABLE XVII. TABLE FOR OBTAINING THE TRUE DIRECTION AND FORCE OF THE WIND FROM THE DECK OF A MOVING VESSEL*

Each data cell below (columns 0–15) gives two figures: **True direction, points off the bow** and **True force, Beaufort scale**. Column 16 gives only the True force, Beaufort scale.

Apparent force of the wind, Beaufort scale	Speed of the vessel, knots	0	1	2	3	4	5	6	7	8	9	10	11	12	13	14	15	16
0	10	16 3	16 3	16 3	16 3	16 3	16 3	16 3	16 3	16 3	16 3	16 3	16 3	16 3	16 3	16 3	16 3	3
	15	16 4	16 4	16 4	16 4	16 4	16 4	16 4	16 4	16 4	16 4	16 4	16 4	16 4	16 4	16 4	16 4	4
	20	16 5	16 5	16 5	16 5	16 5	16 5	16 5	16 5	16 5	16 5	16 5	16 5	16 5	16 5	16 5	16 5	5
1	10	16 3	16 3	16 3	15 3	15 3	15 3	15 3	15 3	15 3	15 3	15 3	15 3	15 4	16 4	16 4	16 4	4
	15	16 4	16 4	16 4	15 4	15 4	15 4	15 4	15 4	15 4	15 4	15 4	15 4	16 4	16 4	16 5	16 5	5
	20	16 5	16 5	16 5	16 5	16 5	16 5	15 5	15 5	15 5	16 5	16 5	16 5	16 5	16 5	16 6	16 6	6
2	10	16 2	15 2	14 2	14 2	13 3	13 3	13 3	13 3	14 4	14 4	14 4	14 4	15 4	15 4	15 4	16 4	4
	15	16 3	16 3	15 3	15 3	14 4	14 4	14 4	14 4	14 4	14 4	15 5	15 5	15 5	15 5	15 5	16 5	6
	20	16 4	16 4	15 4	15 4	15 4	15 5	15 5	15 5	15 5	15 5	15 5	16 6	16 6	16 6	16 6	16 6	6
3	10	16 1	12 1	11 1	11 2	11 2	11 3	12 3	12 3	13 4	13 4	14 4	14 4	15 5	15 5	16 5	16 5	5
	15	16 2	15 2	14 3	13 3	13 3	13 3	13 4	13 4	13 4	14 5	14 5	14 5	15 6	15 6	16 6	16 6	6
	20	16 4	16 4	15 4	15 4	14 4	14 4	14 4	14 5	14 5	14 5	14 6	14 6	15 6	15 6	16 7	16 7	7
4	10	0 1	3 2	6 2	7 3	8 3	9 4	10 4	11 4	11 5	12 5	12 5	13 5	14 6	14 6	15 6	15 6	6
	15	16 1	11 1	10 2	10 3	11 4	11 4	11 4	12 5	12 5	13 6	13 6	14 6	14 7	15 7	15 7	16 7	7
	20	16 2	14 3	13 3	12 4	12 4	12 5	12 5	13 5	13 6	13 6	14 6	14 7	14 7	15 7	15 7	16 7	7
5	10	0 3	2 3	4 4	5 4	7 4	8 4	9 5	10 5	10 5	11 6	12 6	13 6	13 6	14 7	15 7	15 7	7
	15	0 2	4 3	6 3	8 3	9 4	9 5	10 5	11 5	11 6	12 6	13 7	13 7	14 7	14 7	15 8	16 8	8
	20	16 1	10 2	10 3	10 3	10 4	11 4	11 5	11 5	12 6	12 6	13 7	13 7	14 8	14 8	15 8	16 8	8
6	10	0 4	2 4	3 4	5 5	6 5	7 5	8 6	9 6	10 6	11 7	12 7	12 7	13 7	14 7	15 8	15 8	8
	15	0 3	2 3	5 4	6 4	7 5	8 5	9 6	10 6	11 7	12 7	12 7	13 8	13 8	14 8	15 8	16 8	9
	20	0 2	4 2	7 3	8 4	9 4	10 5	10 5	11 6	11 7	12 7	12 8	13 8	13 8	14 9	14 9	15 9	9
7	10	0 5	1 5	3 5	4 6	5 6	6 6	7 7	8 7	9 7	10 7	11 8	12 8	13 8	14 8	14 8	15 8	8
	15	0 4	2 4	4 5	5 5	6 6	6 6	7 7	8 7	9 7	10 7	11 8	12 8	13 9	13 9	14 9	15 9	9
	20	0 3	3 3	4 4	5 4	6 5	8 5	9 6	9 7	10 7	11 8	12 8	12 9	13 9	14 10	15 10	16 10	10
8	10	0 6	1 6	3 7	4 7	5 7	6 7	7 8	7 8	8 8	9 8	10 9	11 9	12 9	13 9	14 9	14 9	9
	15	0 6	2 6	3 6	5 6	6 7	7 7	7 8	8 8	9 9	10 9	11 9	12 9	13 10	14 10	15 10	15 10	10
	20	0 5	2 5	4 5	6 6	7 6	8 7	9 8	10 8	11 9	11 9	12 10	13 10	13 10	14 10	15 11	15 11	11
9	10	0 8	1 8	3 8	4 8	5 8	6 8	7 9	8 9	9 9	10 9	11 10	12 10	13 10	14 10	14 10	15 10	10
	15	0 7	2 7	3 7	4 7	6 7	7 8	8 8	9 9	10 10	11 10	12 10	13 11	14 11	15 11	15 11	16 11	11
	20	0 6	2 6	3 6	5 6	7 7	7 8	8 8	9 9	10 10	11 10	12 10	13 11	13 11	14 11	15 11	15 11	11
10	10	0 9	1 9	2 9	4 9	5 9	6 9	7 10	8 10	9 10	10 10	11 11	12 11	13 11	13 11	14 11	15 11	11
	15	0 8	1 8	3 8	4 8	5 9	6 9	7 9	8 10	9 10	10 11	11 11	12 11	13 11	14 12	14 12	15 12	12
	20	0 7	2 7	3 7	5 8	6 8	7 9	8 9	9 10	10 10	11 11	12 12	13 12	14 12	15 12	15 12	16 12	12
11	10	0 10	1 10	2 10	3 11	5 11	6 11	7 11	8 11	9 11	10 11	11 12	12 12	12 12	13 12	13 12	14 12	12
	15	0 9	1 9	3 9	4 10	5 10	6 10	7 11	8 11	9 11	10 12	11 12	12 12	12 13	13 14	14 14	15 12	12
	20	0 9	1 9	3 9	4 9	5 10	6 10	7 11	8 11	9 11	10 11	11 12	12 12	12 13	13 14	14 14	15 16	12
12	10	0 10	1 10	2 10	3 11	5 11	6 11	7 11	8 11	9 12	10 12	12 12	12 12	12 13	13 14	14 15	15 16	12
	15	0 10	1 10	3 10	4 10	5 10	6 11	7 11	8 11	9 12	10 12	11 12	12 12	12 13	13 14	14 14	15 12	12
	20	0 9	1 9	3 9	4 10	5 10	7 11	8 11	9 11	9 11	10 11	11 12	12 12	12 13	13 14	14 14	15 16	12

First figure column indicates speed of the vessel, knots. Second column gives direction, points off the bow. Third column, true force, Beaufort scale. Proper allowance should be made for compass variation.

* Including new values determined by the Bureau of Aeronautics, Navy Department, in 1927.

3. When the apparent wind is forward of the beam, the true wind is less than the apparent.

4. If the apparent wind is dead astern, the true wind is dead astern and is stronger than the wind created by the ship.

Table XVII permits the determination of the true wind when the apparent wind force and direction and the ship's heading are known. Obviously the table gives approximate results, its accuracy being ordinarily limited.

Factors Affecting Wind Motion

The wind motion of the atmosphere is a continuous and cyclical tendency on the part of the atmosphere to stabilize itself and to reach equilibrium. The process has been in operation since the birth of the

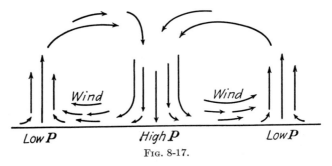

FIG. 8-17.

atmosphere and will continue to operate as long as inequalities in temperature exist over the earth's surface. As Humphreys has stated it, "Atmospheric circulation is a gravitational phenomenon, induced and maintained by temperature differences."

Whether on a large or small scale, warmer air always rises, leaving a relative deficiency of air at the surface; colder air always subsides or sinks, causing a relative excess of air at the ground level. To equalize this excess and scarcity of air over different areas, the air naturally spreads out from areas where an overabundance exists to areas where lesser amounts prevail. This spreading out of the air is our wind.

Actually, there are three primary factors governing wind motion: (1) the pressure gradient, (2) the rotation of the earth, and (3) the centrifugal force of the wind. We shall consider these influences in the order given.

PRESSURE GRADIENT.—The effect of relatively cold air, descending under the influence of gravity, is to cause an increase in the air pressure at that locality. The effect of *rising* air is to cause a *decrease* in pressure. Thus, all winds are a result of horizontal differences in pressure, and all winds tend to blow from high to low. Figure 8-17 illustrates the typical

WINDS—OBSERVATION AND THEORY   141

wind circulation system, as it occurs on both small and large scales in the atmosphere.

Recall that the horizontal pressure change per unit distance was defined earlier as the pressure gradient, and that this pressure gradient extends in the direction of the greatest change in pressure, or directly from high to low.

The pressure gradient is therefore a direct force on the air, moving it from higher to lower pressures, in the tendency to reach equilibrium. The pressure gradient is as much a force as is the force of gravity. If we know the difference in pressure between two points and if we know the distance between the points, we can actually calculate the force of the pressure gradient on the air between those points. The greater this pressure difference between two points, the greater will be this force tending to push the air from higher to lower pressure areas.

Clearly, all winds are thus initiated by the pressure gradient. Their original direction of motion is in the line of the pressure gradient, directly from high to low, or perpendicular to the isobars.

The velocity of the wind will depend on the magnitude of the pressure gradient. Hence, the steeper the gradient, the greater the wind velocity; the gentler the gradient, the less the wind velocity.

On weather maps, the steepness of the pressure gradient is manifested by the spacing of the isobars. Thus, close isobars indicate a steep horizontal pressure difference and nearly always show associated high wind velocities.

The pressure gradient is the only generating force on a wind. It initiates the wind and determines its velocity and the original direction of motion. But winds do not follow the direct path dictated by the pressure gradient. If this were the only influence in operation, winds would blow perpendicularly to the isobars and be parallel to the gradient. Let us therefore consider the other influences that deflect winds from the path in which they originally tend to move.

ROTATION OF THE EARTH.—The earth is a spinning globe, with a rotational velocity of 1,000 miles per hour at the equator. This velocity diminishes with increasing latitude, becoming zero at the poles. Over the surface of this rotating sphere the winds move in response to pressure differences.

As a consequence of the rotation of this sphere, winds do not follow their original path down the pressure gradient but suffer a deflection. Rotation is thus treated as a deflecting force, and its effect can be calculated as though it were a force. The rotational deflection is *not* an actual force; it is only an *apparent* one resulting from the turning of the earth beneath the moving air.

The effect of the rotation of the earth was first stated by Professor

William Ferrel. According to "Ferrel's Law" of rotational deflection all winds in the Northern Hemisphere are deflected to the right of the direction of the pressure gradient, or the direction in which the wind originally tends to move; in the Southern Hemisphere this deflection is to the left.

Cause of Rotational Deflection. Coriolis Force.—The apparent force resulting from rotation, which causes wind deflection, is known as the "Coriolis force." An exact quantitative treatment and explanation of this force require the application of technical physics beyond the scope of this chapter. However, a rather simple descriptive treatment of the problem will aid in understanding the cause of deflection—or the Coriolis force. By this explanation we shall attempt to show the reason for (1)

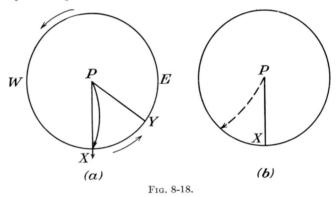

FIG. 8-18.

the existence of deflection, (2) the direction in which deflection occurs (right or left), and (3) the variation of the amount of deflection with latitude.

It might be well to examine the explanation from two viewpoints: (1) by considering the special case of the behavior of winds moving in a north-south direction in the vicinity of the North Pole and (2) by extending the results of the special case, to the general case of the deflection of winds moving in any direction and in any latitude. For convenience, we shall first substitute the motion of a bullet for the motion of the wind, since a bullet, being a more tangible object, may help to simplify the explanation.

1. A relatively small area of the earth around the poles can be considered as a plane surfaces. Figure 8-18 shows the North Pole at the center of the projection, the perimeter of the circle being a few degrees of latitude to the south, and rotating as shown by the arrows.

Assume that P-X is the direction of an observer's meridian at a given instant. Assume also that a bullet is shot from P, along the meridian PX, and that it takes 1 hour to reach X. During this interval however, the meridian originally located along the direction PX, has rotated 15° eastward and is now at $P\text{-}Y$. The bullet, which does not partake of this rotation, continues along the line PX and appears, to the observer firing the gun, to be deflected farther and farther to the right, describing the curved path shown by the curved line PX. Actually, any observer on the earth is never aware of rotation, so that the bullet seems to describe the curving path indicated by the broken line in (*b*).

Any observer situated in a relatively fixed position off in space will see the bullet trace the straight path from P to X in 1 hour.

Note that the direction of deflection will in every such case be to the *right* of the original direction of motion.

In the case of a bullet moving toward the North Pole from point X, we can see the results again in a similar diagram, Fig. 8-19.

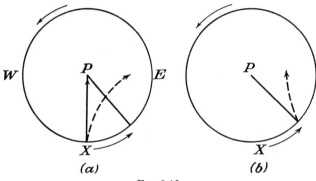

(*a*)   (*b*)

Fig. 8-19.

Now the bullet is shot from X toward P. Again X describes in that time an angle of 15° to the east, which we shall assume to be 100 miles, linearly, at that latitude. As the bullet moves from X to P, in accordance with the law of inertia, it partakes of the eastward rotational spin of 100 miles an hour, in addition to its direct forward motion, and after 1 hour reaches a point 100 miles to the right of P, appearing again to be deflected to the right of its original direction of motion along the meridian.

We need now only substitute moving air for this grand-scale shooting, and we arrive at the behavior of winds under the influence of rotational deflection. It is of interest to note that corrections for this deflection are required for long-range rifle fire. It is negligible over short distances.

2. Having examined the special case of the deflection involved in north-south wind motion at the poles, let us now relate this to the general case of deflection at any latitude, regardless of direction. We again consider the earth's surface about a given point to be a plane; and this plane is perpendicular to a radius of the earth passing through the point. Figure 8-20 shows three such planes: at the equator, at some

middle latitude position, and at the pole. The lines r_1, r_2, r_3 are radii of the earth, perpendicular to each of the planes, respectively.

In the course of the earth's rotation, it is clear that the polar plane, as shown by the arrow will describe one complete rotation about the radial axis r_3, which in this case coincides with the earth's axis (the plane considered in the first case). Note however, that the plane at the equator shows no rotation whatever about the axis, r_1, in the course of rotation about the earth's axis. Any other plane between the equator and the pole shows some degree of rotation about a radius perpendicular to the plane, *e.g.*, the plane perpendicular to r_2. In other words, anywhere but at the equator the earth's rotation about its axis may be resolved into a

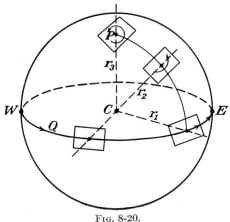

Fig. 8-20.

component about a radial axis perpendicular to the surface at any point. The amount of this rotation of a plane at the earth's surface about a radial axis thus varies from 0° at the equator to 360° at the poles, in one day. Do not confuse this rotation of an arbitrary plane at the earth's surface, about a radial axis, with the rotation of the earth as a whole, about the earth's axis!

To summarize: Any arbitrary plane on the earth's surface can be considered as rotating about a radial axis of the earth, perpendicular to the plane. This rotation is but a component of the actual rotation of the earth about the true axis. At the equator, this component becomes zero.

It is not difficult to conceive of the rotation of the polar plane and the lack of rotation of the equatorial plane. But the movement of a plane between the equator and the poles requires a bit more concentration. The fact that this rotation actually exists has been proved by means of the Foucault pendulum experiment, which it might be well to review. Once a long, freely swinging pendulum is set in motion, it will continue to vibrate in a *fixed* plane—fixed as regards some object in space, such as a star. If such a pendulum is set swinging directly over the North Pole, the surface beneath will slowly rotate toward the left, about the fixed plane of vibration, and make a complete rotation in one day. At the equator, the surface beneath the pendulum will remain unchanged with respect to the plane of vibration. Between the equator and the poles, the surface beneath the swinging pendulum shows a partial rotation about the pendulum, the amount of this rotation increasing with increase in latitude. Actually, to the observer who partakes of the rotation of the earth, and thus of the rotation of any plane at the earth's surface, it is the plane vibration of the pendulum that *appears* to be displaced (toward

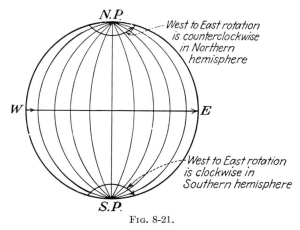

Fig. 8-21.

the right) rather than the surface beneath! Wind deflection results from the same process.

We have thus shown that any number of arbitrary planes can be taken on the earth's surface, which can be considered as rotating about an axis perpendicular to the plane, just as a plane at the pole rotates about the earth's axis. The only difference is that the degree of rotation of these arbitrary planes grows less as the latitude decreases. At any instant, the wind anywhere on the earth's surface can be considered as moving directly toward, or away from, the axis of some arbitrary plane. The wind will then be deflected in the same manner as the wind near the North Pole, in the first case, above. However, if the rotation of the plane grows less with decrease in latitude, the wind deflection resulting from such rotation also diminishes.

It can be shown by simple physics, that the rotational deflection, or Coriolis force, varies as the sine of the latitude.

Since the direction of rotation of the earth is clockwise in southern latitudes, the resulting deflection of wind in the Southern Hemisphere is counterclockwise, or to the *left* of the path of motion. Figure 8-21 illustrates the fact that, although both hemispheres rotate from west to east as a unit, the Northern Hemisphere appears to have a counterclockwise, and the Southern a clockwise motion.

A deeper consideration of the problem of rotation shows that the deflection also varies with the effects associated with centrifugal action from circular wind motion and frictional effects. Although the direction

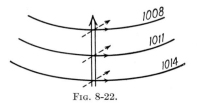

FIG. 8-22.

of the wind is altered by the influence of rotation, the velocity of the wind is entirely unaffected. Only the pressure gradient and frictional effects have any noteworthy influence on the wind velocity.

Thus Figure 8-22 represents a pressure pattern in the Northern Hemisphere. The long double arrow is the direction of the force or pressure gradient. As the wind begins, the deflection forces cause deviation to the right; the higher the wind velocity, the more the deflection.

Recall that, near the ground, wind speed is retarded by friction causing less deflection for surface winds than for the freely moving upper winds. The typical surface-wind motion yielded by the gradient and rotation forces are shown by the small broken arrows. This wind crosses the isobars at a slight angle, the drift *always* being from the higher to lower pressure side.

The more rapidly moving upper air, however, suffers more deflection and actually blows at right angles to the originating force, being *parallel* to the isobars. Such a wind blowing parallel to the isobars as a result of the balancing of the pressure gradient by the rotational deflection is called a "geostrophic wind."

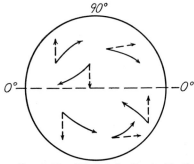

FIG. 8-23.—Wind deflection in Northern and Southern Hemispheres resulting from Coriolis force. The dotted lines show the direction of the pressure gradient, and the solid lines show the resulting wind motion.

CENTRIFUGAL FORCE.—The third primary factor influencing wind motion is the centrifugal force of the wind itself. Centrifugal force on a rotating or revolving particle is that force exerted radially outward from the center or axis of rotation or revolution. When a weight is swung about on a string, there is this familiar force tending to pull the weight out from the center of the spin (Fig. 8–24).

Centrifugal force varies directly with the square of angular velocity.

In cases where circular or curved isobars prevail, the effect of centrifugal force becomes important.   As soon as the wind starts to blow under the directive force of the gradient, rotation causes a deflection so that the wind assumes a curving motion, finally following more or less closely the isobars about the central low-pressure area.   Then, centrifugal force begins to operate and deflects the wind still farther from the direction of the gradient, for this force acts opposite to the pressure gradient. The greater the curvature and velocity of the wind motion, the greater is this outward force, and the greater is the deflection produced.   If, as in the Northern Hemisphere, the original rotational deviation is to the right, then centrifugal force enhances this deflection.   A similar effect to the left occurs in the Southern Hemisphere.

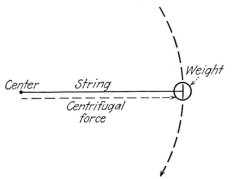

Fig. 8-24.—The principle of centrifugal force.

Winds whose motion is the result of the equilibrium of these three forces—pressure gradient, rotational or Coriolis force, and centrifugal force—are known as "gradient winds" and blow parallel to the isobars in the upper air, but show a drift toward lower pressure in surface air, owing to friction.   In surface air, friction reduces the wind velocity and hence the wind deflection.   This deflection of the surface winds causes them to flow across the isobars at a slight angle.

In summary we note that there are three primary factors that exert a pronounced influence on the direction and velocity of winds: the pressure gradient, the Coriolis force resulting from the rotation of the earth, and the centrifugal force of wind moving in a curving path.   The pressure gradient determines the velocity of the wind (with modifications from friction); the next two factors affect only the direction of the wind and are thus deflecting forces.

CHAPTER 9

PRIMARY OR TERRESTRIAL WIND CIRCULATION

The wind goeth toward the south, and turneth about unto the north; it whirleth about continually, and the wind returneth again according to his circuits.
—*Ecclesiastes*, I, 6.

There are blowing, and have been blowing from time immemorial, certain steady winds that may be permanent throughout the year or may vary with the seasons. Owing to their constancy and the large areas they cover, they are known as "primary" or "terrestrial" winds. Such winds have their origin in definite *permanent* or *semipermanent high- and low-pressure belts* which tend to surround the earth. In turn, these pressure belts originate from the unequal heat and temperature distribution over the earth's surface, pointed out in an earlier chapter. And so we return to this fundamental factor of the heating of the earth. It will be recalled from Chap. 2 on Temperature, that isotherms (equal-temperature lines) would resemble parallels of latitude, indicating a uniform poleward temperature decrease, only if the earth were uniform in surface composition, *i.e.*, all water. But the true picture showed very erratic isotherms indicating an irregular temperature decrease. This is explained by the presence of land and water bodies. This departure from uniform surface heating has a pronounced effect on the primary pressure and wind systems, causing in many cases, vast modifications of the ideal conditions.

We can therefore best understand these winds if they are examined from two viewpoints. First, the ideal wind and pressure system that would develop on a uniform (all water) earth will be considered. Then the actual modifications of this ideal system, resulting from the uneven heating of land and water, will be studied.

Maury has very aptly reviewed the disturbing effect of land on the freedom of wind behavior. "When we travel out on the oceans, and get beyond the influence of the land upon the winds, we find ourselves in a field particularly favorable for studying the general laws of atmospheric circulation. Here, beyond the reach of the great equatorial and polar currents of the sea, there are no unduly heated land surfaces, no mountain ranges, or other obstructions to the circulation of the atmosphere—nothing to disturb it in its natural courses. The sea, therefore, is the field for observing the operations of the general laws which govern

148

the movements of the great aerial ocean. Observations on land will enable us to discover the exceptions. But from the sea we get the rule. Each valley, every mountain range and local district, may be said to have its own peculiar system of calms, winds, rains and droughts. But not so the surface of the broad ocean; over it, the agents which are at work are of a uniform character."

Ideal Primary Pressure and Wind System

PRIMARY PRESSURE BELTS.—The earth is greatly overheated in a belt which, on our homogeneous sphere, would lie along the equator. Local heating results in rising air which lowers the pressure. The polar

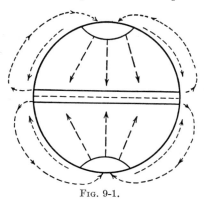

areas in both hemispheres are relatively very cold with consequent descending air and higher pressures. This pronounced heating in the equatorial belt and cooling in the polar regions produces the *general* or *primary air circulation.* The warm air in the hot tropical belt rises and spreads out to northward and southward at high altitudes. The cold descending polar air flows equatorward when reaching the ground (Fig. 9-1).

FIG. 9-1.

Even our ideal picture is not quite so simple as is pictured above. There are other high- and low-pressure belts between the equator and the poles, which interfere. Being characterized essentially by rising or falling air, they will naturally be areas of calms. These belts, pictured in the Fig. 9-2, will now be considered in further detail.

Doldrums.—Throughout the year there is a belt of relative low pressure surrounding the earth. The air is hot and humid and causes rising, expansion, and constant adiabatic cooling. This cooling results in frequent heavy showers, particularly in late afternoon, when the overheating is most pronounced. Most of the air motion in the doldrums is *vertical* and yields but light and variable winds, having in general a slight westward drift. Thus, the doldrums are known more technically as the "belt of equatorial calms." The oppressive, hot, sticky atmosphere with calm winds and slick glassy seas were named "doldrums" in the olden days of sailing ships.

The following extract is from the log of Commodore Arthur Sinclair, aboard the frigate "Congress," on a cruise to South America in 1817–1818, and describes the murky atmosphere beneath the equatorial cloud band. "This is certainly one of the most unpleasant regions in our globe. A dense, close atmosphere, except for a few hours after a thunderstorm, during which time torrents of rain fall, when the air becomes a little refreshed; but a hot glowing sun soon reheats it again, and but for your awnings, and the little air put in circulation by the continual flapping of the ship's sails, it would be most insufferable. No person who has not crossed this region can form an adequate idea of its unpleasant effects. You feel a degree of lassitude unconquerable, which not even the sea bathing, which everywhere else proves so salutory and renovating, can dispel. Except when in actual danger of shipwreck I never spent twelve

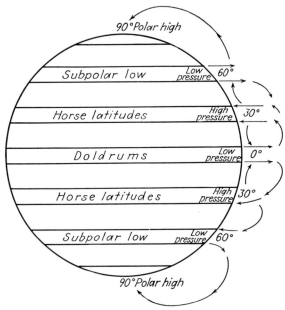

Fig. 9-2.—The primary or permanent pressure systems, with the resulting wind motion shown in cross section.

more disagreeable days in the professional part of my life than in these calm latitudes."

Horse Latitudes.—At approximately 30°N. and S., we have two belts of high average pressure. These belts of high pressure owe their origin to descending air, which warms adiabatically as it falls. Consequently, there is again a lack of definite wind motion, yielding the name of "subtropical calms" for these areas. Being formed of descending, warming air, the horse latitudes are very dry and clear belts. As the air falls, it becomes warmer and increases its capacity for water vapor with a resultant decreasing relative humidity. This dry air, thirsty for water vapor, is responsible for the prevalence of the great deserts of the earth that are in or close to the horse latitudes. According to the most common tale handed down, the name "horse latitudes" was derived from the historic days of sailing ships. After being becalmed in these belts for long periods the horses were often thrown overboard (to sink or swim), in order to lighten the vessel and conserve water.

Subpolar Lows (Arctic and Antarctic Lows).—At about 60°N. and S. exist two low-pressure belts: the subpolar or actic and the antarctic low-pressure areas, respectively.

Polar High-pressure Caps.—From incomplete evidence available it appears that in both hemispheres there are two high-pressure areas

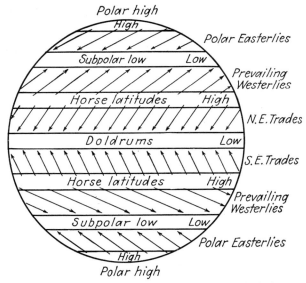

FIG. 9-3.—The ideal primary or terrestrial pressure and wind systems.

in the vicinity of the poles. The poles themselves are not necessarily at the center of the pressure areas.

PRIMARY WIND BELTS.—Clearly, on a uniform earth there would be a uniform pressure gradient extending from the horse latitudes toward the doldrums on the equatorial sides, and to the subpolar lows on the polar sides. There is also a gradient extending from the polar caps to the subpolar lows in both hemispheres. This large-scale pressure pattern accounts for the general circulation system illustrated in Fig. 9-3.

Note once again that this grand motion of the atmosphere is merely its tendency to restore equilibrium, for "nature abhors a vacuum."

Northeast and Southeast Trades.—The pressure gradient between the high of the horse latitudes and the low of the doldrums causes a flow of air which *tends* to move directly southward. But remember the deflective forces! Although the pressure gradient is north-south, the winds are deflected to the *right* in the Northern Hemisphere and develop a motion to the *southwest*, rather than the south, becoming *northeast* winds. These are the "northeast trades."

In the Southern Hemisphere, the winds blowing equatorward from the southern horse latitudes are deflected to the *left* (as are all well-behaved winds in that hemisphere) and become *southeast* winds—the "southeast trades." The trade winds exhibit great constancy over the oceans, both in direction and velocity, with an average Beaufort force of 4.

The term "trade wind" has no direct relation to commerce as it implies. The meaning originally attached to the word "trade" as applied to winds was that of constancy. The expression "to blow trade" meant to blow steadily or constantly. Hence, when the ancient mariner discovered these steady marine winds and used them to his advantage, he gave them this distinctive name.

Prevailing Westerlies.—Another important wind flow develops between the horse latitudes and the subpolar lows in both hemispheres. In the Northern Hemisphere these winds are again deflected strongly to the right and become west to southwest winds. These winds are the "prevailing westerlies."

In the Southern Hemisphere, as shown in the illustrations, the winds traveling southward from the horse latitudes are deflected to the *left* and become west to northwest winds, again the prevailing westerlies. The prevailing westerlies, or just "westerlies," as they are often known, have an average force of 5 to 6 in the Southern Hemisphere, whereas they are much less constant in the Northern Hemisphere, for reasons to be seen shortly.

Polar Easterlies.—In both hemispheres there is a flow of air from the polar highs to the subpolar lows. The deflecting forces, although to the right and left in the Northern and Southern Hemispheres, respectively, result in easterly winds, known as "polar easterlies."

Modifications of the Ideal Pressure and Wind System

Figures 9-4 and 9-5, illustrating the January and July world pressure and winds, indicate the actual modifications of our ideal system. It should be noted that even these are but average conditions for the month and do not show daily fluctuations. From the interrelationship of temperature, pressure, and wind, we may naturally expect that the least irregularities or changes will occur in regions where large uniform water expanses exist. In such regions the temperature gradient is uniform, showing east-west isotherms throughout the year. Consequently, the pressure gradient will remain uniform and yield constant and steady winds.

Since the polar highs and polar easterlies are beyond the normal field

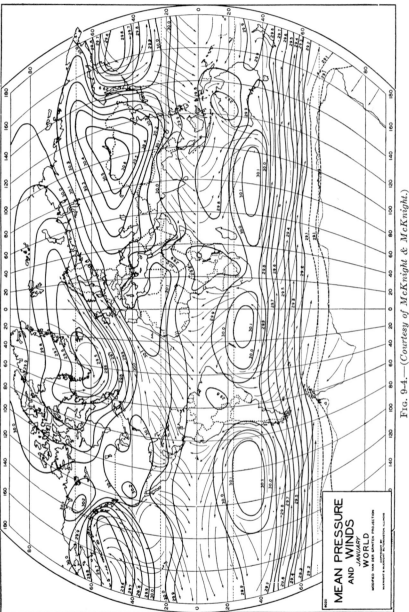

FIG. 9-4.—(Courtesy of McKnight & McKnight.)

MEAN PRESSURE
AND WINDS
JANUARY
WORLD
MODIFIED VAN DER GRINTEN PROJECTION
COPYRIGHT BY
McKNIGHT & McKNIGHT, BLOOMINGTON, ILLINOIS

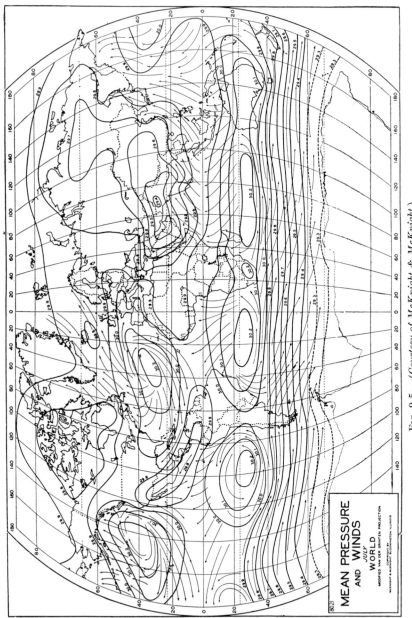

FIG. 9-5.—*(Courtesy of McKnight & McKnight.)*

of navigation and hence of observation, evidence indicating the true condition in these regions is relatively sparse.

SOUTHERN HEMISPHERE MODIFICATIONS. *Horse Latitudes.*—It is seen on Fig. 9-5 that there exists an almost continuous belt of high pressure about 30°S. For this season, the highest average pressure is just above 30.2 inches, since the innermost isobar equals 30.2. This high-pressure unit represents the horse latitudes of the Southern Hemisphere.

Since July is the winter period in this region we may expect a slight change 6 months later. Then (in January) the relatively small land masses covered by the horse latitudes will be much warmer than the oceans. This situation yields rising air which thus lowers the pressure somewhat. Now, by consulting the January maps it is seen that the highest isobaric pressure is 30.1 inches and that the central high-pressure zones no longer extend over the warmer continents.

Prevailing Westerlies (Roaring Forties).—Owing to the constancy of the southern horse latitudes and the uniformity of the water surface southward to the subpolar low, a strong and uniform pressure gradient exists permanently between these belts. This pressure gradient is easily seen on either Fig. 9-4 or 9-5 where the parallel east-west isobars indicate a uniform and relatively strong pressure fall between 30° to 60°S.

The winds blowing from the horse latitudes to the antarctic or subpolar low are therefore very steady and very strong throughout the year, with an average velocity of 5 to 6 on the Beaufort scale, as mentioned earlier. These winds are particularly steady and strong between 40° and 55°S., giving rise to the name "roaring forties" for these latitudes. The winds themselves are sometimes known as the "roaring forties."

Southeast Trades.—The winds that blow from the southeast to northwest, originating in the high-pressure belt near 30°S., are the southeast trades.

We can see from Fig. 9-5 that the doldrums lie to the *north* of the equator. This displacement originates from the predominance of the heated land masses in the Northern Hemisphere. As a result, it is evident that the southeast trades must *cross the equator* to reach their goal, the doldrums. But all winds are deflected to the right in the Northern Hemisphere. Consequently, the trades "hook" to the right, becoming southwest, upon crossing into the Northern Hemisphere.

Such winds are known as "hooked trades." This is clearly developed on Fig. 9-5 where the southeast trades in the Indian Ocean, in the Atlantic west of Africa, and in the Pacific west of South America, hook to the right where they cross the equator.

NORTHERN HEMISPHERE MODIFICATIONS.—The ideal wind and pressure belts suffer their greatest distortion in the Northern Hemisphere. This fact is a direct result of the presence of large land masses associated with equally large water areas. When we recall the pronounced difference in temperature between land and water from summer to winter, it is clear that pronounced pressure changes will also result. Dependent on such pressure changes, definite wind variations develop. A glance at Figs. 9-4 and 9-5 is sufficient to show the disconformity and irregularity of the pressure and wind areas of the Northern Hemisphere, as compared to the Southern.

Doldrums.—Owing to the predominance of land in the Northern Hemisphere (as compared to the Southern), the average annual position

Fig. 9-6.—Sky conditions typical of islands in the trade-wind belts; fair-weather cumulus and fractocumulus with traces of high-level cirrus. (*Official U.S. Navy Photograph.*)

of the doldrums is *north* of the equator. At times of course, it may lie on, or partly to the south of the equator, during the southern summer.

On Fig. 9-5 we note that between the horse latitudes of the two hemispheres lies a not-too-well-defined belt of low pressure averaging 29.9 inches. This same belt is indicated somewhat more clearly on the January map where it approximates the position of the equator.

Horse Latitudes.—The horse latitudes here undergo marked changes from summer to winter. In summer (the July map), the water areas are relatively colder than the continents and therefore develop higher pressure. Two well-formed branches of this high exist over the Pacific and over the Atlantic centered over the Azores. These sections of the northern horse latitudes are known as the "Pacific high" and the "Azores high," respectively.

The pressure over North America is considerably lower than that of the ocean areas in this belt. The greatest and most distinct pressure change from summer to winter takes place over Asia, where the horse latitudes are not only not high but actually very low, forming a low-pressure area with the lowest isobaric reading at 29.4 inches. This, of course, is a consequence of the intense heating of the large Asiatic continent in summer.

In the northern winter (January map), the relatively colder continents are higher in pressure, with the now cold Asiatic area increasing from its very low pressure to a pronounced high of 30.6 inches. The Pacific and Azores highs are correspondingly weaker.

Northeast Trades.—Over the Atlantic and eastern Pacific the trades are more or less uniform. The stronger pressure gradient in summer between the Pacific and the Azores highs and the doldrums tends to strengthen the winds in that season. They are more constant there than over the land areas, where temperature and pressure changes are more severe.

Indian Monsoon.—*Monsoon winds are winds whose direction reverses with the seasons.* Such a reversal in wind direction obviously requires a reversal of the pressure gradient, since winds always blow from high to low. There are many areas on the earth where such pressure variations occur, following changes in land temperature from winter to summer. By far the most notable and widespread pressure change is that responsible for the Indian monsoon.

We have observed that from winter to summer there is a unique variation of pressure from high to low. This is the direct cause of the famous monsoon. During the winter the winds blow normally from the northeast, originating in the high over Asia. But in the summer, as seen on Fig. 9–5, the pressure is low over Asia, and the winds have completely reversed arriving from the southwest, after hooking across the equator. This air originates its motion in the southern horse latitudes and follows the continuous pressure gradient into central Asia, thus combining trade and monsoon winds.

After blowing across the open tropical ocean this southwest summer monsoon wind is extremely humid and warm. Upon striking the high plateaus and mountains of India, the air is forced to ascend and cools adiabatically as it does so. This cooling lowers the air temperature beneath the dew point, resulting in the well-known rainy season of the Indian summer.

The winter monsoon, blowing from the northeast in central Asia is cold and dry, owing to its continental origin. The monsoon winds become light and variable during the period of change, in spring and autumn.

Another strong, though not so widespread monsoon, exists west and southwest of the African bulge, in the Atlantic. Here, again owing to the migration of the doldrums, with change of seasons, this area is covered by the northeast trades in winter, and the hooked south to southwest trades in the summer. This is clearly evinced on the world wind maps.

Prevailing Westerlies.—The prevailing westerlies of the Northern Hemisphere are erratic and variable. Their source, the horse latitudes, varies considerably with the seasons. Their goal, the arctic or subpolar low, as described below, also suffers excessive change. As a result of this unsteady pressure gradient, the westerlies are correspondingly unsteady. Further, the prevalence of migrating cyclones and anticyclones (see Chap. 10) in the belt of the westerlies seriously affects and distorts the ideal pattern in these latitudes.

Despite the irregularity of the pressure gradient and the influence of cyclonic and anticyclonic disturbances, this belt does exhibit winds, which on the average are westerly in direction.

Subpolar Low.—The behavior of the subpolar low resembles that of the horse latitudes in its seasonal variations. We can see from the maps that two very strongly defined lows exist in the winter over the North Atlantic and Pacific. During this season the oceans are relatively warmer than the cold continents and the subpolar lows are known as the "Iceland low" and the "Aleutian low," respectively. In the summer, these lows dwindle almost into insignificance as the water temperature becomes relatively cold. It is the steady pressure gradient associated with the Iceland low in winter that is responsible, to a great extent, for the severe winds and gales common to the North Atlantic in winter.

The Jet Stream.—The "jet stream," discovered in the 1940s, is a relatively narrow east-moving upper air current with reported velocities as high as 100 to 300 mph. The narrow jets may extend for thousands of miles in fairly straight, or in sinuous paths. The jet stream is a middle-latitude feature whose axis varies from about 25 to 30 degrees north in winter to 45 degrees north in summer with a definite decrease in velocity accompanying the northward migration. Highest jet velocities usually develop between 20,000 to 40,000 feet. Observations in the Southern Hemisphere, although much fewer, indicate the existence of a similar upper air feature. This is a subject of concentrated research at present.

CHAPTER 10

SECONDARY WINDS

Over many particular areas of the earth a system of secondary winds, whose causes lie particularly in local conditions, are superposed on the general circulation. These secondary winds frequently mask completely, or overshadow, the expected primary winds in such regions. They are often of more significance as a result of their very irregularity, both in velocity and direction.

We can arrange these secondary winds as follows:

1. Those dependent on the migrating low- and high-pressure areas of the middle latitudes—the cyclones and anticyclones, and

2. Those dependent directly on temperature differences over adjacent areas.

Cyclonic and Anticyclonic Winds

It will be recalled from Chap. 7 on Atmospheric Pressure that the pressure distribution in the middle latitudes or, more specifically, between the horse latitudes and the subpolar lows, is very irregular. Further, these pressure variations tend to move eastward, as irregular waves of low or high pressure.

The pressure gradients associated with these irregular highs and lows are responsible for winds of widely varying velocities and continuously shifting directions. So pronounced are these winds that they completely modify the direction and velocity of the prevailing westerlies, particularly in the Northern Hemisphere.

The actual origin and development of these low- and high-pressure wind systems will be considered in a later chapter.

CYCLONES.—We have noted that wind motion is governed by three fundamental factors: the pressure gradient, the rotation of the earth, and the centrifugal force developed by the curving motion following rotational deflection. Let us examine the application of these influences to actual pressure configurations in the middle latitudes, considering first, the low-pressure area. Figure 10-1 shows a well-formed, circular low-pressure area in the Northern Hemisphere. As shown by the isobars, the pressure is lowest in the center and increases radially outward.

In response to the pressure gradient, the air moves in to the center of the low from all directions. Just as water on the rim of a bowl drains downward toward the center under the influence of gravity, so does the air flow inward to the center of a low under the indirect influence of gravity and the direct influence of the gradient.

Since the earth is rotating, the forces of deflection (rotation and centrifugal force) come into operation as soon as the motion of the wind is originated. As explained above, the wind in the Northern Hemisphere deviates to the right of its initial tendency of motion (or pressure gradient).

As shown in Fig. 10-1, the actual surface wind in a low-pressure area follows the path indicated by the solid arrows. The broken arrows indicate the pressure gradient or original direction tendency. It is evident that the wind direction makes a slight angle with the isobars. Should the wind *velocity* increase, its deflection also *increases*, and causes the wind path to be almost parallel to the isobars. Therefore the wind in a low actually has a circular path about the center rather than a radial inward motion. This is similar to the motion of a water stream flowing into the center of a rotating bowl.

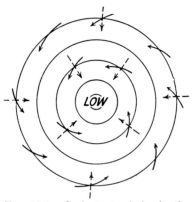

Fig. 10-1.—Cyclonic circulation in the Northern Hemisphere.

In any low-pressure area in the Northern Hemisphere, owing to the deflection to the right, the wind will have a counterclockwise motion about the center of the low. This wind motion about a low-pressure area is known as a "cyclonic" wind system or "cyclonic circulation." From this, the low-pressure area itself has derived the name "cyclone." The terms "low-pressure area," "low," "depression," and "cyclone" are used interchangeably.

In the Southern Hemisphere, as explained previously, winds are deflected to the left of the pressure gradient. Consequently the cyclonic wind circulation in the Southern Hemisphere is in a *clockwise* direction about the center of the low.

A cyclone is therefore merely an area of low atmospheric pressure, characteristic of the temperate middle latitudes. Cyclones usually extend over hundreds of thousands of square miles, frequently covering a good portion of the country at one time.

The term "cyclone" implies no particularly dangerous or destructive storm conditions. Any low-pressure area with its attendant winds is a cyclone. At times of course, the steep pressure gradients that often develop do yield gale winds in lows, but these relatively large "weather areas" should not be confused with the much smaller, more destructive "tropical cyclone" or "hurricane," which we shall study shortly. In distinction to the tropical cyclone, the larger, milder, middle-latitude low is frequently referred to as the "extratropical cyclone."

ANTICYCLONES.—An area of high atmospheric pressure may be likened to an inverted bowl of water, in which the water will everywhere flow outward and downward from the center when the container is removed. Similarly, in high-pressure areas or highs, the wind tends to blow radially outward from the center. Again the deflecting factors cause the wind to leave the expected path and deviate to the right in the Northern Hemisphere and to the left in the Southern Hemisphere.

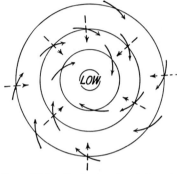

FIG. 10-2.—Cyclonic circulation in Southern Hemisphere.

In Fig. 10-3, the circular area of high pressure has a uniform pressure gradient outward from the center. In the Northern Hemisphere the winds, being deflected to the right, assume a *clockwise* circulation about the high-pressure center.

In the Southern Hemisphere the circulation is of a counterclockwise nature owing to left-hand wind deflection. Since the wind circulation

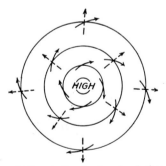

FIG. 10-3.—Anticyclonic circulation in Northern Hemisphere.

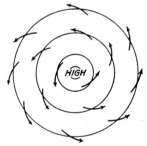

FIG. 10-4.—Anticyclonic circulation in Southern Hemisphere.

in high-pressure areas is opposite in direction to the wind behavior in low-pressure areas, the former are frequently called "anticyclones."

WEATHER MAP EXAMPLES OF HIGHS AND LOWS.—Figures 10-5 to 10-7 show three successive daily marine weather maps, with pressure and wind distribution over a large portion of the earth's surface. Note the different patterns assumed by the isobars in depicting the pressure distribution over the North Atlantic and adjacent areas, together with the wind circulation about the several high- and low-pressure areas.

These figures also show the typical gale conditions so prevalent over the North Atlantic during the winter season.   The low centered at 40°N.

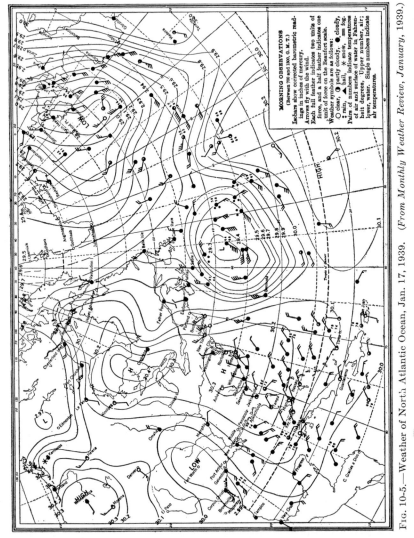

FIG. 10-5.—Weather of North Atlantic Ocean, Jan. 17, 1939.   (*From Monthly Weather Review, January, 1939.*)

55°W. is already an intense cyclone, with gale winds prevailing, on the chart for January 17.   The center of the low has deepened from 29.3 to 28.3 inches by January 19.   The pressure gradient has also steepened considerably with further strengthening of the winds.

Note also, the general west to east or northeast drift of all the pressure configurations shown. The slight angle made between the wind and the isobars is nicely indicated.

STORMS AND GALES OF ANTICYCLONIC ORIGIN.—We commonly associate bad weather and high winds with low-pressure areas and low or

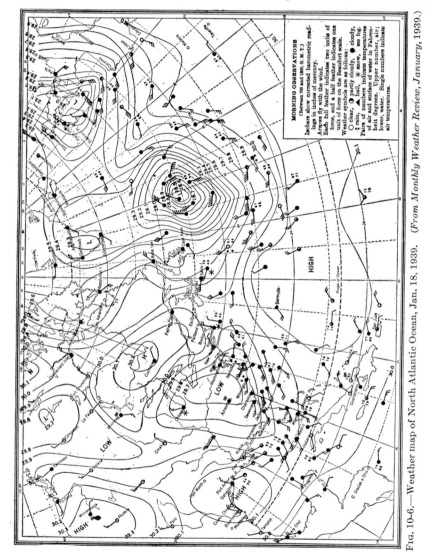

FIG. 10-6.—Weather map of North Atlantic Ocean, Jan. 18, 1939. (*From Monthly Weather Review, January,* 1939.)

falling barometers. Frequently, in certain areas strong gale winds are encountered with anticylonic, or rising, barometric conditions.

Invasions of huge cold air masses (which will be considered in detail in a later chapter) often extend far south through the belt of prevailing westerlies and even into the tropics.   These dense cold air masses are sources of high atmospheric pressure with the attendant clockwise circulation in the Northern Hemisphere.

If these high-pressure areas develop over the continents, the outflow

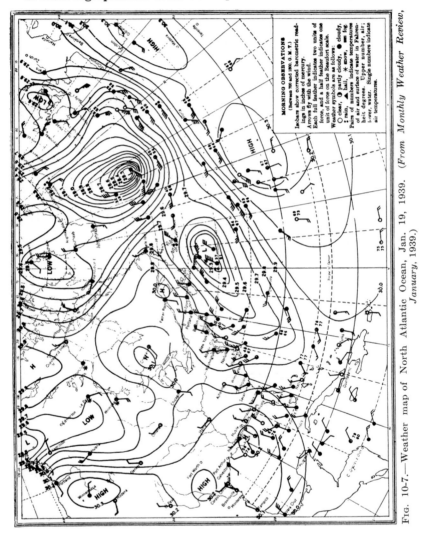

Fig. 10-7.—Weather map of North Atlantic Ocean, Jan. 19, 1939.   (From *Monthly Weather Review, January*, 1939.)

of air toward the sea may often have gale force, particularly if a well-formed cyclone or low preceded the advance of the cold anticyclone.

When strong high-pressure areas form over the Middle Western states, as happens frequently just before, during, and following the winter months, severe cold winds pour southward into the Gulf of Mexico, often

FIG. 10-8.—United States warships ride out a winter storm on the North Atlantic off Iceland, February, 1943. (*Official U.S. Navy Photograph.*)

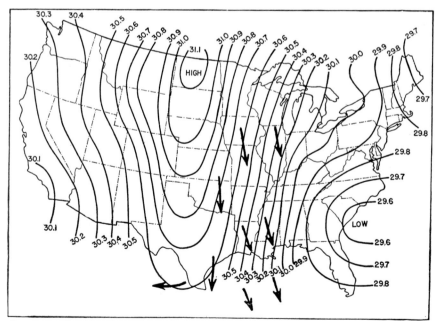

FIG. 10-9.—Pressure distribution giving rise to a strong norther of anticyclonic origin in the Gulf of Mexico. (*Courtesy of U.S. Weather Bureau.*)

CHARTS SHOWING STRONG WIND AND GALE OBSERVATIONS
FOR THE OCEANS.   Figs. 10–10 to 10–15.   *(Courtesy of U.S. Navy.)*

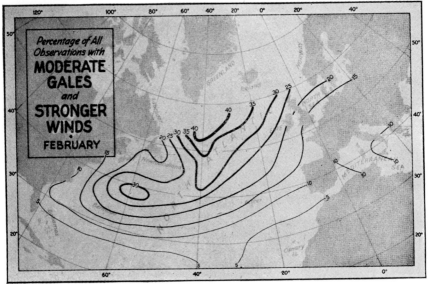

Fig. 10-10.

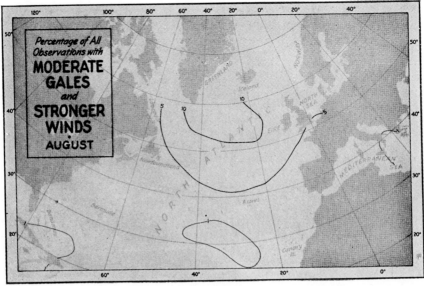

Fig. 10-11.

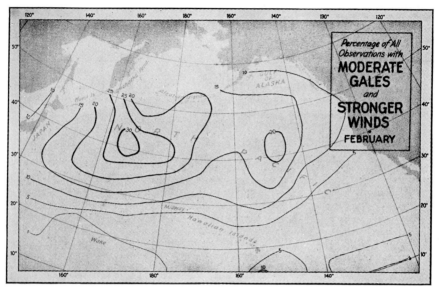

FIG. 10-12.

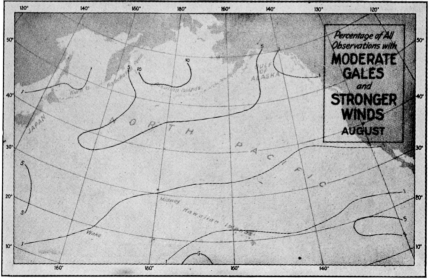

FIG. 10-13.

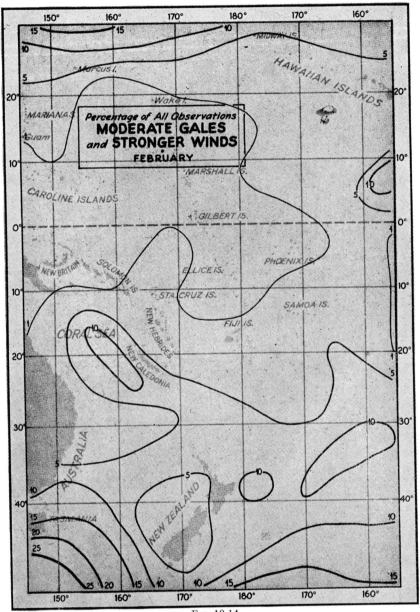

FIG. 10-14.

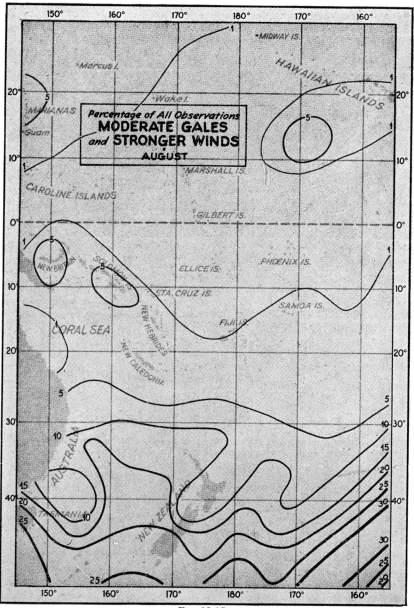

Fɪɢ. 10-15.

reaching whole gale force. The advancing edge of these anticyclonic storms is often attended with a heavy cloud bank and severe squalls. Precipitation may accompany the strong to gale north winds.

Winds in the Gulf of Mexico originating from such conditions are called "northers." A typical pressure situation giving rise to such storm winds in the Gulf is shown in Fig. 10-9.

Effect of Moving Lows and Highs (Cyclones and Anticyclones)

We mentioned earlier that the periodic pressure variations, with maxima at 10 A.M. and 10 P.M. and minima at 4 P.M. and 4 A.M., are overshadowed by pressure changes of greater magnitude in the middle latitudes (between 30° and 60°). The reason for this overshadowing can now be made more clear.

The highs and lows just considered travel through the atmosphere as huge pressure waves with a motion generally from *west to east* and with an average velocity of 20 to 30 miles an hour. The effect of low-pressure areas usually *disappears* above heights of 2½ to 4 miles, where the primary circulation is reasserted. Figures 10-18 to 10-21 showing wind motion at different levels illustrate this effect. The complete weather conditions attending the passage of these highs and lows will be studied in more detail in a later chapter. However, we can now examine some of the pressure and wind changes attending the passage of these atmospheric disturbances.

The continuous and irregular pressure variations experienced in middle latitudes are the result of the successive passage of highs and lows, which are rarely of uniform size, shape, and pressure gradient. Moreover, they travel with varying velocities. Consequently the amount and duration of these pressure variations, as registered on recording instruments, vary considerably from day to day. The barometer falls as a low or cyclone approaches. The rate at which the barometer rises or falls depends upon the pressure gradient and the velocity of the pressure areas approaching from the west. Cloudiness, precipitation, and bad weather usually accompany a low, and fair weather, a high.

Noticeable and significant wind shifts also attend the passage of these pressure areas. Let us consider a low or cyclone in the Northern Hemisphere, moving from west to east, as in Fig. 10-16.

As the area moves, the part of the low indicated by the dashed line will pass over the observer at X. With a falling barometer, the observer will experience winds setting in from the southeast and *veering* to southwest, west, and northwest as the low passes. If the *center* passes over the observer, the wind will *reverse* in direction, approximately from southeast to northwest.

In the same way, it is clear that, if the low or cyclone center passes *south* of the observer, a *backing* wind will be experienced, with the winds shifting from an easterly direction to north or northwest.

Based on the above principle the following general rules are issued by the U.S. Weather Bureau:

1. When the wind sets in from points between south and southeast with steadily falling barometer, a storm is approaching from the west or northwest, and its center will pass near or north of the observer within 12 to 24 hours, with the wind veering northwest by way of south and southwest.

2. When the wind sets in from points between east and northeast and the barometer falls steadily, a storm is approaching from the south or southwest, and its center will pass near or south or east of the observer within 12 to 24 hours with wind backing northwest by way of north.

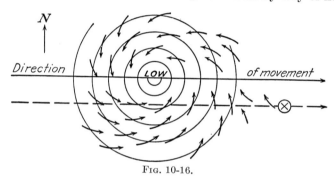

Fig. 10-16.

LAW OF BUYS-BALLOT.—This is also known as the "law of storms" and enables the observer to obtain a fairly accurate approximation of the bearing of the lowest pressure, or storm center.

Owing to its counterclockwise motion, the wind blows inward at a slight angle with the isobars in a cyclone. Thus, when facing the wind the observer in the Northern Hemisphere will always find the lowest pressure on his right. In the Southern Hemisphere, as a consequence of the clockwise cyclonic circulation in those latitudes, the low will be on his left.

More specifically, in the Northern Hemisphere, when facing the wind, the observer will have the low or storm center bearing 8 to 10 points (90° to 120°) on his right, and in the Southern Hemisphere, an equivalent distance on his left.

Since the winds at higher altitudes, being unhampered by friction, achieve higher velocities, they are, as explained previously, deflected more and have paths parallel to the isobars. Consequently, a discrepancy usually exists between the surface wind direction and the direction exhibited by the movement of the *lower clouds*.

Thus, to apply the law of storms to observations of lower cloud motion: face the wind (as shown by the low clouds) and the low pressure will be 8 points or 90° on the right in the Northern Hemisphere, and an equivalent distance on the left in the Southern Hemisphere.

Note the emphasis on observation of the lower cloud movement. Recall that cyclone areas gradually disappear with altitude. Hence the high clouds will often be under the influence of the primary winds, rather than the secondary cyclonic winds nearer the surface. It is therefore important to note that in the belt of the prevailing westerlies the cirrus, cirrostratus, and cirrocumulus clouds invariably move from the west, under the influence of these winds, although different conditions may prevail at ground level.

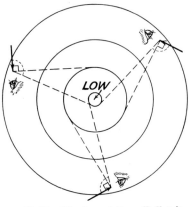

FIG. 10-17.—The law of Buys-Ballot in Northern Hemisphere.

Figures 10-18 to 10-21 show average wind conditions at different levels and tend to indicate the contrast between the irregularity of surface winds and the uniformity of upper winds.

The weather conditions of the belt of prevailing westerlies, particularly in the Northern Hemisphere, are *always* under the influence of cyclones or anticyclones. One or the other is invariably present. Further and more detailed study of the weather conditions associated with these atmospheric features will be found in a following chapter.

Winds Caused by Local Temperature Differences

All winds are of course basically the result of differences in temperature. There are, however, certain important local wind types that are caused directly by temperature distinctions resulting either from variations in composition or topography of the earth's surface, or both.

LAND AND SEA BREEZES.—Shore and coastal areas frequently exhibit winds whose direction reverses from day to night. They can be considered as a kind of daily monsoon since their origin is similar to that of monsoon winds. They differ in that monsoons result from large *seasonal* pressure changes, whereas land and sea breezes are a consequence of lesser *daily* changes in pressure. In any case, changes in temperature are responsible for all such winds.

During the daytime, in the summer season, a pronounced temperature difference develops. As the sun shines down on adjacent land and sea borders, the land rapidly becomes warmer than the neighboring water.

WIND CHARTS OF FOUR DIFFERENT LEVELS

Observations on Nov. 12, 1942. *(Courtesy of U.S. Navy.)*

SURFACE

Fig. 10-18.

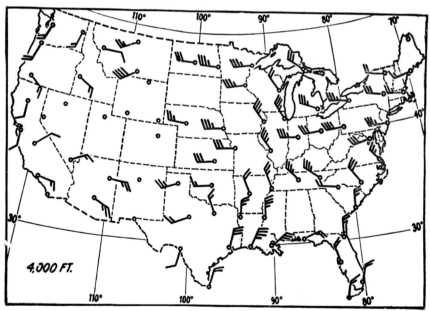

4,000 FT.

Fig. 10-19.

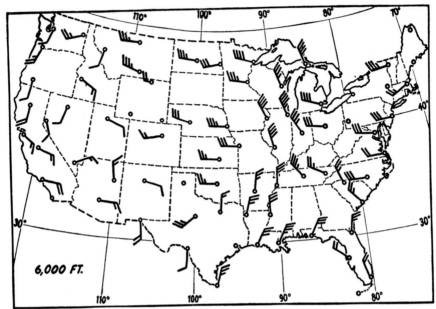

6,000 FT.

Fig. 10-20.

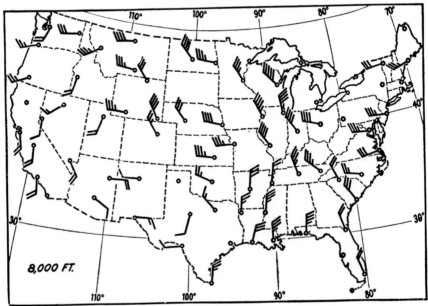

8,000 FT.

Fig. 10-21.

As this continues, convection causes the air over land to expand and to
rise as it becomes less dense.   Thus the atmospheric pressure becomes
lower over the land than over the bordering sea.   This establishes a
pressure gradient with pressure higher over the sea and lower over the
land.   Such a wind blowing in the daytime as a result of temperature
differences between land and water is known as a "sea breeze."

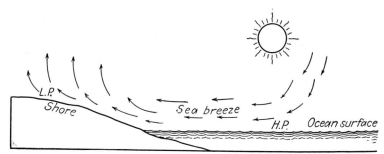

Fig. 10-22.—Development of sea breeze during differential daytime heating of a shore belt.

Sea breezes become stronger during the late afternoon as temperature
differences increase.   They are frequently felt many miles inland from
the shore zone.   Large lakes show similar winds although they may not
be on so great a scale.   Such winds usually have a definite moderating
influence on the climate of the narrow shore area that they affect.   The
cooler onshore winds lower the maximum temperature otherwise expected
in summer afternoons.

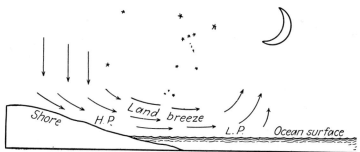

Fig. 10-23.—Development of land breeze during differential nocturnal cooling of a shore
belt.

Land breezes are *offshore night* winds that develop as the land cools
by radiation at night.   We have learned previously that land cools more
rapidly than water.   Consequently the land, which was warmer during
the day, at night becomes colder than the adjoining water.   The air
over the land gradually becomes colder and therefore denser than that
offshore.   Hence, the pressure gradient is now reversed with pressure
higher over the land, yielding offshore winds known as "land breezes."

Land breezes are experienced to within only a few miles offshore, although they are frequently very strong along actual beach areas.

Land and sea breezes are often particularly well developed over tropical and subtropical islands, such as those in the West Indies and the Pacific. Marked temperature differences form between these islands and the surrounding oceans during sunny days, which differences reverse at night. The sea breeze dies down at or shortly after sunset as the heating effects of the sun disappear. This often happens with extreme regularity.

A relatively important navigational aid results from this daily heating coupled with the sea breeze. As the warm sea air reaches the heated island during the daytime, it partakes of the convectional air

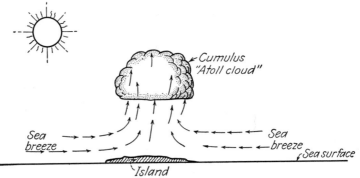

Fig. 10-24.—Formation of cumulus cloud over a heated island.

motion over the island and rises. The rising air produces adiabatic cooling and yields cumulus clouds as it cools to the dew point. Such clouds are daily characteristics of these small islands and can be seen from great distances when the low land beneath is completely invisible. They are sometimes called "atoll clouds" owing to their prevalence over the coral atolls of tropical waters. Brief heavy showers may develop if the heating is sufficient to cause towering cumulonimbus clouds to form from the original cumulus.

FOEHN AND CHINOOK WINDS.—These are warm *dry* winds descending the leeward slopes of mountains. The air in falling to the floor of an adjacent valley or plain, after coming across the mountain top, warms adiabatically at the rate of 1°F. for each 185 feet of descent. Thus if the wind descends the side of a mountain several thousands of feet high, it will be considerably warmer and hence drier than the air prevailing in that area. In the winter and early spring such warm dry winds are responsible for rapid melting of the snow, clearing the soil for spring farming. In Europe the name "foehn" is applied to this wind, while in the United States and Canada along the eastern or lee slopes of the Rockies, the Indian name "chinook" is used.

The chinook may originate from winds that ascend the windward slopes and descend the leeward slopes of a mountain range. If the air in ascending cools sufficiently to reach the dew point, further rising will cause cooling according to the reduced moist adiabatic rate. But on descending the lee slopes the dry air now warms only according to the dry rate and may reach a much higher temperature than the air at the same level on the approach side. Figure 10-25 illustrates the development of a chinook wind on the leeward slopes of a mountain after condensation occurred on the opposite windward side. Note the temperature increase of the wind after descending at the dry adiabatic rate.

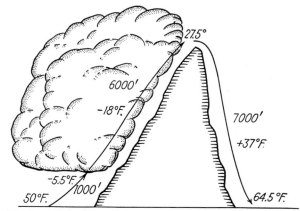

Fig. 10-25.—Adiabatic conditions responsible for the warm chinook wind.

Mountain and Valley Breezes.—As implied by the name, these breezes exist in mountainous areas, or areas of strong topographic relief. During daytime heating, valley areas become relatively overheated. Consequently, the warmed air rises up the sides of the valley (or mountain) during periods of sunshine. These breezes may be weak or strong depending on the nature of the topography. Such air movements, originating at the valley floor, are called "valley breezes."

During the night in the same areas, the air on the mountain sides, in contact with the cooling slopes, cools faster than the surrounding air or that in the sheltered valley below. Hence the air along the slopes settles downward, being more pronounced on nights when good radiation weather prevails and permits rapid cooling of the mountain sides, and consequently of the adjacent air. Again, local topography may favor the development of rather strong nocturnal mountain breezes.

Both valley and mountain breezes are sometimes slowed considerably by the effect of adiabatic cooling in the rising valley breeze, and adiabatic heating in the case of the settling mountain breeze.

Local Wind Types

All winds, regardless of their location, can be explained by the facts and principles developed in this and the preceding chapter. At the root of the whole matter lie the basic temperature differences followed by pressure irregularities. Many local winds have such marked and definite characteristics in the localities of their occurrence, that colloquial names are ascribed to them. Brief definitions (from U.S. Weather Bureau) of these local winds are given since they are so frequently encountered.

BORA.—A cold wind of the northern Adriatic blowing down from the high plateaus in the north. A similar wind occurs on the northeastern coast of the Black Sea.

CAT'S-PAW.—A slight and local breeze which shows itself by the rippling of the sea surface.

CHUBASCO.—A violent squall on the west coast of tropical and sub-tropical North America.

CORDONAZO.—A hurricane wind blowing from a southerly quadrant on the west coast of Mexico as a result of a hurricane passing off the coast.

ETECIANS.—Northerly winds blowing in summer over the eastern Mediterranean.

GREGALE.—A stormy northeast wind on the Mediterranean.

HARMATTAN.—A dry dusty wind of the west coast of Africa, blowing from the deserts.

KHAMSIN.—A hot, dry, southerly wind occurring in Egypt, in spring-time.

LESTE.—A hot, dry, easterly wind of the Madeira and Canary Islands.

LEVANTER.—A strong easterly wind of the Mediterranean, especially in the Straits of Gibraltar, where damp foggy weather also attends the wind.

MISTRAL.—A stormy, cold, northerly wind blowing down from the mountains of the interior along the Mediterranean Coast from the mouth of the Ebro to the Gulf of Genoa.

NORTHER.—A stormy northerly wind of sudden onset occurring during the colder half of the year over the region from Texas, southward across the Gulf of Mexico and the western Caribbean. These winds are dependent on the strengthening of the cold-weather high-pressure area prevailing over the southern United States.

PAMPERO.—A northwest squall blowing over or from the pampas of South America. Off the coast of Argentina they are most prevalent from July to September.

PAPAGAYO.—A strong to violent northeast wind blowing during the colder months in the Gulf of Papagayo, on the northwest coast of Costa Rica and in adjacent Pacific coastal waters.

SHAMAL.—A northeast wind of Mesopatamia and the Persian Gulf.

SIMOON.—An intensely hot and dry wind of Asiatic and African deserts.

SIROCCO.—This is applied to various warm winds in the Mediterranean area, particularly in North Africa.

TEHUANTEPECER.—A strong to violent northerly wind of Pacific waters off southern Mexico and northern Central America, confined mostly to the Gulf of Tehuantepec and occurring during the colder months.

Tornadoes and Waterspouts

Tornadoes and waterspouts are closely related phenomena. When the motion of a tornado carries it out to sea, it is called a "waterspout." However, not all waterspouts are true tornadoes but may result from other causes, as well. As such, we shall consider them under separate headings.

TORNADOES.—Tornadoes are by far the most violent and destructive manifestations of all nature. Nothing else is comparable to their fury. Fortunately the path of this "atmospheric monster" is so narrow that the total damage left in its wake is not nearly as great as that of less violent but larger storms.

Tornadoes are common mostly to the lower middle latitudes of both hemispheres, although, even here, their occurrence is limited in location. The storm itself is a gigantic whirling funnel of air extending earthward from heavy black cumulonimbus clouds. The air motion is characterized by a cyclonic upward spiral, causing rapid expansion, cooling, and condensation, which forms the dark cloud of the tornado funnel. A downpour of rain and hail is the common associate of the tornado, occurring just before and after its passage. The accompanying lightning and thunder are related more directly to the parent cumulonimbus cloud than to the tornado itself.

The width of the storm at the ground level averages about 300 yards, although it may vary anywhere from 20 or 30 yards to a mile. The forward velocity of motion varies from 25 to 40 miles per hour. Curiously, it often travels in an erratic, skipping path, so that the tapering end of the funnel may hop over one area and descend to wreak further havoc, often exhibiting a writhing, serpentine appearance, as it does so.

The pressure and winds of a tornado can rarely be measured directly but must be inferred from observation. The extremely high velocity of the whirling air causes a marked decrease in pressure at the center.

A steep pressure gradient results owing to the short horizontal distance over which the fall in pressure occurs. Thus, in many cases the destructive effect of the storm has been ascribed to the explosive action of air under normal pressure within a building, as the outside pressure falls rapidly with the passage of the storm.

The wind velocity is excessive, not only in a horizontal direction but vertically as well. Thus, very heavy objects, in some cases a team of horses and a wagon, have been lifted gently and carried some distance, being held aloft by rising air, and then deposited, just as gently. These cases lead to estimates of up to 200 miles per hour for the velocity of the vertically rising air. The horizontal winds are in excess of this. Dry straws have been driven through wooden telegraph poles under the

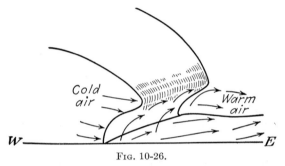

Fig. 10-26.

impact of the driving winds. Theoretical calculations show that wind speeds from 300 to 500 miles per hour may be required for this result.

In the Northern Hemisphere, tornadoes occur in the warm air in the southern section of a cyclone (northern section in the Southern Hemisphere), being more common in the spring and early summer than in any other period. After formation, tornadoes usually travel east to northeastward, or in accordance with the direction of motion of the low-pressure area.

It is not accidental that tornadoes usually form when and where they do. Rather, the conditions of formation are opportune at that time and place. These conditions necessary for tornado formation are (1) warm humid air flowing into the cyclone from the south or southwest and (2) a mass of cold air advancing from the west, into the warm air, at a level above the ground. We shall learn later in greater detail that the southern section of a cyclone often consists of a tongue of warm air protruding northward into cold surrounding air. Further, the cold air to the west moves eastward faster than the warm tongue preceding it. Also, the cold air frequently travels faster at high levels than at the ground, where its speed is retarded by friction. This situation is indicated in Fig. 10-26.

a b

c

FIG. 10-27.—Four stages in the development of a tornado, Gothenberg, Neb., June 24, 1930. (*Courtesy of U. S. Weather Bureau.*)

Without entering into an involved explanation, we may note that the tornado whirl originates in the warm air at the level of the overrunning cold upper air layer, as a result of the contrasting properties and the contrasting directions of motion. Typical violent thundersqualls develop along this upper cold-air boundary at the same time, and it is from the base of one of these thunderclouds that the dark vortex descends.

Clearly, tornado conditions are not localized but may exist at many places along the upper cold-air line, which may at times be some 50 miles ahead of the cold-air line at the ground. Consequently, it is not uncommon to have many tornadoes traveling simultaneously across country along a fairly well-defined line.

WATERSPOUTS.—Waterspouts are among the most curious of marine phenomena and have given rise to speculations and legends of all sorts in order to explain their origin and nature. They are actually of two types, depending on their origin. One type occurs, as explained above, when a tornado moves beyond the confines of the continent; in this case it has all the violence and other features of the true tornado. The more common type of spout is a simpler convectional feature of the atmosphere that may occur at almost any time or place, in temperate or tropical latitudes. Further, it may be associated with fair weather or foul.

The tornado and the tornado-type waterspout always exhibit cyclonic rotation owing to the nature of their origin. However the air in the convection-type spout may rotate in either cyclonic or anticyclonic motion, depending on the manner of formation. Having examined the features of the tornado, we shall consider now the features of the waterspout of second type.

Individual waterspouts may vary considerably as to features of origin and structure, although certain typical characteristics can be given. The spout is most frequently associated with a heavy cloud of the cumulus family, resulting from local convection. From the cloud base, the spout tapers downward in the form of a narrow, dark cone. Running through the center of this cone is a long hollow tube of relatively low pressure which is responsible for a certain amount of sea water being sucked into the spout for a short vertical distance. The rapidly rotating winds also carry sea water aloft in the form of spray, picked up from the surface. However, the dark appearance of the spout is a result of neither sea water carried upward nor the cloud base protruding downward. It is rather the result of condensation in the moist air, whirling into and around the low-pressure center, as it spirals upward and expands.

Waterspouts are commonly observed to originate in two sections. The upper part is seen to develop as a small protuberance, funneling downward from the cloud base, in a halting, hesitating fashion. Directly below, at this time, an agitation of the water surface occurs, characterized by a boiling and tossing of spray, together with the formation of a low mound of water rising into the center of the yet invisible lower vortex. Then, from near the center of this disturbance, a second, dark, vapor-laden cone forms, but this one funnels upward, being an inverted counterpart of the one above. The tapering ends of the two cones continue to extend and finally unite, resembling a drawn-out hourglass at first and then a continuous, elongated whirling tube.

The spout follows in the direction taken by the overlying parent cloud mass. It rarely lasts longer than 30 to 60 minutes, the end coming rather abruptly. The tube may thin out and separate into two sections, the upper retreating into the cloud, and the lower falling back to the water surface. At times, the entire spout may appear to rise or roll directly up into the cloud. Thunderstorm conditions often attend the spout, being associated with the cumulonimbus cloud above.

In the violence exhibited, waterspouts are extremely variable. Often they are no stronger than common dust whirls or whirlwinds frequently observed over land surfaces. Occasionally the spout may contain wind motion of great strength, sufficient to destroy small craft and create much damage on larger vessels. It is doubtful whether any modern ocean-going vessel need have much to fear from waterspouts of ordinary convectional origin. There is, in fact, no record of any modern ship suffering disaster as a result of such an encounter.

CHAPTER 11

TROPICAL CYCLONES—HURRICANES

Tropical cyclones are the most violent storms experienced by the mariner. In West Indian waters these storms are known as "hurricanes"; in the East Indian and Japanese waters they are called "typhoons"; in the Indian Ocean they are called "cyclones"; off Australia, "willy-willies." Technically they are "tropical cyclones." Owing to common American usage we shall use the terms "hurricane" and "tropical cyclone" interchangeably.

Although essentially a feature of the lower latitudes, these storms are so important to the mariner that much time will now be devoted to their study. To do this we shall consider their nature; their origin, occurrence, path, and frequency; the conditions of the dangerous and navigable semicircles; the indications of approaching hurricanes; and finally, the problem of locating the center of such a storm. The task of maneuvering within the storm itself is encountered in seamanship and is treated in texts on that subject. However, that task will be much simplified by an accurate understanding of hurricane conditions.

Although tropical-cyclone conditions frequently exist, they are often called "tropical disturbances" or "tropical storms." Not until the severity of the storm reaches great violence, is it called a "hurricane."

Nature of Tropical Cyclones

Tropical cyclones are small low-pressure areas forming revolving storms, very nearly circular in shape. This circular shape is indicated by the isobars that show the pressure distribution within the area. The tropical cyclone thus differs from the cyclones of the middle latitudes, whose shapes are much varied. The *tropical* cyclone should not be confused with this middle-latitude cyclone, which is far milder.

The tropical cyclone averages something over 300 miles in diameter, differing again from the much larger *extratropical* cyclones. Neither the size nor the shape is the characteristic feature of such storms, but rather the extremely high and damaging winds that prevail therein. It is to these severe winds that hurricanes owe their fame.

What is there about such storms that causes such intense winds? The steep pressure gradient is responsible for them, since the pressure drop from the outside to the center of the storm may vary from 0.5 to

2 inches. If the storm is approximately 300 miles in diameter, the pressure drop is experienced over only 150 miles. A pressure change of even 0.5 inch over 150 miles is a very large one. This steep gradient is attended by and responsible for the destructive high-velocity winds. It will be remembered that the wind velocity is determined by the steepness of the pressure gradient. Thus, when the gradient is so steep as to produce wind velocities of 75 miles per hour or greater, the wind is said to have hurricane force (Beaufort of 12).

The lowest pressure recorded for a hurricane center in the Western Hemisphere was 26.35 inches, in the Florida Keys during the storm of

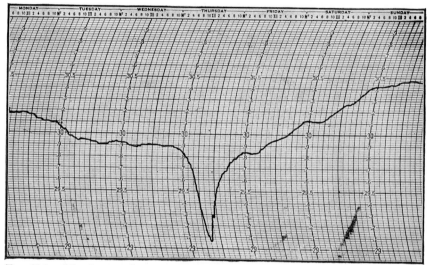

Fig. 11-1.—Microbarograph trace showing passage of tropical cyclone at Kings Point, N. Y., September 14, 1944.

September 2, 1935. The lowest pressure ever recorded in any tropical cyclone occurred during the typhoon of August 18, 1927, near Luzon, when the barometer fell to 26.185 inches.

Figure 11-1 shows the microbarograph trace during the passage of the hurricane of September 14, 1944, over Kings Point, New York. Although the lowest point is not below 29.07 inches, the fall in pressure is very rapid as shown by the steepness of the trace. This steep pressure drop was responsible for winds from 60 to 90 miles per hour during peak periods.

Not only is the pressure gradient steep, but it becomes steeper nearer the center as illustrated in the tropical cyclone shown in Fig. 11-2.

As the wind spirals into the low-pressure center in the normal counterclockwise motion for a low in the Northern Hemisphere, its velocity steadily increases as a consequence of the intense and steepening pressure gradient. With this increasing velocity the wind becomes deflected more and more and assumes a path practically parallel with the isobars. Thus there remains a small circular calm area about 10 miles in diameter, in the center of the storm itself. Figure 11-3 shows clearly the increasing wind velocity, with its gusty variations, as the center approaches, and the sudden drop to practically dead calm in the center, followed by the abrupt increase.

The winds about this calm center may be of the order of 100 miles an hour. Mountainous waves, often 40 to 50 feet in height, may alternately

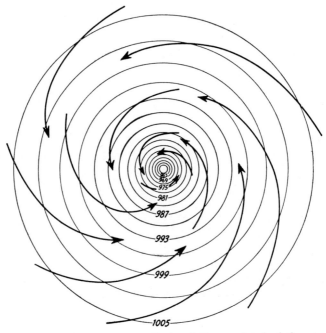

FIG. 11-2.—The steepening pressure gradient and the associated wind system within a tropical cyclone (Northern Hemisphere).

raise and drop the vessel from crest to trough, straining in the process every seam and fiber of the ship. The waves themselves, however, are not hampered in their movement by pressure gradient and deflective force. They continue rolling *into the calm center* with but little loss in velocity and height. In addition they come in from all directions. Hence, although the *air* is calm, the *seas* within the calm central area are high and confused, making maneuvering very difficult despite the quiet air. Owing to the circular motion, the winds on the opposite sides of the center always blow in opposite directions.

The following quotation is from the report of the second officer on a ship passing through the hurricane of September 19, 1941, off western Mexico:

"The barometer fell so rapidly that it could be seen moving down— from 29.25 to 27.67.   At 4:30 the ship passed through the center of the cyclone.   The wind died down to almost 0 and the low clouds opened up so that high cirrus could be seen through a small opening.   There was a peculiar yellow light and the sea became bright green in color. The extremely low atmospheric pressure caused discomfort in the ears. High confused swells broke aboard the ship with terrific force from all

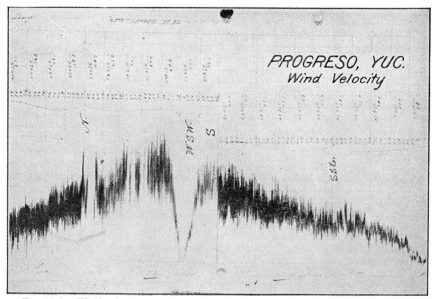

PROGRESO, YUC.
Wind Velocity

F<small>IG</small>. 11-3.—Wind velocity recording showing intensity and gustiness of winds preceding and following the calm center of the Yucatan hurricane, August 26, 1938.   (*Monthly Weather Review, January,* 1939.)

sides.   In about 10 to 15 minutes the center passed and the wind came from the southwest, force 12 and over."

It is often said that the winds set in with greater violence as the center passes over a vessel or station.   The truth is that as the center is approached the winds build up to maximum violence more or less slowly, compared to the change from dead calm to the maximum velocity as the center passes.   At the same time, the destructive effect of a sudden high wind is greater than that of a wind building up slowly to the same velocity.   Thus a line may snap under a sudden strain while it has withstood the same strain developed gradually.   If the calm storm center passes across the vessel, preparations should always be made in anticipation of this sudden onslaught of the winds and their reversal.

Many a vessel has keeled over and submerged following this sudden attack and reversal of the wind.

As the wind spirals into the low-pressure storm center, the air rises as well. This rising motion is most nearly vertical surrounding the storm center. Rising air always cools, and in the humid marine air this cooling results in condensation in the form of clouds. These clouds vary from thin cirrostratus in the outer portions of the storm through altostratus and nimbostratus to cumulonimbus where the steep, almost vertically rising air is encountered around the storm center. The calm center, having no generally rising air, will be relatively clear. Thus this calm center has a clear opening or shaft penetrating the surrounding heavy clouds and is called the "eye of the storm. The surrounding dense black cumulonimbus mass which rings the calm center is often called the

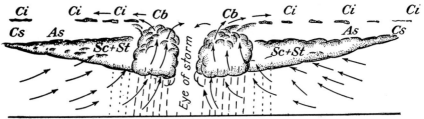

Fig. 11-4.—Cross section of atmospheric conditions in a typical tropical cyclone.

"bar" of the storm, since it appears as a dense cloud bank when viewed from a distance.

The cross section in Fig. 11-4 indicates this air motion responsible for the cloud formations. It should be noted that the tops of the central cumulonimbus clouds produce cirrus at their peaks. These cirrus clouds blow outward from the storm center in all directions. Being masked by the storm clouds, the cirrus forms are not visible until the margin of the hurricane is reached. Rain falls in the inner central area of the storm, becomes very heavy in the ring surrounding the center, and is often attended by lightning and thunder in this area. The intensity of the rains attending the hurricane is very great. So heavy are they in fact, that visibility is often reduced to the distance of the proverbial "hand before one's face." At night these conditions are doubly awesome and dangerous to the navigator.

Origin, Path, Occurrence, and Frequency of Tropical Cyclones

Tropical cyclones originate near the doldrums but always from 6° to 10° away from the equator. Hurricanes never form directly on or very close to this line.

The exact cause of the original hurricane whirl is still not perfectly understood. However, the origin is closely associated with the influx of a cold mass of air, often at high altitudes, into the doldrum area, meeting the excessively warm moist air of the tropics. The resulting instability as a result of this meeting, together with the energy liberated by condensation from the warm air, plays a major part in the birth of these violent tropical storms. The fact that they are strictly marine in origin further increases the difficulty of continued observation and thus of completely explaining their inception.

As the storm grows and increases in intensity, the steady supply of the latent heat of the rising warm air at the storm center maintains the energy of the tropical cyclone.

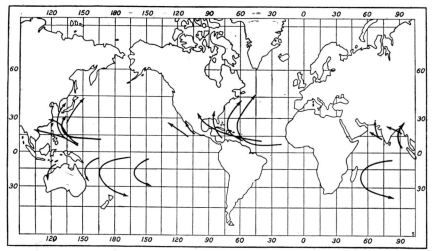

Fig. 11-5.—The principal hurricane regions of the world and their average paths of motion.

Once the hurricane forms, it travels away from the equator north-ward in the Northern Hemisphere, southward in the Southern. At the same time, it follows the general air movements. Thus, as the hurricane moves away from the equator, it migrates into the trade-wind belt and curves off to the west with those winds.

Upon crossing the horse latitudes the hurricane encounters the westerlies and therefore recurves to the eastward. These paths in both hemispheres are illustrated in Fig. 11-9. The parabolic storm track is characteristic of a well-behaved hurricane.

After crossing the horse latitude zone and recurving, the tropical cyclone usually begins to spread out and diminish in intensity, although marked violence may still exist.

We have stated that the hurricane follows the general air circulation. Suppose that a high-pressure area, or anticyclone, exists in the westerlies

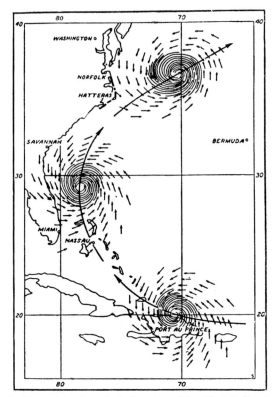

Fig. 11-6.—Typical track and wind system of the West Indian hurricane.

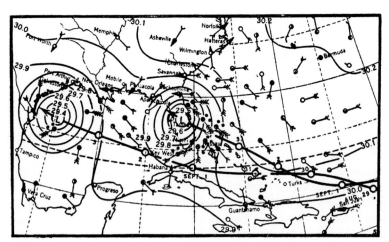

Fig. 11-7.—Weather map showing two tropical cyclones in progress at the same time. Each feather on the wind arrows represents one unit of Beaufort force. (*Courtesy of U. S. Weather Bureau.*)

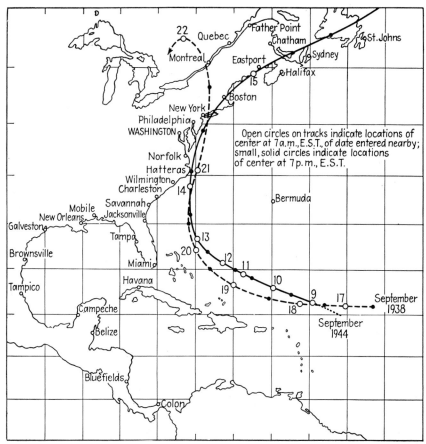

Fig. 11-8.—Tracks of the destructive September hurricanes of 1938 and 1944. (*Courtesy of U.S. Weather Bureau.*)

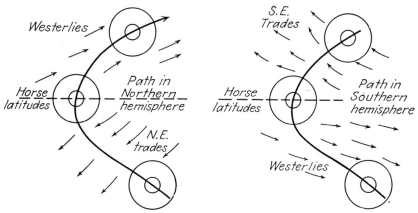

Fig. 11-9.—Typical parabolic hurricane tracks for the Northern and Southern Hemispheres.

just above the horse latitudes where the storm should normally recurve. Recall that in the Northern Hemisphere the anticyclone winds spiral clockwise or move west and northwestward, and west to southwestward in the Southern Hemisphere, where the hurricane should recurve (see Fig. 11-10).

Consequently a well-developed "high" on the normal path of a hurricane may seriously affect its normal recurvature. The presence of a low will have no particular effect on the hurricane motion.

Actually the true path of a tropical cyclone is determined not so much by the surface winds, as by the upper winds. Recall the source from which the hurricane draws its supply of energy—the heat liberated

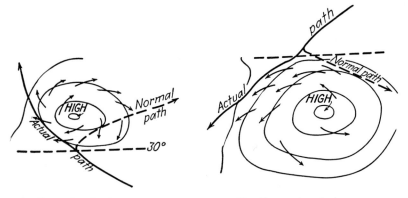

Northern hemisphere   Southern hemisphere

Fig. 11-10.—Effect of anticyclonic conditions on the normal recurvature of tropical cyclones.

at the cloud level or condensation level. The true heart of the storm is at this level, where the continuous influx of warm, rising humid air liberates a steady supply of latent heat, which maintains the fury of the storm. Hence it is the air movement at this cloud level that actually determines the course of the storm. At times this may vary widely from the wind motion at the ground and so lead to erroneous conclusions concerning its motion. The use of planes or balloon soundings of the upper air drift is thus very important.

The average velocity of tropical cyclones is from 10 to 30 miles per hour. However, they may frequently remain stationary for a time, or may exceed this average. In low latitudes, after their formation, hurricanes usually move very slowly. As they move toward higher latitudes, this forward motion increases, frequently accelerating very rapidly upon crossing the horse latitudes. The hurricanes of the eastern Atlantic coast area of 1938 and 1944 roared over Long Island at velocities of about 60 miles per hour. In addition, such unusual storms generally maintain their full hurricane intensity until relatively high latitudes are reached.

There are six regions on the earth where tropical cyclones are most commonly encountered: (1) the North Atlantic Ocean, including the West Indian waters; (2) the Southeastern North Pacific, just west of Mexico; (3) the North Pacific Ocean, including the area extending through the China Sea from the East Indies to Japan; (4) the Arabian Sea and the Bay of Bengal, flanking India; (5) the South Indian Ocean, east of Madagascar; (6) the South Pacific and Australian waters. It is notable that such storms are strictly marine in occurrence and that the South Atlantic is free of them.

The tropical cyclones of the Western Pacific area are often smaller though more violent than the West Indian type. Often, several typhoons may course the oceans simultaneously.

Table XVIII shows the frequency of tropical cyclones over given intervals for each of the six regions.

TABLE XVIII. OCCURRENCE OF TROPICAL CYCLONES OF THE SIX REGIONS[1]

	January	February	March	April	May	June	July	August	September	October	November	December	Annual average number	Length of record, years
1. North Atlantic Ocean	0	0	0	0	4	24	25	71	112	91	23	2	7	50
2. Southeastern North Pacific Ocean	0	0	0	0	3	17	17	25	50	26	2	1	5	27
3. North Pacific Ocean (Far East)	15	8	11	13	26	36	109	151	129	117	59	37	20	36
4. Arabian Sea	*	*	*	*	5	11	3	0	2	10	8	2	2	23
Bay of Bengal	*	*	*	*	21	42	65	55	70	51	37	17	10	36
5. South Indian Ocean	113	115	98	68	25	3	*	*	*	7	33	58	7	70
6. Australian waters to 160°E. longitude	54	49	58	29	7	7	*	*	*	4	10	22	3	84
South Pacific Ocean east of 160°E. longitude	69	47	64	18	2	2	*	*	*	4	8	31	2	105

[1] From U.S. Government Publication, Hydrographic Office, No. 9.

Dangerous and Navigable Semicircles

Along its path or track, a hurricane is readily resolved into two semicircles. Looking in the direction of motion of the storm, we obtain the right and left semicircles, which are respectively on the eastern and western sides of this path in the Northern Hemisphere. The reverse is true in the Southern Hemisphere (Fig. 11-11).

In the Northern Hemisphere the right semicircle is the *dangerous*, and the left, the *navigable*, semicircle. Of course, both semicircles are dangerous, but for certain reasons the right is the more so in the Northern and the left the more so in the Southern Hemisphere.

Consider a storm to be in the Northern Hemisphere and moving at 30 miles per hour along the indicated path (Fig. 11-12).   Let us assume the winds to reach a good average hurricane force of 100 miles per hour about the center.

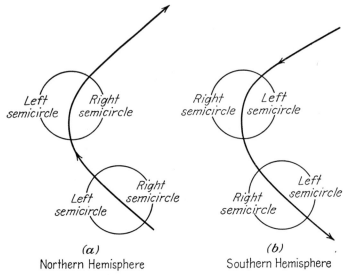

(a)
Northern Hemisphere

(b)
Southern Hemisphere

FIG. 11-11.

1. Clearly the wind motion in the right half with respect to a vessel on the ocean will have a velocity of 130 miles per hour.   This results from the combined motion of the wind about the storm center added to the forward velocity of the storm itself.   In the left semicircle the wind and the storm move in opposing directions, resulting in an effective velocity of 70 miles per hour, a difference from the right side of 60 miles per hour. Of course this is the *maximum* difference between the two sides, where the wind is parallel to the storm track.

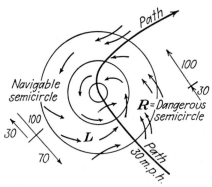

FIG. 11-12.—The dangerous and navigable semicircles for a tropical cyclone in the Northern Hemisphere.

2. The direction of the wind and that of the resulting ocean currents in the storm area are such as to cause the vessel in the right half to drift around and into the storm path forward of the center.   In the left half this motion is to the rear of the storm center.

3. Since the tropical cyclones recurve to the right in the Northern

Hemisphere, it is evident that a vessel in the right, especially the forward right quadrant, might find itself directly on or very close to the track of the center as it recurves.

For these reasons the right semicircle is considered dangerous. Since the winds spiral in a *clockwise* direction about a low in the Southern Hemisphere, it is easily seen that for the same reasons the left semicircle will be more dangerous in that hemisphere.

Indications of Approaching Tropical Cyclones

No one definite clue exists to presage the approaching hurricane. However, there is a combination of observed effects, which, when occurring simultaneously, serve as very good warning. If only one of the phenomena to be considered is encountered, the observer will do well to be on the alert for other possible indications. This is especially true if the vessel is in or near any of the localities where tropical cyclones prevail.

SWELL.—Swell, or ground swell, consists of long, low, undulating waves that have outrun the winds producing them. The stronger the wind, the higher and longer are the resulting waves. Consequently, in a hurricane zone, any swell differing in length and direction from the swell characteristic of that locality, is a possible warning. The storm itself has been in the direction from which the swell moves. Thus ground swell with a period of 10 to 15 seconds, when encountered in the Caribbean or the Gulf of Mexico, is said to be a certain sign of a tropical cyclone in that area. The "period" is the time between successive swell crests.

STATE OF SKY—CLOUDS.—We have noted previously that the cirrus clouds spread out far in advance of the storm itself and are often, when in combination with an abnormal swell, accurate warnings of an existing tropical cyclone. If the storm is approaching, the cirrus often take the form of long bands radiating from the position of the storm center. As the storm approaches, the cirrus give way to increasing cirrostratus. These form a typical film or veil over the sky and cause halos about the sun or moon. Under these conditions, the sky is frequently a brilliant red at sunrise or sunset.

PRESSURE CHARACTERISTICS.—With the continued approach of the storm to within a few hundred miles, unusual barometric conditions are frequently observed. In tropical waters any barometric fluctuation differing from the normal diurnal variation from 10 A.M. to 4 P.M. to 10 P.M. to 4 A.M., especially if coincident with the above indications, serves as a further herald of the hurricane. As the edge of the storm area itself is actually encountered, the barometer may rise abruptly and then fall, or simply be erratic, or it may fall much faster than normal.

If a hurricane is definitely approaching, the barometer will, after a possible initial unsteadiness, fall more and more rapidly as the ever-steepening pressure gradient moves in.

An approximate idea of the distance to the storm center can be gained by noting this increasing hourly rate of fall. Table XIX furnishes a

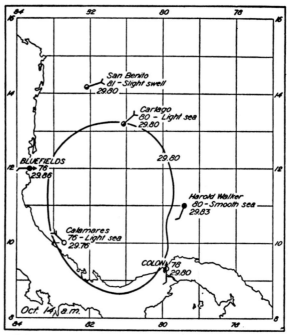

FIG. 11-13.—Pressure and wind conditions at 7 A.M., October 14, 1926, showing gentle cyclonic wind circulation of an incipient disturbance. The amount of filling of the small circles at the heads of the arrows indicates the state of the sky. (*Courtesy of U.S. Weather Bureau.*)

rough guide to this distance by showing the average relationship between rate of fall and distance to center.

TABLE XIX.   RELATION OF PRESSURE CHANGE TO TROPICAL CYCLONE DISTANCE

Hourly Rate of Fall, In.	Distance to Center, Miles
0.02–0.06	250–150
0.06–0.08	150–100
0.08–0.12	100– 80
0.12–0.16	80– 50

WIND CHARACTERISTICS.—With a coming hurricane the wind usually shifts in direction from the prevailing direction and increases in velocity. This change is a noticeable one in view of the normal steadiness of the trades that prevail in the tropics and subtropics. The wind increases in squalls or gusts, becoming more and more violent closer to the center.

GENERAL INDICATIONS.—In general, the air surrounding a tropical cyclone is cooler, drier, and clearer than the atmosphere encompassed within the storm area. As a vessel enters the storm zone, a change to warmer, more humid air is experienced.

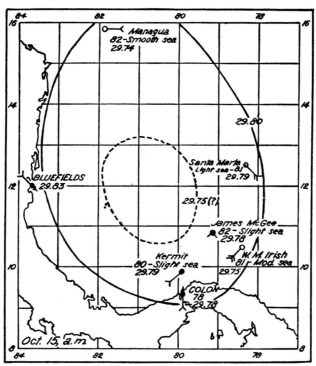

FIG. 11-14.—Pressure and wind conditions at 7 A.M., October 15, 1926. Lower pressures and slightly more vigorous wind circulation are evident. Conditions of the sea surface are indicated here and on the following time figures. Dotted line indicates probable central area of storm. (*Courtesy of U.S. Weather Bureau.*)

Although none of the above weather features alone will positively identify the presence of a hurricane, a combination of them is a fairly dependable sign.

Locating the Storm Center

Once the existence of a tropical cyclone is determined, the observer has the important task of locating its center, and his position with relation to this center.

In the absence of reports from other ships or stations, the observer must rely upon his own observations. From the law of Buys-Ballot, if one faces the wind, the low-pressure or storm center is 8 to 10 points on the right. One observation will yield only a line of position, somewhere along which the storm center lies. The force of the wind and the rate of fall of the pressure indicate the approximate distance of the storm center *provided it is approaching directly.*

Under hurricane conditions the true *wind* direction can often best be determined by the motion of the *lower* clouds. Recall that the upper wind blows more freely and consequently is parallel to the isobars. Thus by facing into the low cloud movement one may judge the storm center to be directly (8 points or 90°) on the right in the Northern Hemisphere, and to have a similar bearing on the left in the Southern Hemisphere.

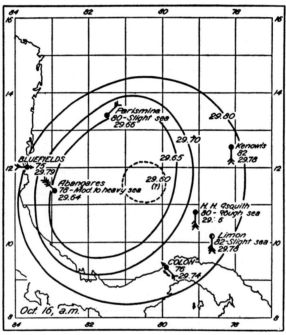

Fig. 11-15.—Conditions at 7 A.M., October 16, 1926. Marked increase in winds with further decrease in pressure is seen. (*Courtesy of U.S. Weather Bureau.*)

It should be remembered that the wind deflection increases as the velocity increases, causing the winds to blow around with or parallel to the isobars. Hence, for high-velocity winds the storm center is more nearly 8 points to the right, when one faces the wind.

In Fig. 11-18 the determination of the hurricane center is shown by applying the above rule to observations from two vessels.

The more numerous the reports, the more accurately can the storm center be located. Figure 11-19 indicates an example of this situation.

Occasionally, the exact position of the center of the tropical cyclone is secured when some vessel happens to be within it.

The observer can usually locate his position with reference to the storm center and the dangerous and navigable semicircles by a knowledge

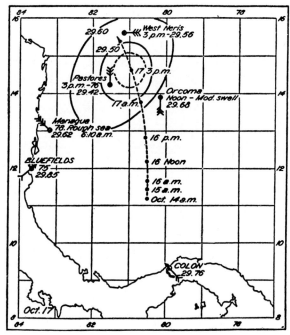

FIG. 11-16.—Conditions on October 17, 1926, showing, in addition, the track of the storm center with dots indicating its position at the times given. A rapid increase in intensity followed with the storm passing over Havana and Bermuda, exhibiting winds of full hurricane force. (*Courtesy of U.S. Weather Bureau.*)

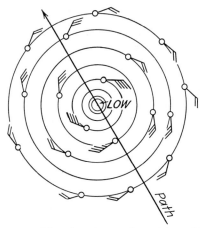

FIG. 11-17.—Wind diagram useful in locating one's position within a hurricane in the Northern Hemisphere.

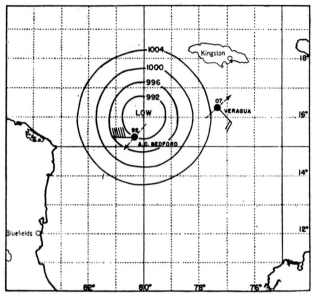

FIG. 11-18.—Center of hurricane located by observations from two ships. Dashed arrows show direction of swell. (*Courtesy of U.S. Weather Bureau.*)

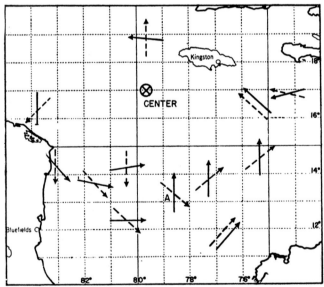

FIG. 11-19.—Direction of wind (solid arrows) and direction of swell (dashed arrows) in hurricane of Fig. 11-18. (*Courtesy of U.S. Weather Bureau.*)

of the wind direction and the nature of the wind *shifts*. It is clear that if the wind direction remains constant, with the force increasing steadily, he must be on the storm track *ahead* of the center. With a steady wind direction but with a diminishing velocity, he is *behind* the center.

When in any position other than on the track of the center, *shifting* of the wind will occur. In the Northern Hemisphere, when the wind sets in from points southerly to easterly, the ship is most likely in the right or dangerous semicircle. Northerly and westerly winds place the

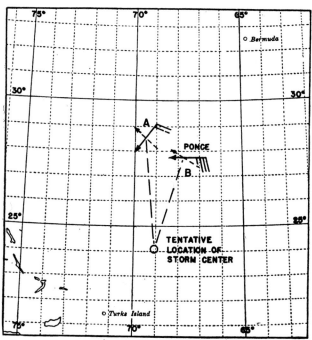

Fig. 11-20.—Center of hurricane located by two observations from same ship at a 12-hour interval. (*Courtesy of U.S. Weather Bureau.*)

observer in the left semicircle. This results from the normal counter-clockwise whirl of the winds about the hurricane or any low-pressure center in the Northern Hemisphere, shown once again in the Fig. 11-17.

East to northeast winds indicate the forward right quadrant of the storm, one of the most dangerous areas. The student should construct a similar picture for a tropical cyclone in the Southern Hemisphere, remembering the clockwise circulation prevailing there about a low-pressure center.

A significant relationship exists between wind and swell about a tropical cyclone. It was mentioned previously that the swell is one of the earliest indications of an approaching hurricane, the center of the storm being in the direction from which the swell approaches. When within the area encompassed by the storm winds, the wind usually bears to the left of the swell (for conditions in the Northern Hemisphere). In general, in the Northern Hemisphere with a progressive tropical cyclone in the vicinity, the deviation of wind from swell is usually 2 to 3 points, in the forward semicircle; 3 to 5 points in the left rear quadrant; and 1 to 2 points in the right rear quadrant. Remember that left and right are determined by the observer as he looks in the line of progression of the storm. This is general information and might not apply to particular storms. Figures 11-18 to 11-20 are illustrative of wind and swell conditions prevailing in the centers of two different Caribbean hurricanes.

Examples of Tropical Cyclones

The map sequences of August 25 to 30, 1930, and September 13 to 15, 1944, Figs. 11-21 to 11-26, are instances typical of many North Atlantic hurricanes. The first sequence illustrates a more normal condition of recurvature, with the influence of the storm being restricted almost wholly to deep-sea areas. Such a storm, although characterized by extremely high wind velocities, leaves more room for maneuvering than the storm to be considered below. A study of these charts will clarify further many of the principles illustrated above.

The weather maps for September 13 to 15, 1944, Figs. 11-27 to 11-29, show successive stages in the life of the violent tropical cyclone that traveled along the Atlantic Coast during those dates. The storm was first observed in a premature condition by Army Air Force observers, when it was many degrees to the east and somewhat south of its position on the thirteenth. This is a well-known and typical example of a hurricane failing to recurve, as a result of the surrounding atmospheric circulation. This hurricane followed a low-pressure trough between an area of high pressure over the continent to the west, and an area of high pressure over the Atlantic to the east. A storm of this type is obviously of great danger all along the seaboard area embraced by its wind system. It is of particularly great danger to shipping. Far more ships are subjected to the influence of such a coastal storm than to that of the type considered just previously. Whether it be coastal traffic or ocean-going vessels in or near harbors, the room for maneuvering to avoid the brunt of the hurricane is greatly reduced.

We may note in the case of this hurricane that the seaboard and waters immediately adjacent were traversed by the navigable semicircle of the storm, the dangerous semicircle lying to the east, where the winds were far stronger. The coastal conditions might have been much worse had the storm center been farther to the west, permitting the dangerous half to cover the coast.

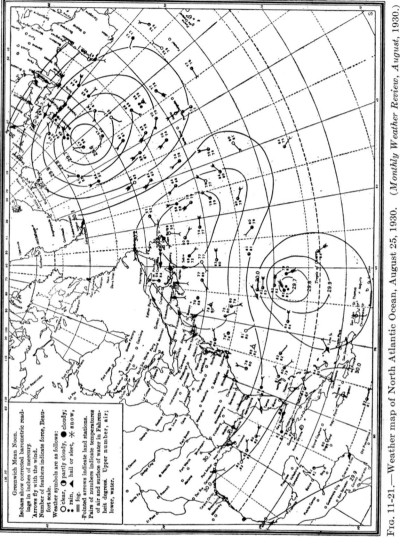

FIG. 11-21.—Weather map of North Atlantic Ocean, August 25, 1930.   (*Monthly Weather Review, August, 1930.*)

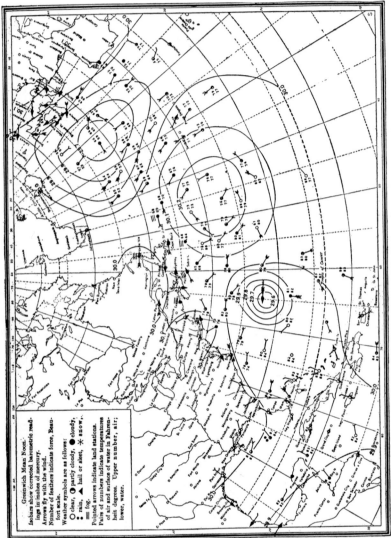

Greenwich Mean Noon.
Isobars show corrected barometric readings in inches of mercury.
Arrows fly with the wind.
Number of feathers indicate force, Beaufort scale.
Weather symbols are as follows:
○ clear, ◑ partly cloudy, ● cloudy,
●● rain, ▲ hail or sleet, ✳ snow.
☰ fog.
Pointed arrows indicate land stations.
Pairs of numbers indicate temperatures of air and surface of water in Fahrenheit degrees. Upper number, air; lower, water.

FIG. 11-22.—Weather map of North Atlantic Ocean, August 26, 1930.   (Monthly Weather Review, August, 1930.)

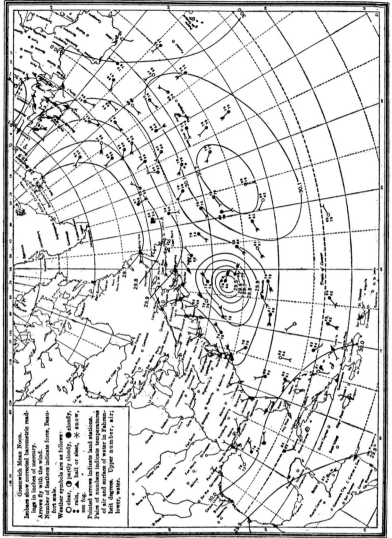

FIG. 11-23.—Weather map of North Atlantic Ocean, August 27, 1930. (*Monthly Weather Review, August, 1930.*)

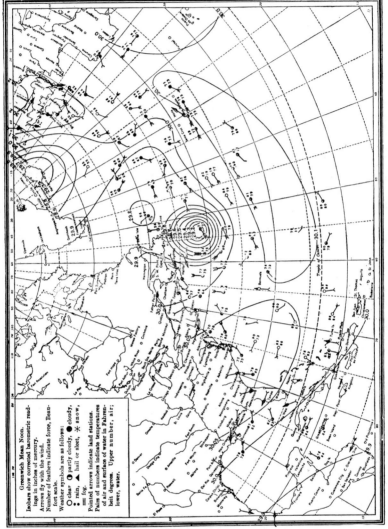

FIG. 11-24.—Weather map of North Atlantic Ocean, August 28, 1930. (*Monthly Weather Review, August, 1930.*)

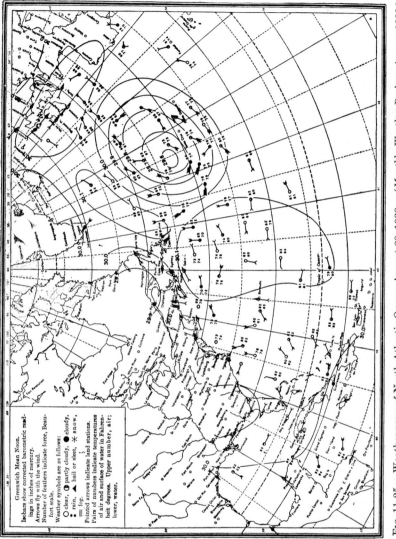

(Monthly Weather Review, August, 1930.)

Fig. 11-25.—Weather map of North Atlantic Ocean, August 29, 1930.

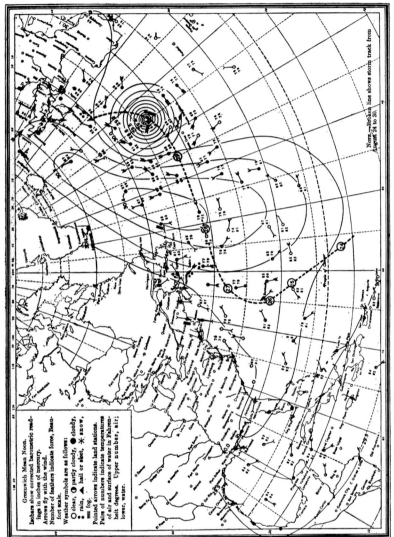

Greenwich Mean Noon.
Isobars show corrected barometric readings in inches of mercury.
Arrows fly with the wind.
Number of feathers indicate force, Beaufort scale.
Weather symbols are as follows: ○ clear, ◐ partly cloudy, ● cloudy, ⦁ rain, ▲ hail or sleet, ✳ snow, ≡ fog.
Pointed arrows indicate land stations.
Pairs of numbers indicate temperature of air and surface of water in Fahrenheit degrees. Upper number, air; lower, water.

Note.—Broken line shows storm track from August 24 to 30.

Fig. 11-26.—Weather map of North Atlantic Ocean, August 30, 1930.   (*Monthly Weather Review, August, 1930.*)

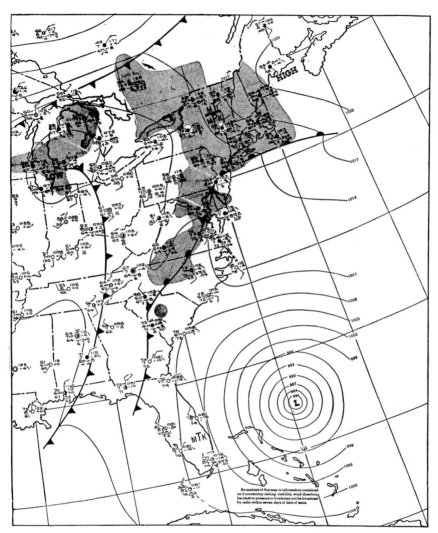

FIG. 11-27.—Weather map of September 13, 1944.

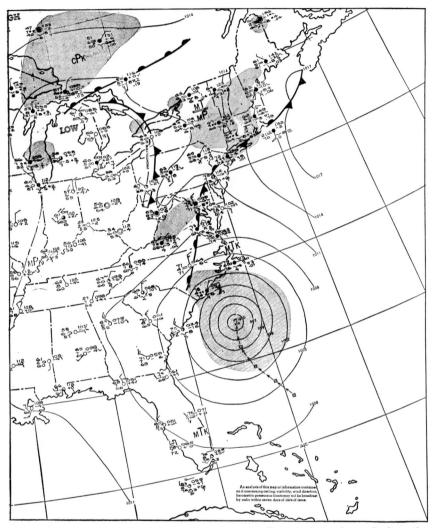

FIG. 11-28.—Weather map of September 14, 1944.   Crosses along the path show the
position of the storm center at 6-hour intervals.

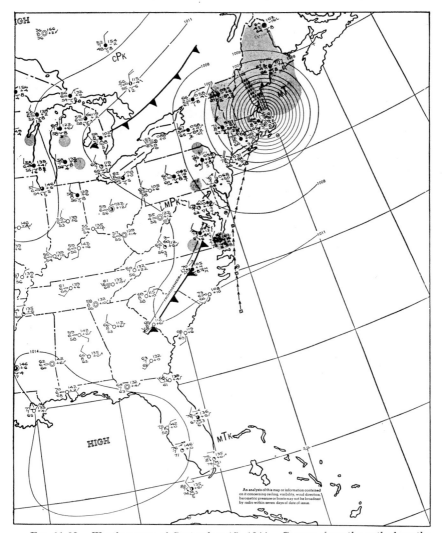

Fig. 11-29.—Weather map of September 15, 1944. Crosses along the path show the position of the storm center at 6-hour intervals. Note the increase in the forward velocity of the storm.

CHAPTER 12

WEATHER CODING AND NOTATION

Importance of Reports

The gathering of accurate observations taken over large areas is an absolute prerequisite to the analysis and forecasting of weather conditions, since these conditions move generally eastward. An extensive network of land stations has been established to collect these weather data and then relay them to the central bureau for assembly into a weather map which is the basis of interpretation and forecasting.

But remember that the earth's surface is about three-quarters water. How then is this vital information obtained over oceanic areas? Obviously merchant ships constitute the major source for these observations. It is the task of the ship's officers to take *accurate* weather observations. The resultant charts and their analysis can certainly be no more accurate and dependable than the original observations themselves.

Of great importance to the mariner are the pilot charts of the seas. In addition to the navigational aids provided by them, they show average conditions of wind and weather over the oceans. Again merchant ships provide practically the only important source for the determination of these data. Having learned the instruments and methods of observing the weather elements, let us now see how this information is recorded and distributed.

The U.S. Weather Bureau derives its data from two distinct channels: (1) ships at sea, and island stations whether American or foreign, and (2) the regular Weather Bureau land stations and airport weather stations.

Marine Reports

For purposes of efficiency and uniformity in the transmission of weather data, the International Meteorological Congress adopted the International Weather Code. Ships and stations of all nationalities can freely interchange weather messages. Each code table giving the numerical values to be used in preparing and decoding reports is designated by a standard international code letter or symbol. A complete description of the meaning of the different symbols together with the actual code tables follows this discussion.

In actual practice, every item of the code may not be reported, and the arrangement of the items may vary, depending on the nature

212

of the observations and the equipment available. However, in marine or international weather transmission the arrangement must conform to one of the five forms listed under the code description. Notice that the code message is divided for convenience into groups of five symbols each. In an actual weather message these symbols will of course be replaced by numerals from the corresponding code tables.

In order to facilitate observations and reports at sea the U.S. Weather Bureau provides American ships with three standard items: (1) the ship code card, (2) the ship's weather log (form 1210 AB), and (3) the radio weather form (form 1204).

The ship code card contains in compact form all the code tables reproduced below.

The weather log (1210 AB) is reproduced here on pages 216 and 217. At sea it should be filled out four times a day, if possible, at 0000, 0600, 1200, and 1800, GCT. The student should practice taking and recording at least one complete set of observations, thereby filling out one row on this form. Special fog, gale, and storm reports are entered on the reverse side of the sheet. At the conclusion of each voyage all sheets containing any information are detached and forwarded to the Weather Bureau. A new sheet should be used for each ocean. Form 1210 AB is filled out in conjunction with the ship code card, which contains code tables for the different elements to be observed. Each code table contains code figures to fit any condition of the elements at the time of observation.

Remember to enter the proper number of code figures in the box for each item. The symbol for latitude is $L_aL_aL_a$, not just L_a. This means that three figures should be entered for the latitude position. In each case the number of symbol letters representing each item indicates the number of code figures to be inserted.

Form 1210 AB suffices for average weather and pilot charts; for the preparation of large-scale daily weather maps for forecasting purposes the information on this form must be relayed immediately to the Weather Bureau. To this end, the items are transcribed from the universal and supplemental groups on form 1210 AB (Fig. 12-1) to the radio form 1204 (Fig. 12-3). The code is copied so that a group of five code numbers appears in each box of the radio form. Missing items are replaced by a slant (/). The first box in the radio form will thus contain code figures representing items Y, Q, $L_aL_aL_a$; the second box, figures for $L_oL_oL_o$, GG, etc. No punctuation or decimal marks appear on the radio form! *Clearly then, a particular weather item is indicated not only by a code number, but also by its position in the sequence.*

One line on form 1210 AB is filled in and recopied onto form 1204, which is shown on page 220, from the data given in the example appearing on page 214.

Description of data	Symbol letter	Code table		Observation as coded
Day of week.............	Y	1	Tuesday	3 ⎫
Octant of globe...........	Q	2	North latitude 0° to 90°W	0 ⎬ 1st
Latitude..................	L_a L_a L_a	.....	North 47°38′	4 ⎫ group 7 ⎬ 6 ⎭
Longitude................	L_o L_o L_o	.....	West 46°22′	4 ⎫ 6 ⎬ 2d 3 ⎭ group
Time of observation (GCT)	G G	.....	0000 GCT	0 ⎫ 0 ⎭
Total cloud amount........	N	3	7 eighths	7 ⎫
Wind direction (true) in 10's of degrees	d d	4	354°	3 ⎬ 3d 5 ⎭ group
Wind speed in knots........	f f	5	Moderate breeze	1 ⎫ 3 ⎭
Visibility................	V V	6	1 nautical mile	9 ⎫ 5 ⎬
Present weather...........	w w	7	Rain showers—moderate	8 ⎬ 4th 1 ⎭ group
Past weather..............	W	8	Cloudy	2 ⎭
Barometric reading........	P P P	9	1,007.1 mb. (29.74 in.)	0 ⎫ 7 ⎬ 1 ⎭ 5th
Temperature of air F.°......	T T	.....	42°F....................	4 ⎫ group 2 ⎭
Amount of low cloud, whose height is reported by h	N_h	3	5 eighths	5 ⎫
Type of low cloud.........	C_L	10	Stratocumulus	5 ⎬
Height of base of low cloud above sea	h	11	2,500 ft.	5 ⎬ 6th
Type of middle cloud.......	C_M	12	Altocumulus and altostratus at different levels.	7 ⎬ group
Type of high cloud........	C_H	13	Strands of cirrostratus, scattered, not increasing.	1 ⎭
Direction toward which ship is moving	D_s	14	Southwest	5 ⎫
Ship's speed.	v_s	15	13 knots	5 ⎬ 7th
Barometric tendency during last 3 hr.	a	16	Falling then rising	5 ⎭ group
Amount of barometric change during last 3 hr.	p p	17	1.2 mb.	1 ⎫ 2 ⎭
Identifying figure..........	8	.....		8 ⎫
Amount of significant cloud layer	N_s	3	5 eighths	5 ⎬
Significant cloud..........	C	17	Stratocumulus	6 ⎬ 8th group
Height of significant cloud layer	h_s h_s	18	2,500 ft.	2 ⎫ 5 ⎭

Description of data	Symbol letter	Code table		Observation as coded
Identifying figure	0	......		0 ⎫
Difference between air and sea temperature	{ T_s T_s	}	3°F. below	5 ⎪ 3 ⎬ 9th
Dew point temperature.....	{ T_d T_d	}	40°F.	4 ⎪ group 0 ⎭
Identifying figure..........	1	......		1 ⎫
Direction of waves........	{ d_w d_w	} 4	350°	3 ⎪ 5 ⎬ 10th
Period of waves...........	P_w	20	5 sec.	2 ⎪ group
Height of waves...........	H_w	21	3 ft. (1 m.)	2 ⎭
Identifying term..........	ICE	......		I C E
Description of kind of ice...	c_2	22	Drift ice	3 ⎫
Effect of ice on navigation..	K	23	Navigation unobstructed for steamers	1 ⎪
Bearing of ice limit........	D_i	24	Ice limit toward NW	7 ⎬ 11th
Distance to ice limit.......	r	25	1½ miles	1 ⎪ group
Orientation of ice limit......	e	26	Ice NE. to SW. with ice to the NW.	1 ⎭

NOTE: As a rule, the group $8N_sC_hsh_s$ will be omitted from ships' radio messages.

Although the observer can often make fairly accurate local weather interpretation and receive forecasts by radio, it is still more helpful if he too is aware of surrounding weather conditions. For this purpose the Weather Bureau rebroadcasts the coded information received from all the ships immediately after receipt. From this knowledge rough but significant weather maps can be plotted and interpreted by the meteorologically trained officer.

The stations broadcasting weather reports regularly, at present, are given in both U.S. Weather Bureau and International Meteorological Organizations volumes.

FIG. 12-1.

FIG. 12-2.

INTERNATIONAL CODE FOR RADIO WEATHER [JAN. 1, 1949]

Reports from Ships

DESCRIPTION OF CODE.—Codes given below have been assigned FM (Form of Message) numbers for identification purposes. These identification numbers are not to be included in coded messages prepared for transmission by radio. It will be noted that Codes FM 22 and FM 23 are abridged forms of Code FM 21. Each item of data is given a distinctive symbol. The symbols and group arrangements are as follows:

FM 21: $YQL_aL_aL_a$ $L_oL_oL_oGG$ Nddff VVwwW PPPTT $N_hC_Lhc_MC_H$ D_sv_sapp ($8N_sCh_sh_s$) ($0T_sT_sT_dT_d$) ($1d_wd_wP_wH_w$)—ICE followed by plain language or (c_2KD_ire)

FM 22: $YQL_aL_aL_a$ $L_oL_oL_oGG$ Nddff VVwwW PPPTT $N_hC_Lhc_MC_H$

FM 23: $YQL_aL_aL_a$ $L_oL_oL_oGG$ Nddff VVwwW

The groups enclosed in parentheses ( ) are drop-out groups which are omitted from the coded message when data therefore are not observed. The omission of any drop-out group(s) from the message will be apparent to the recipient of the message because the first figure of each of these groups is a distinct identifying figure, *e.g.*, "0," "1," etc. There is one exception; some ships using Code FM 21 do not have barographs; hence data for the group D_sv_sapp are omitted from the message. In case the group D_sv_sapp is omitted from the report in Code FM 21, 30 is added to the time of observation (GG). For example, in an 0600 GCT report when GG will be coded as 36, *i.e.*, 06 + 30.

In addition, the groups $8N_sCh_sh_s$ and $1d_wd_wP_wH_w$ may be repeated in the observation message when there is more than one significant cloud layer below 20,000 feet or more than one train of waves respectively to report. Repetition of groups in the message will be obvious since each of these groups contains the identifying figure "8" or "1," as the case may be.

Weather reports from ships at sea included in U.S. Weather Bureau bulletins broadcast for the benefit of merchant shipping will as a rule, contain only the first five groups of Code FM 21.

EXPLANATION OF SYMBOL LETTERS

a   Characteristic of barometric tendency during the period of 3 hours preceding the time of observation (Table 19).

C   Significant cloud (Table 18).

C_H Clouds of types cirrus, cirrostratus, cirrocumulus (Table 13).

C_L Clouds of types stratocumulus, stratus, cumulus, cumulonimbus (Table 10).

C_M Clouds of types altocumulus, altostratus, nimbostratus (Table 12).

c_2 Description of kind of ice (Table 22).

D_i Bearing of ice limit (Table 24).

D_s Ship's course—direction toward which ship is moving (Table 14).

dd   Direction (true) in 10's of degrees, FROM which wind is blowing. Scale 00–36. (See Table 4.)

d_wd_w Direction from which waves are coming (Table 4).

e   Orientation of ice limit from reporting ship (Table 26).

ff   Wind speed in knots (Table 5).

GG   Greenwich civil time of observation (00 = midnight, 06 = 6 a.m., 12 = noon, and 18 = 6 p.m., etc.).

H_w Mean maximum height of waves (Table 21).

h   Height above ground (or sea) of the lowest cloud (Table 11).

h_sh_s Height above station (or ship) of the significant cloud layer (Table 19).

K   Effect of ice on navigation (Table 23).

$L_aL_aL_a$ Latitude, in degrees and tenths, the tenths being obtained by dividing the number of minutes by 6 and neglecting the remainder.

$L_oL_oL_o$ Longitude, in degrees and tenths, the tenths being obtained as for latitude, $L_aL_aL_a$. The initial "1" is omitted if longitude of ship is 100 degrees or more.

N Total amount of sky covered with cloud, in eighths (Table 3).

N_h Amount of low cloud, in eighths, the height of which is reported by h (Table 3).

N_s Amount, in eighths, of the significant cloud layer (Table 3).

PPP Barometric pressure, in tens, units, and tenths of millibars (initial 9 or 10 omitted). The values refer to sea level and include all corrections for index errors, temperature, and gravity (Table 9).

P_w Period (in seconds) of waves (Table 20).

pp Amount of barometric change during the 3 hours preceding the time of observation expressed in units of one-tenth of a millibar. When the amount of change equals 9.9 millibars or more, an extra group "99ppp" is inserted in the message and the total amount of change coded "ppp." For example, if the amount of change is 9.9 millibars, "app 99ppp" is coded "799 99099"; 10.2 millibars is coded "799 99102." (See Table 17.)

Q Octant of the globe in which the ship is located (Table 2).

r Distance of ice from the ship (Table 25).

TT Temperature of the air, in whole degrees Fahrenheit.

T_dT_d Temperature of the dew point in whole degrees Fahrenheit.

T_sT_s Difference between air temperature and sea temperature in whole degrees Fahrenheit. If the air temperature is below the sea temperature, 50 is added to the value of the difference in coding the data. For example, if air temperature is 5°F. above sea temperature, T_sT_s is coded as 05; if air temperature is 11°F. below the sea temperature, T_sT_s is coded as 61; *i.e.*, 11 + 50.

VV Visibility or horizontal distance at which objects can be seen in daylight or at which lights can be seen at night (Table 6).

v_s Speed of ship in knots (Table 15).

W Past weather (Table 8).

ww Present weather at the time of observation (Table 7).

Y Day of the week (Table 1).

Conventional Group Arrangement of Coded Message

1ST GROUP: $YQL_aL_aL_a$:
Day of Week (Y)
Octant of globe (Q)
Latitude ($L_aL_aL_a$)

2ND GROUP: $L_oL_oL_oGG$:
Longitude ($L_oL_oL_o$)
Greenwich Civil Time (GG)

3RD GROUP: Nddff:
Total cloud amount (N)
Wind direction (dd)
Wind speed (ff)

4TH GROUP: VVwwW:
Visibility (VV)
Present weather (ww)
Past weather (W)

5TH GROUP: PPPTT:
Barometric pressure (PPP)
Temperature (TT)

CONVENTIONAL GROUP ARRANGEMENT OF CODED MESSAGE.—(*Continued*)

6TH GROUP: $N_hC_LhC_MC_H$
    Amount of low cloud (N_h)
    Type of (low) cloud (C_L)
    Height of (low) cloud (h)
    Type of (middle) cloud (C_M)
    Type of (high) Cloud (C_H)

7TH GROUP: $D_sv_s$app:
    Ship's course (D_s)
    Ship's speed (v_s)
    Barometer characteristic (a)
    Amount of change in the barometer (pp)

8TH GROUP: $8N_sCh_sh_s$:
    Identifying figure (8)
    Amount of significant cloud layer (N_s)
    Type of significant cloud (C)
    Height of significant cloud layer (h_sh_s)

9TH GROUP: $OT_sT_sT_dT_d$:
    Identifying figure (0)
    Difference between air and sea temperature (T_sT_s)
    Dew-point temperature (T_dT_d)

10TH GROUP: $1d_wd_wP_wH_w$
    Identifying figure (1)
    Direction from which waves are coming (d_wd_w)
    Period of waves (P_w)
    Height of waves (H_w)

11TH GROUP: c_2KD_ire:
    Identifying word (ICE)
    Description of kind of ice (c_2)
    Effect on navigation (K)
    Bearing of ice limit (D_i)
    Distance of ice limit from reporting ship (r)
    Orientation of ice limit (e)

WB Form 1904	U. S. DEPARTMENT OF COMMERCE, WEATHER BUREAU		No. _____

RUSH (Government Message)

| PREFIX | VESSEL OF ORIGIN | No. | OPERATOR | | CHECK | FILING | | FORWARDING | | COASTAL STATION |
			SENDING	RECEIVING		DATE	TIME	DATE	TIME	ROUTED VIA
RADIO					Govt.		M.		M.	

Observer,   SENT TO _____ (*Ship or station*)   (*Call letters*)

30476	46300	73513	95812	07142
55571	55512	05340	13522	ICE 31711

(SEE INSTRUCTIONS ON THE BACK OF THIS FORM)

FIG. 12-3.

TABLE XX. TABLES FOR DECODING RADIO WEATHER REPORTS FROM SHIPS AT SEA
IN INTERNATIONAL CODE*

CODE TABLE 1. SYMBOL Y—DAY OF THE WEEK

Day	Code Figures
Sunday	1
Monday	2
Tuesday	3
Wednesday	4
Thursday	5
Friday	6
Saturday	7

CODE TABLE 2. SYMBOL Q—OCTANT OF THE GLOBE

Longitude	Code Figures
North latitude:	
0°W.–90°W.	0
90°W.–180°W.	1
180°E.–90°E.	2
90°E.–0°E.	3
South latitude:	
0°W.–90°W.	5
90°W.–180°W.	6
180°E.–90°E.	7
90°E.–0°E.	8

* NOTE: Many of these codes are used in the same form for regular land station reports. The additional codes used in these reports are given in the next section.

CODE TABLE 3. SYMBOL N—TOTAL CLOUD AMOUNT

Symbol N_h—Amount of low cloud, the height of which is reported by h

Symbol N_s—Amount of significant cloud layer

Code figures	Cloud amount (eighths of sky covered)	Approximate cloud amount (tenths of sky covered)
0	None	None
1	1	1
2	2	2–3
3	3	4
4	4	5
5	5	6
6	6	7–8
7	7	9
8	8	10
9	Sky obscured	Sky obscured

NOTES

1. "Fragments of clouds" are coded as 1.

2. "Overcast but with openings" is coded as 7.

3. The full International specification for code figure 9, is "Sky obscured or cloud amount cannot be estimated owing to darkness."

CODE TABLE 4.

Symbol dd—True direction, in 10's of degrees, FROM which wind is blowing (00–36)

Symbol $d_w d_w$—Direction, in 10's of degrees, FROM which waves come

Code figures	Direction	Code figures	Direction
00	Calm	19	185° to 194°
01	5° to 14°	20	195° to 204°SSW.
02	15° to 24°NNE.	21	205° to 214°
03	25° to 34°	22	215° to 224°
04	35° to 44°	23	225° to 234°SW.
05	45° to 54°NE.	24	235° to 244°
06	55° to 64°	25	245° to 254°WSW.
07	65° to 74°ENE.	26	255° to 264°
08	75° to 84°	27	265° to 274°W.
09	85° to 94°E.	28	275° to 284°
10	95° to 104°	29	285° to 294°WNW.
11	105° to 114°ESE.	30	295° to 304°
12	115° to 124°	31	305° to 314°
13	125° to 134°	32	315° to 324°NW.
14	135° to 144°SE.	33	325° to 334°
15	145° to 154°	34	335° to 344°NNW.
16	155° to 164°SSE.	35	345° to 354°
17	165° to 174°	36	355° to 4°N.
18	175° to 184°S.		

Used only with $d_w d_w$

49	Waves confused, direction indeterminate	99	Waves confused, direction indeterminate, but higher than 14 ft. (4½ m.)

NOTE: In case a vessel is equipped with an anemometer and the true wind speed exceeds 99 knots, 50 will be added to "dd" and only the wind speed in excess of 100 knots will be coded. For example, if direction = 163° and speed = 121 knots, the wind will be coded as "6621" (dd = 16 + 50; ff = 121 − 100).

CODE TABLE 5.   SYMBOL ff—WIND SPEED IN KNOTS

Code figures	Beaufort number	Description	Equivalent speed, knots
00	Zero	Calm	0
02	One	Light airs	1–3
05	Two	Light breeze	4–6
09	Three	Gentle breeze	7–10
13	Four	Moderate breeze	11–16
18	Five	Fresh breeze	17–21
24	Six	Strong breeze	22–27
30	Seven	High wind (moderate gale)	28–33
37	Eight	Gale (fresh gale)	34–40

CODE TABLE 5.—(*Continued*)

Code figures	Beaufort number	Description	Equivalent speed, knots
44	Nine	Strong gale	41–47
52	Ten	Whole gale	48–55
60	Eleven	Storm	56–63
68	Twelve	Hurricane	64 and above

NOTE: In case a vessel is equipped with an anemometer and the true wind speed exceeds 99 knots, 50 will be added to "dd" and only the wind speed in excess of 100 knots will be coded. For example, if the direction = 163° and speed = 121 knots, the wind will be coded as "6621" (dd = 16 + 50; ff = 121 − 100).

CODE TABLE 6. SYMBOL VV—VISIBILITY

Code figures	Visibility range
90	Less than 50 yd. (50 m.)
91	50 yd. (50 m.)
92	200 yd. (200 m.)
93	¼ nautical mile (500 m.)
94	½ nautical mile (1,000 m.)
95	1 nautical mile (2,000 m.)
96	2 nautical miles (4,000 m.)
97	5 nautical miles (10 km.)
98	10 nautical miles (20 km.)
99	25 nautical miles or more (50 km.)

CODE TABLE 7. SYMBOL ww—PRESENT WEATHER

ww = 00–49: No precipitation at the station at the time of observation

00–19: No precipitation, fog, duststorm, sandstorm or drifting snow at the station (or ship) at the time of observation or during the preceding hour, except for 09

No hydrometeors except clouds

00 Cloud development not observed or not observable
01 Clouds generally dissolving or becoming less developed
02 State of sky on the whole unchanged
03 Clouds generally forming or developing

Characteristic change of the state of sky during the past hour

Haze, dust, sand, or smoke

04 Visibility reduced by smoke, *e.g.*, veldt or forest fires, industrial smoke or volcanic ashes
05 Dry haze
06 Widespread dust in suspension in the air, not raised by wind at or near the station (or ship) at the time of observation

CODE TABLE **7.**—(*Continued*)

07 Dust or sand raised by wind at or near the station (or ship) at the time of observation, but no well developed dust devil(s), and no duststorm or sandstorm seen

08 Well developed dust devil(s) seen at or near the station (or ship) within last hour, but no duststorm or sandstorm

09 Duststorm or sandstorm within sight of station (or ship) or at station (or ship) during the last hour

10 Light fog (visibility 1,000 m.; 1,100 yd. or more)

11 Patches of $\left.\begin{array}{l}\text{11 Patches of} \\ \text{12 More or less} \\ \text{continuous}\end{array}\right\}$ Shallow fog at the station (or ship) not deeper than about 2 meters (6½ ft.) on land or 10 meters (33 ft.) at sea

13 Lightning visible, no thunder heard

14 Precipitation within sight, but not reaching ground at the station (or ship)

15 Precipitation within sight, reaching ground, but distant [*i.e.*, estimated to be more than 5 km. (3 miles) from station (or ship)]

16 Precipitation within sight, reaching ground, near to but not at the station (or ship)

17 Thunder heard, but no precipitation at the station (or ship)

18 Squall(s)

19 Funnel cloud(s) (tornado or $\left.\right\}$ Within sight during the past hour waterspout)

20–29: Precipitation, fog, or thunderstorm at the station (or ship) during the preceding hour but *not* at the time of observation

20 Drizzle (not freezing)

21 Rain (not freezing)

22 Snow $\left.\right\}$ Not falling as showers

23 Rain and snow

24 Freezing drizzle or freezing rain

25 Shower(s) of rain

26 Shower(s) of snow, or of rain and snow

27 Shower(s) of hail or of hail and rain

28 Fog

29 Thunderstorm (with or without precipitation)

30–39: Duststorm, sandstorm, or drifting snow

30 Slight or moderate duststorm or sandstorm $\left.\right\}$ Has decreased during the preceding hour

31 Slight or moderate duststorm or sandstorm $\left.\right\}$ No appreciable change during the preceding hour

32 Slight or moderate duststorm or sandstorm $\left.\right\}$ Has increased during the preceding hour

33 Severe duststorm or sandstorm $\left.\right\}$ Has decreased during the preceding hour

34 Severe duststorm or sandstorm $\left.\right\}$ No appreciable change during the preceding hour

35 Severe duststorm or sandstorm $\left.\right\}$ Has increased during the preceding hour

36 Slight or moderate drifting snow $\left.\begin{array}{l}\text{ } \\ \text{ }\end{array}\right\}$ Generally low

37 Heavy drifting snow

CODE TABLE 7.—(Continued)

38 Slight or moderate drifting
     snow   } Generally low
39 Heavy drifting snow

40–49: Fog at time of observation
  40 Fog at a distance at the time of observation, but not at the station (or ship) during the last hour, the fog extending to a level above that of the observer
  41 Fog in patches
  42 Fog, sky discernible
  43 Fog, sky not discernible } Has become thinner during the preceding hour
  44 Fog, sky discernible
  45 Fog, sky not discernible } No appreciable change during the preceding hour
  46 Fog, sky discernible
  47 Fog, sky not discernible } Has begun or has become thicker during the preceding hour
  48 Fog, depositing rime, sky discernible
  49 Fog, depositing rime, sky not discernible

50–99: Precipitation at the station (or ship) at the time of observation

50–59: Drizzle at time of observation
  50 Drizzle, not freezing, intermittent
  51 Drizzle, not freezing, continuous } Slight at time of observation
  52 Drizzle, not freezing, intermittent
  53 Drizzle, not freezing, continuous } Moderate at time of observation
  54 Drizzle, not freezing, intermittent
  55 Drizzle, not freezing, continuous } Thick at time of observation
  56 Drizzle, freezing, slight
  57 Drizzle, freezing, moderate or thick
  58 Drizzle and rain, slight
  59 Drizzle and rain, moderate or heavy

60–69: Rain at time of observation
  60 Rain, not freezing, intermittent
  61 Rain, not freezing, continuous } Slight time of observation
  62 Rain, not freezing, intermittent
  63 Rain, not freezing, continuous } Moderate at time of observation
  64 Rain, not freezing, intermittent
  65 Rain, not freezing, continuous } Heavy at time of observation
  66 Rain, freezing, slight
  67 Rain, freezing, moderate or heavy
  68 Rain or drizzle and snow, slight
  69 Rain or drizzle and snow, moderate or heavy

70–79: Solid precipitation not in showers at time of observation
  70 Intermittent fall of snow flakes
  71 Continuous fall of snow flakes } Slight at time of observation
  72 Intermittent fall of snow flakes
  73 Continuous fall of snow flakes } Moderate at time of observation
  74 Intermittent fall of snow flakes
  75 Continuous fall of snow flakes } Heavy at time of observation
  76 Ice needles (with or without fog)
  77 Granular snow (with or without fog)
  78 Isolated starlike snow crystals (with or without fog)
  79 Ice pellets

CODE TABLE 7.—(*Continued*)

80–99: Showery precipitation, or precipitation with current or recent thunderstorm

80　Rain shower(s), slight
81　Rain shower(s), moderate or heavy
82　Rain shower(s), violent
83　Shower(s) of rain and snow mixed, slight
84　Shower(s) of rain and snow mixed, moderate or heavy
85　Snow shower(s), slight
86　Snow shower(s), moderate or heavy
87　Shower(s) of soft or small hail with or without rain or rain and snow mixed } Slight

88　Shower(s) of soft or small hail with or without rain or rain and snow mixed } Moderate or heavy

89　Shower(s) of hail with or without rain or rain and snow mixed, not associated with thunder } Slight

90　Shower(s) of hail, with or without rain or rain and snow mixed, not associated with thunder } Moderate or heavy

91　Slight rain at time of observation
92　Moderate or heavy rain at time of observation
93　Slight snow or rain and snow mixed or hail at time of observation
94　Moderate or heavy snow, or rain and snow mixed or hail at time of observation } Thunderstorm during the preceding hour but not at time of observation

95　Thunderstorm, slight or moderate, without hail but with rain and/or snow at time of observation
96　Thunderstorm, slight or moderate, with hail at time of observation
97　Thunderstorm, heavy, without hail but with rain and/or snow at time of observation
98　Thunderstorm combined with duststorm or sandstorm at time of observation
99　Thunderstorm, heavy, with hail at time of observation } Thunderstorm at time of observation

CODE TABLE 8.　SYMBOL W—PAST WEATHER

Code figures	Description	Code figures	Description
0	Clear or few clouds	5	Drizzle
1	Partly cloudy or variable sky	6	Rain
2	Cloudy or overcast	7	Snow or rain and snow mixed or sleet
3	Sandstorm or duststorm or drifting or blowing snow	8	Shower(s)
4	Fog, smoke or thick dust haze	9	Thunderstorm with or without precipitation

CODE TABLE 9. SYMBOLS PP—CORRECTED BAROMETER READING
Symbol PPP—Corrected barometer reading
Coded in "tens," "units," and "tenths" of millibars, initial 9 or 10 omitted. For
example, 982.1 millibars is coded as 821; 1,010.9 millibars as 109, etc.

Inches	Millibars	Inches	Millibars	Inches	Millibars	Inches	Millibars
27.50	931.3	27.94	946.2	28.38	961.1	28.82	976.0
27.51	931.6	27.95	946.5	28.39	961.4	28.83	976.3
27.52	931.9	27.96	946.8	28.40	961.7	28.84	976.6
27.53	932.3	27.97	947.2	28.41	962.1	28.85	977.0
27.54	932.6	27.98	947.5	28.42	962.4	28.86	977.3
27.55	933.0	27.99	947.9	28.43	962.8	28.87	977.7
27.56	933.3	28.00	948.2	28.44	963.1	28.88	978.0
27.57	933.6	28.01	948.5	28.45	963.4	28.89	978.3
27.58	934.0	28.02	948.9	28.46	963.8	28.90	978.7
27.59	934.3	28.03	949.2	28.47	964.1	28.91	979.0
27.60	934.6	28.04	949.5	28.48	964.4	28.92	979.3
27.61	935.0	28.05	949.9	28.49	964.8	28.93	979.7
27.62	935.3	28.06	950.2	28.50	965.1	28.94	980.0
27.63	935.7	28.07	950.6	28.51	965.5	28.95	980.4
27.64	936.0	28.08	950.9	28.52	965.8	28.96	980.7
27.65	936.3	28.09	951.2	28.53	966.1	28.97	981.0
27.66	936.7	28.10	951.6	28.54	966.5	28.98	981.4
27.67	937.0	28.11	951.9	28.55	966.8	28.99	981.7
27.68	937.4	28.12	952.3	28.56	967.2	29.00	982.1
27.69	937.7	28.13	952.6	28.57	967.5	29.01	982.4
27.70	938.0	28.14	952.9	28.58	967.8	29.02	982.7
27.71	938.4	28.15	953.3	28.59	968.2	29.03	983.1
27.72	938.7	28.16	953.6	28.60	968.5	29.04	983.4
27.73	939.0	28.17	953.9	28.61	968.8	29.05	983.7
27.74	939.4	28.18	954.3	28.62	969.2	29.06	984.1
27.75	939.7	28.19	954.6	28.63	969.5	29.07	984.4
27.76	940.1	28.20	955.0	28.64	969.9	29.08	984.8
27.77	940.4	28.21	955.3	28.65	970.2	29.09	985.1
27.78	940.7	28.22	955.6	28.66	970.5	29.10	985.4
27.79	941.1	28.23	956.0	28.67	970.9	29.11	985.8
27.80	941.4	28.24	956.3	28.68	971.2	29.12	986.1
27.81	941.8	28.25	956.7	28.69	971.6	29.13	986.5
27.82	942.1	28.26	957.0	28.70	971.9	29.14	986.8
27.83	942.4	28.27	957.3	28.71	972.2	29.15	987.1
27.84	942.8	28.28	957.7	28.72	972.6	29.16	987.5
27.85	943.1	28.29	958.0	28.73	972.9	29.17	987.8
27.86	943.4	28.30	958.3	28.74	973.2	29.18	988.2
27.87	943.8	28.31	958.7	28.75	973.6	29.19	988.5
27.88	944.1	28.32	959.0	28.76	973.9	29.20	988.8
27.89	944.5	28.33	959.4	28.77	974.3	29.21	989.2
27.90	944.8	28.34	959.7	28.78	974.6	29.22	989.5
27.91	945.1	28.35	960.0	28.79	974.9	29.23	989.8
27.92	945.5	28.36	960.4	28.80	975.3	29.24	990.2
27.93	945.8	28.37	960.7	28.81	975.6	29.25	990.5

CODE TABLE 9.—(*Continued*)

Inches	Millibars	Inches	Millibars	Inches	Millibars	Inches	Millibars
29.26	990.9	29.70	1,005.8	30.14	1,020.7	30.58	1,035.6
29.27	991.2	29.71	1,006.1	30.15	1,021.0	30.59	1,035.9
29.28	991.5	29.72	1,006.4	30.16	1,021.3	30.60	1,036.2
29.29	991.9	29.73	1,006.8	30.17	1,021.7	30.61	1,036.6
29.30	992.2	29.74	1,007.1	30.18	1,022.0	30.62	1,036.9
29.31	992.6	29.75	1,007.5	30.19	1,022.4	30.63	1,037.3
29.32	992.9	29.76	1,007.8	30.20	1,022.7	30.64	1,037.6
29.33	993.2	29.77	1,008.1	30.21	1,023.0	30.65	1,037.9
29.34	993.6	29.78	1,008.5	30.22	1,023.4	30.66	1,038.3
29.35	993.9	29.79	1,008.8	30.23	1,023.7	30.67	1,038.6
29.36	994.2	29.80	1,009.1	30.24	1,024.0	30.68	1,038.9
29.37	994.6	29.81	1,009.5	30.25	1,024.4	30.69	1,039.3
29.38	994.9	29.82	1,009.8	30.26	1,024.7	30.70	1,039.6
29.39	995.3	29.83	1,010.2	30.27	1,025.1	30.71	1,040.0
29.40	995.6	29.84	1,010.5	30.28	1,025.4	30.72	1,040.3
29.41	995.9	29.85	1,010.8	30.29	1,025.7	30.73	1,040.6
29.42	996.3	29.86	1,011.2	30.30	1,026.1	30.74	1,041.0
29.43	996.6	29.87	1,011.5	30.31	1,026.4	30.75	1,041.3
29.44	997.0	29.88	1,011.9	30.32	1,026.8	30.76	1,041.7
29.45	997.3	29.89	1,012.2	30.33	1,027.1	30.77	1,042.0
29.46	997.6	29.90	1,012.5	30.34	1,027.4	30.78	1,042.3
29.47	998.0	29.91	1,012.9	30.35	1,027.8	30.79	1,042.7
29.48	998.3	29.92	1,013.2	30.36	1,028.1	30.80	1,043.0
29.49	998.6	29.93	1,013.5	30.37	1,028.4	30.81	1,043.3
29.50	999.0	29.94	1,013.9	30.38	1,028.8	30.82	1,043.7
29.51	999.3	29.95	1,014.2	30.39	1,029.1	30.83	1,044.0
29.52	999.7	29.96	1,014.6	30.40	1,029.5	30.84	1,044.4
29.53	1,000.0	29.97	1,014.9	30.41	1,029.8	30.85	1,044.7
29.54	1,000.3	29.98	1,015.2	30.42	1,030.1	30.86	1,045.0
29.55	1,000.7	29.99	1,015.6	30.43	1,030.5	30.87	1,045.4
29.56	1,001.0	30.00	1,015.9	30.44	1,030.8	30.88	1,045.7
29.57	1,001.4	30.01	1,016.3	30.45	1,031.2	30.89	1,046.1
29.58	1,001.7	30.02	1,016.6	30.46	1,031.5	30.90	1,046.4
29.59	1,002.0	30.03	1,016.9	30.47	1,031.8	30.91	1,046.7
29.60	1,002.4	30.04	1,017.3	30.48	1,032.2	30.92	1,047.1
29.61	1,002.7	30.05	1,017.6	30.49	1,032.5	30.93	1,047.4
29.62	1,003.1	30.06	1,018.0	30.50	1,032.9	30.94	1,047.8
29.63	1,003.4	30.07	1,018.3	30.51	1,033.2	30.95	1,048.1
29.64	1,003.7	30.08	1,018.6	30.52	1,033.5	30.96	1,048.4
29.65	1,004.1	30.09	1,019.0	30.53	1,033.9	30.97	1,048.8
29.66	1,004.4	30.10	1,019.3	30.54	1,034.2	30.98	1,049.1
29.67	1,004.7	30.11	1,019.6	30.55	1,034.5	30.99	1,049.5
29.68	1,005.1	30.12	1,020.0	30.56	1,034.9		
29.69	1,005.4	30.13	1,020.3	30.57	1,035.2		

NOTE: 1 inch = 33.86395 millibars; 1 millibar = 0.02952993 inch; 1 millimeter = 0.039370 inch; 1 inch = 25.4005 millimeters; 1 millibar = 0.7500616 millimeter; 1 millimeter = 1.33322387 millibars.

Code Table 10. Symbol C_L—Clouds of Types Stratocumulus, Stratus, Cumulus, and Cumulonimbus

Code figure	Technical language specifications	Plain language specifications
0	No clouds C_L	No stratocumulus, stratus, cumulus, or cumulonimbus clouds
1	Cumulus humilis	Cumulus with little vertical development and seemingly flattened
2	Cumulus congestus, with or without cumulus humilis, or stratocumulus at the same level of base	Cumulus of considerable development, generally towering, with or without other cumulus or stratocumulus; bases all at the same level
3	Cumulonimbus calvus, with or without cumulus, stratocumulus, or stratus	Cumulonimbus with tops lacking clear-cut outlines but distinctly not cirriform or anvil-shaped; with or without cumulus, stratocumulus, or stratus
4	Stratocumulus cumulogenitus or vesperalis	Stratocumulus formed by the spreading out of cumulus; cumulus also often present. (Note: Since the spreading out of the scattered parcels of air that have been warmed by the surface may take place, as in stratocumulus vesperalis as soon as the condensation level is reached, observers should be warned that, though cumulus may normally have been seen earlier, the formation of a particular piece of stratocumulus vesperalis may not come from a cumulus)
5	Stratocumulus other than cumulogenitus and vesperalis	Stratocumulus not formed by the spreading out of cumulus
6	Stratus and/or fractostratus, but not fractostratus of bad weather	Stratus or fractostratus or both, but not fractostratus of bad weather
7	Fractostratus and/or fractocumulus of bad weather ("scud"), usually under altostratus and nimbostratus	Fractostratus and/or fractocumulus of bad weather ("scud"), usually under altostratus and nimbostratus. By "bad weather" is meant the conditions usually prevailing before, during, or after precipitation)
8	Cumulus humilis or congestus and stratocumulus other than cumulogenitus and vesperalis with bases at different levels	Cumulus and stratocumulus other than those formed by the spreading out of cumulus, with bases at different levels
9	Cumulonimbus capillatus (often with anvil) with or without cumulus, stratocumulus, stratus, or "scud"	Cumulonimbus having a clearly fibrous (cirriform) top, often anvil-shaped, with or without cumulus, stratocumulus, stratus, or "scud"

Note: When the sky is obscured by rain, snow, fog, duststorm, smoke, or other phenomena and clouds of C_L type cannot be observed, a slant (/) will be reported for C_L.

CODE TABLE 11.   SYMBOL h—HEIGHT OF BASE OF LOW CLOUD ABOVE SEA

Code figures	Feet	Meters
0	0–150	0–50
1	150–300	50–100
2	300–600	100–200
3	600–1,000	200–300
4	1,000–2,000	300–600
5	2,000–3,000	600–1,000
6	3,000–5,000	1,000–1,500
7	5,000–6,500	1,500–2,000
8	6,500–8,000	2,000–2,500
9	No low cloud below 8,000	No low cloud below 2,500

NOTES

1. If the height of the base of cloud is exactly equal to a height given in the table, the higher code figure is used.   For example, a height of 6000 feet is coded as 3.

2. With fog such that sky cannot be seen "h" is coded as 0 and N_h as 9.

CODE TABLE 12.   SYMBOL C_M—CLOUDS OF TYPES ALTOCUMULUS, ALTOSTRATUS, AND NIMBOSTRATUS

Code figure	Technical language specifications	Plain language specifications
0	No clouds C_M	No altocumulus, altostratus, or nimbostratus clouds
1	Altostratus translucidus	Thin altostratus (semitransparent everywhere) through which the sun or moon would be seen dimly as through ground glass
2	Altostratus opacus, or nimbostratus	Thick altostratus, or nimbostratus (through portions of the sheet the position of the sun or moon may be indicated by a light patch)
3	Altocumulus translucidus more or less stable and at a single level	Thin (semitransparent) altocumulus; cloud elements not changing much; at a single level
4	Altocumulus translucidus in patches (often lenticular) continually transforming and/or occurring at different levels	Thin (semitransparent) altocumulus in patches (often almond- or fish-shaped); cloud elements continually changing and/or occurring at more than one level
5	Altocumulus translucidus in bands or in a layer systematically invading the sky and usually thickening as a whole, even partly into altocumulus opacus or duplicatus	Thin (semitransparent) altocumulus in bands or in a layer gradually spreading over the sky and usually thickening as a whole; it may become partly opaque or double-layered
6	Altocumulus cumulogenitus	Altocumulus formed by the spreading out of cumulus

CODE TABLE 12.—(*Continued*)

Code figure	Technical language specifications	Plain language specifications
7	Altocumulus duplicatus or opacus, not increasing; or altostratus and altocumulus	Any of the following cases: (*a*) double-layered altocumulus, usually opaque in parts, not increasing; (*b*) a thick (opaque) layer of altocumulus, not increasing; (*c*) altostratus and altocumulus both present at the same or different levels
8	Altocumulus cumuliformis (floccus or castellatus)	Altocumulus in the form of cumulus-shaped tufts or altocumulus with turrets
9	Altocumulus of a chaotic sky; generally at different levels; cirrus densus in patches usually present	Altocumulus of a chaotic sky; generally at different levels; dense cirrus in patches is usually also present

NOTE: When the sky is obscured by rain, snow, fog, duststorm, smoke, or other phenomena and clouds of C$_M$ type cannot be observed, a slant (/) is reported for C$_M$.

CODE TABLE 13. SYMBOL C$_H$—CLOUDS OF TYPES CIRRUS, CIRROSTRATUS, AND CIRROCUMULUS

Code figures	Technical language specifications	Plain language specifications
0	No clouds C$_H$	No cirrus, cirrocumulus, or cirrostratus clouds
1	Cirrus filosus, scattered and not increasing	Filaments or strands of cirrus, scattered and not increasing (often "mares' tails")
2	Cirrus densus in patches or twisted sheaves usually not increasing, sometimes presumably being the remains of the upper part of cumulonimbus	Dense cirrus in patches or twisted sheaves usually not increasing; possibly but not certainly the remains of the upper part of cumulonimbus
3	Cirrus nothus: either the remains of cumulonimbus or part of a distant cumulonimbus the rest of which is not visible	Cirrus, often anvil-shaped; either the remains of the upper portions of cumulonimbus or part of a distant cumulonimbus the rest of which is not visible. (If there is doubt as to the cumulonimbus origin or association, code C$_H$2 should be used)
4	Cirrus (often cirrus uncinus) systematically invading the sky and usually thickening as a whole	Cirrus (often hook-shaped) gradually spreading over the sky and usually thickening as a whole
5	Cirrus, often in polar bands, and/or cirrostratus systematically invading the sky and usually thickening as a whole, but the continuous layer not reaching 45° altitude	Cirrus and cirrostratus, often in bands converging toward the horizon; or cirrostratus alone; in either case gradually spreading over the sky and usually thickening as a whole, but the continuous layer not reaching 45° altitude

CODE TABLE 13.—(*Continued*)

Code figures	Technical language specifications	Plain language specifications
6	Cirrus, often in polar bands, and/or cirrostratus systematically invading the sky and usually thickening as a whole, and the continuous layer exceeding 45° altitude	Cirrus and cirrostratus, often in bands converging toward the horizon; or cirrostratus alone; in either case gradually spreading over the sky and usually thickening as a whole, and the continuous layer exceeding 45° altitude.
7	Cirrostratus covering the whole sky	Cirrostratus covering the whole sky
8	Cirrostratus not increasing and not covering the whole sky	Cirrostratus not increasing and not covering the whole sky; cirrus and cirrocumulus may be present
9	Cirrocumulus the dominant cirroform cloud	Cirrocumulus alone or cirrocumulus with some cirrus or cirrostratus, but the cirrocumulus being the main cirriform cloud present. (Cirrocumulus may be present in C_H1 to C_H8)

NOTE: When the sky is obscured by rain, snow, fog, duststorm, smoke, or other phenomena and clouds of type C_H cannot be observed, a slant (/) will be reported for C_H.

CODE TABLE 14. SYMBOL D_s—SHIP'S COURSE, DIRECTION TOWARD WHICH SHIP IS MOVING

Code figures	True direction	Code figures	True direction
0	Ship hove to	5	SW.
1	NE.	6	W.
2	E.	7	NW.
3	SE.	8	N.
4	S.	9	No information

CODE TABLE 15. SYMBOL v_s—SHIP'S SPEED

Code figures	Speed, knots	Code figures	Speed, knots
0	Ship stopped	5	13–15
1	1–3	6	16–18
2	4–6	7	19–21
3	7–9	8	22–24
4	10–12	9	More than 24

CODE TABLE 16. SYMBOL a—CHARACTERISTIC OF CHANGES OF BAROMETER IN THE LAST 3 HR.

Code figures	Description	
0	Rising, then falling	
1	Rising, then steady; or rising, then rising more slowly	Barometer now
2	Unsteady	higher than or the
3	Steady or rising	same as 3 hr.
4	Falling or steady, then rising; or rising, then rising more quickly	ago
5	Falling, then rising	
6	Falling, then steady; or falling, then falling more slowly	Barometer now
7	Unsteady	lower than 3 hr.
8	Falling	ago
9	Steady or rising, then falling; or falling, then falling more quickly	

CODE TABLE 17. SYMBOLS pp—AMOUNT OF BAROMETRIC CHANGE IN THE LAST 3 HOURS

Coded in units of $\frac{1}{10}$ of a millibar. For example, $\frac{1}{10}$ millibar is coded as 01; 1.2 millibars as 12

Amount of rise or fall		Amount of rise or fall		Amount of rise or fall		Amount of rise or fall	
Millibars	Inch	Millibars	Inch	Millibars	Inch	Millibars	Inch
0.2	0.01	3.8	0.11	7.4	0.22	11.0	0.33
0.4	0.01	4.0	0.12	7.6	0.23	11.2	0.34
0.6	0.02	4.2	0.13	7.8	0.23	11.4	0.34
0.8	0.02	4.4	0.13	8.0	0.24	11.6	0.35
1.0	0.03	4.6	0.14	8.2	0.25	11.8	0.35
1.2	0.04	4.8	0.14	8.4	0.25	12.0	0.36
1.4	0.04	5.0	0.15	8.6	0.26	12.2	0.37
1.6	0.05	5.2	0.16	8.8	0.26	12.4	0.37
1.8	0.05	5.4	0.16	9.0	0.27	12.6	0.38
2.0	0.06	5.6	0.17	9.2	0.28	12.8	0.38
2.2	0.07	5.8	0.17	9.4	0.28	13.0	0.39
2.4	0.07	6.0	0.18	9.6	0.29	13.2	0.40
2.6	0.08	6.2	0.19	9.8	0.29	13.4	0.40
2.8	0.08	6.4	0.19	10.0	0.30	13.6	0.41
3.0	0.09	6.6	0.20	10.2	0.31	13.8	0.41
3.2	0.10	6.8	0.20	10.4	0.31	14.0	0.42
3.4	0.10	7.0	0.21	10.6	0.32	14.2	0.43
3.6	0.11	7.2	0.22	10.8	0.32	14.4	0.43

CODE TABLE 17.—(*Continued*)

Amount of rise or fall		Amount of rise or fall		Amount of rise or fall		Amount of rise or fall	
Miilibars	Inch	Millibars	Inch	Millibars	Inch	Millibars	Inch
14.6	0.44	16.2	0.49	17.8	0.53	19.4	0.58
14.8	0.44	16.4	0.49	18.0	0.54	19.6	0.59
15.0	0.45	16.6	0.50	18.2	0.55	19.8	0.59
15.2	0.46	16.8	0.50	18.4	0.55		
15.4	0.46	17.0	0.51	18.6	0.56		
15.6	0.47	17.2	0.52	18.8	0.56		
15.8	0.47	17.4	0.52	19.0	0.57		
16.0	0.48	17.6	0.53	19.2	0.58		

CODE TABLE 18. SYMBOL C—FORM OF SIGNIFICANT CLOUD

Code figures	Form of cloud	Abbreviation
1	Cirrus	Ci.
2	Cirrostratus	Cs.
3	Cirrocumulus	Cc.
4	Altocumulus	Ac.
5	Altostratus	As.
6	Stratocumulus	Sc.
7	Nimbostratus	Ns.
8	Cumulus or fractocumulus	Cu. or Fc.
9	Cumulonimbus	Cb.
0	Stratus or fractostratus	St. or Fs.

CODE TABLE 19. SYMBOL $h_s h_s$—HEIGHT ABOVE STATION (OR SHIP) OF SIGNIFICANT CLOUD LAYER

Code figures	Feet	Meters	Code figures	Feet	Meters
00	100 minus	30 minus	79	7,900	2,370
01	100	30	80	8,000	2,400
02	200	60	81	9,000	2,700
03	300	90	82	Not used	Not used
04	400	120	83	10,000	3,000
05	500	150	84	13,000	4,000
06	600	180	85	16,000	5,006
07	700	210	86	20,000	6,000
08	800	240	87	23,000	7,000
09	900	270	88	26,000	8,000
10	1,000	300	89	30,000 or higher	9,000 or higher
Etc.	Etc.	Etc.	90	0–150	0–50

CODE TABLE 19.—(*Continued*)

Code figures	Feet	Meters	Code figures	Feet	Meters
91	150–300	50–100	96	3,000–5,000	1,000–1,500
92	300–600	100–200	97	5,000–6,500	1,500–2,000
93	600–1,000	200–300	98	6,500–8,000	2,000–2,500
94	1,000–2,000	300–600	99	8,000 or more, or no clouds	2,500 or more, or on clouds
95	2,000–3,000	600–1,000			

NOTES

1. For each code figure 01 to 80, inclusive, in the above table, the height increases 100 feet (30 meters); *i.e.*, figure 21 = 2,100 feet (630 meters); 63 = 6,300 feet (1,890 meters).

2. Code figures 90–99: If the base of cloud is exactly equal to a height given in the table, the higher code figure is used. For example, a height of 600 feet is coded as 93.

CODE TABLE 20. SYMBOL P_w—PERIOD OF WAVES

Code figures	Period, sec.
2	5 less
3	5–7
4	7–9
5	9–11
6	11–13
7	13–15
8	15–17
9	17–19
0	19–21
1	Over 21
x	Calm, or period unable to be determined

NOTE: If the exact number of seconds for the period of the waves corresponds to 2 code figures the lower code figure is reported.

CODE TABLE 21. SYMBOL H_w—MEAN MAXIMUM HEIGHT OF WAVES

Code figures	Height
0	Less than 1 ft. (1/4 m.)
1	1 1/2 ft. (1/2 m.)
2	3 ft. (1 m.)
3	5 ft. (1 1/2 m.)
4	6 1/2 ft. (2 m.)
5	8 ft. (2 1/2 m.)
6	9 1/2 ft. (3 m.)
7	11 ft. (3 1/2 m.)
8	13 ft. (4 m.)
9	14 ft. (4 1/2 m.)
x	Height impossible to determine
	(When 50 is added to $d_w d_w$, the height of waves is coded as follows):

CODE TABLE 21.—(*Continued*)

Code figures	Height
0	16 ft. (5 m.)
1	17½ ft. (5½ m.)
2	19 ft. (6 m.)
3	21 ft. (6½ m.)
4	22½ ft. (7 m.)
5	25 ft. (7½ m.)
6	25½ ft. (8 m.)
7	27 ft. (8½ m.)
8	29 ft. (9 m.)
9	30½ ft. (9½ m.)
x	Height impossible to determine

NOTES

1. Each code figure except "zero" covers a range of ¾ meter; *e.g.*, code figure 1 = ¼ meter to ¾ meter, code figure 2 = ¾ meter to 1¼ meters.

2. If the wave height is exactly between the heights corresponding to 2 code figures, the lower code figure is reported.

3. For wave heights greater than 31 feet (9¾ meters), the code figure for 30½ feet (9½ meters) is reported followed by the word "WAVES" and the actual height of the waves in feet or meters; *e.g.*, "WAVES 37."

CODE TABLE 22.   SYMBOL c_2—DESCRIPTION OF KIND OF ICE

Code figures	Description
0	No ice: ("O" will be used to report "ice blink," and then a direction must be reported)
1	Slush or young ice
2	Fast ice
3	Drift ice
4	Packed (compact) slush or strips of hummock ice
5	Open lead near shore
6	Heavy fast ice
7	Heavy drift ice
8	Hummocked ice
9	Ice jamming

CODE TABLE 23.   SYMBOL K—EFFECT OF THE ICE ON NAVIGATION

Code figures	Description
0	Navigation unobstructed
1	Navigation unobstructed for steamers; difficult for sailing ships
2	Navigation difficult for low-powered steamers; closed to sailing ships
3	Navigation possible only for powerful steamers
4	Navigation possible only for steamers constructed to withstand ice pressure
5	Navigation possible with the assistance of icebreakers

CODE TABLE 23.—(*Continued*)

Code figures	Description
6	Channel open in the solid ice
7	Navigation temporarily closed
8	Navigation closed
9	Navigation conditions unknown (*e.g.*, owing to bad weather)

CODE TABLE 24. SYMBOL D_i—BEARING OF ICE LIMIT

Code figures	Description
0	No ice limit can be stated
1	Ice limit towards NE.
2	Ice limit towards E.
3	Ice limit towards SE.
4	Ice limit towards S.
5	Ice limit towards SW.
6	Ice limit towards W.
7	Ice limit towards NW.
8	Ice limit towards N.
9	Ice limit in several directions

NOTE: If more than 1 ice limit can be stated, the nearest or most important is reported.

CODE TABLE 25. SYMBOL r—DISTANCE TO ICE LIMIT FROM REPORTING SHIP

Code figures	Distance
0	Up to 1 mile
1	1 to 2 miles
2	2 to 4 miles
3	4 to 6 miles
4	6 to 8 miles
5	8 to 12 miles
6	12 to 16 miles
7	16 to 20 miles
8	More than 20 miles
9	Unspecified or no observations

NOTE: If the exact bounding distance for the ice limit corresponds to 2 code figures, the lower code figure is reported.

CODE TABLE 26. SYMBOL e—ORIENTATION OF ICE LIMIT

Code figures	Orientation of ice limit
0	Orientation of ice limit impossible to estimate—ship *outside* the ice
1	Ice edge lying in a direction NE. to SW. with ice situated to the NW.
2	Ice edge lying in a direction E. to W. with ice situated to the northward
3	Ice edge lying in a direction SE. to NW. with ice situated to the NE.
4	Ice edge lying in a direction S. to N. with ice situated to the eastward
5	Ice edge lying in a direction SW. to NE. with ice situated to the SE.
6	Ice edge lying in a direction W. to E. with ice situated to the southward
7	Ice edge lying in a direction NW. to SE. with ice situated to the SW.
8	Ice edge lying in a direction N. to S. with ice situated to the westward
9	Orientation of ice limit impossible to estimate—ship *inside* the ice

Reports from Land Stations

In order to obtain weather data from a sufficiently large area, it may sometimes be necessary to decode a number of land-station reports. The U.S. Weather Bureau, in January, 1949, adopted a new weather code consisting of 13 groups, the first six of which conform to the standard International Code and are known as "Universal Groups"; the second seven are the "Supplementary Groups," part or all of which may be reported.

At present, regular observations are taken four times daily at land stations throughout the United States, Canada, Alaska, the West Indies, and islands of the Pacific, at 0030 GCT, 0630 GCT, 1230 GCT, and 1830 GCT (GCT is Greenwich Civil Time, being 5 hours later than Eastern Standard Time, EST).

The 13 code groups of the Weather Bureau have the following forms:

iii$T_d T_d$ Nddff   VVwwW   PPPTT $N_h C_L h C_M C_H$ $6D_c$app
7RRR$_t$s $8N_s Ch_s h_s$ $9S_p S_{ps} S_p$ $1d_w d_w P_w H_w$ $2h_{85} h_{85} h_{85} a_3$
$3R_{24} R_{24} R_{24} R_{24}$ $4T_x T_x T_n T_n$ (Additional Plain Language Data)

Bulletins containing complete code tables both for marine and land-station reports, and further instruction in their use, are furnished by the U.S. Weather Bureau on request.

DEFINITIONS AND MEANINGS OF LETTER SYMBOLS

iii   Index number which identifies the station
$T_d T_d$ Temperature of the dew point to the nearest whole degree Fahrenheit
N   Total amount of cloud
dd   True direction, in tens of degrees, FROM which the wind is blowing (00–36)

DEFINITIONS.—(*Continued*)

ff   Wind speed in knots

VV   Visibility

ww   Present weather

W   Past weather

PPP   Atmospheric pressure reduced to mean sea level, in tens, units, and tenths of millibars [the hundreds figure(s) are omitted]

TT   Temperature of the air to the nearest whole degree Fahrenheit

N_h Amount of cloud whose height is reported for h

C_1 Clouds of genera (types) Sc., St., Cu., Cb.

h   Height above ground of the base of the cloud

C_m Clouds of genera Ac., As., Ns.

C_h Clouds of genera Ci., Cs., Cc.

6   Indicator for the sixth group

D_c True direction from which clouds are moving, reported to eight points of the compass

a   Characteristic of the barograph trace during the past 3 hours

pp   Amount of barometric tendency (net change) during the 3-hour period ending at the actual time of observation, reported in units and tenths of millibars

7   Indicator figure for seventh group

RR   Amount of precipitaton for the 6-hour period preceding the actual time of observation, in hundredths of an inch

R_t Time precipitation began or ended

s   Total depth of snow on ground at actual time of observation, reported to nearest whole inch

8   Indicator figure for the eighth group

N_s Amount of significant cloud layer

C   Type of significant cloud

$h_s h_s$ Height above station of the layer of significant cloud to which N_s refers

9   Indicator figure for the ninth (special phenomena) group

$S_p S_p$ Special phenomena, general description

$s_p s_p$ Special phenomena, detailed description

1   Indicator figure for the tenth (wave) group

$d_w d_w$ True direction, in tens of degrees, from which the waves come

P_w Period of the waves

H_w Mean maximum height of the waves

2   Indicator figure for the eleventh (850-millibar pressure) group

$h_{85} h_{85} h_{85}$ Height in "tens" of geopotential feet above mean sea level of the 850-millibar pressure surface; in thousands, hundreds, and tens of g feet

a_3 Characteristic of barograph trace during the 3-hour period ending 3 hours prior to the actual time of observation

3   Indicator figure for the twelfth (24-hour precipitation) group

$R_{24} R_{24} R_{24} R_{24}$ Total amount of precipitation for the 24-hour period ending at the time of observation

4   Indicator figure for the thirteenth (maximum and minimum temperature) group

$T_x T_x$ Maximum temperature

$T_n T_n$ Minimum temperature

EXAMPLE OF CODED REPORT

A 0030 GCT observation. [Note that groups eight, ten, and twelve are omitted.]

20169	82971	24216	48973	873//	67499
	73570	90184	24393	47858	

Code figure	Symbol	Data
201	iii	Key West, Fla.
69	T_dT_d	69°F.
8	N	8 oktas (10 tenths)
29	dd	290°
71	ff	71 knots
24	VV	3 miles
21	ww	Rain in last hour but not at time of observation
6	W	Rain
489	PPP	948.9 mb.
73	TT	73°F.
8	N_h	8 oktas (10 tenths)
7	C_L	Fractostratus and/or fractocumulus of bad weather
3	h	656 to 983 ft.
/	C_M	Not observable
/	C_H	Not observable
6	6	
7	D_C	Northwest
4	a	Falling, then rising
99	pp	+20.2 mbs. (see next group)
7	7	
35	RR	0.35 in. (see below), total amount 2.35 in.
7	R_t	Began 6 to 12 hr. ago
0	s	None
9	9	
01	S_PS_P	Velocity of max. wind 84 knots
84	s_ps_p	
2	2	
439	$h_{85}h_{85}h_{85}$	4386 g ft.
3	a_3	Rising or steady
4	4	
78	T_xT_x	78°F.
58	T_nT_n	58°F.

TABLE XXI. ADDITIONAL CODE TABLES IN USE WITH COMPLETE LAND-STATION REPORTS (AUGUST, 1950)*

(The code table numbers given under Table XXI are simply for convenience in reference here and do not correspond to the actual table numbers given by the U.S. Weather Bureau. Codes not found here are included under Table XX.)

* The complete "Synoptic Code (1949 Edition)" with full instructions, and later supplements are available from the U.S. Weather Bureau.

Code Table 1. Symbol TT—Temperature of Air
Symbol T_dT_d—Dew-point Temperature
Symbol T_nT_n—Minimum Temperature
Symbol T_xT_x—Maximum Temperature

All temperatures are coded in whole degrees Fahrenheit, to the nearest whole degree. For temperatures below 0°F. subtract observed value from 100 and code resulting number. *Examples:* −15° is coded 85; −1° is coded 99. For temperatures above 100°F. subtract 100 from observed value and code resulting number. *Examples:* 107° is coded 07; 114° is coded 14. Special Note: When temperatures are given in degrees *centigrade,* "below zero temperatures" are indicated by adding 50 to the observed value.

Code Table 2. Symbol N—Total Amount of Cloud
Symbol N_h—Amount of Cloud Whose Height Is Reported by h
Symbol N_s—Amount of the Significant Cloud Layer

Code figure	Amount of sky covered (in tenths)	Code figure	Amount of sky covered (in tenths)
0	No clouds	5	6
1	1 − and 1	6	7 and 8
2	2 and 3	7	9 and 9+
3	4	8	10
4	5	9	Sky obscured

Code Table 3. Symbol h—Height above Ground of the Base of the Cloud

Code figure	Height in feet	Approximate height in meters
0	0– 149	0– 49
1	150– 299	50– 99
2	300– 599	100– 199
3	600– 999	200– 299
4	1000–1999	300– 599
5	2000–3499	600– 999
6	3500–4999	1000–1499
7	5000–6499	1500–1999
8	6500–7999	2000–2500
9	No clouds, or clouds at 8,000 or higher	No clouds, or clouds at 2,500 or higher

Note: The heights (in feet) given in this code table approximately correspond to those given in International Code 43 and to those given in the ninth decade (*i.e.,* code figures 90–99) of International Code 40.

CODE TABLE 4.   SYMBOL VV—HORIZONTAL VISIBILITY

Code figure	Visibility in statute miles and fractions	Code figure	Visibility in statute miles and fractions
00	Less than ⅛	40	5
01	⅛ and ³⁄₁₆	48	6
02	¼	56	7
03	⅜	64	8
04	½	72	9
05	⅝	80	10, 11, and 12
06	¾	81	13, 14, 15, and 20
08	1	82	25, 30, and 35
10	1¼	83	40 and 45
12	1½	84	50, 55, and 60
14	1¾	85	65 to 90 inclusive
16	2	86	95 to 120 inclusive
18	2¼	87	125 to 185 inclusive
20	2½	88	190 to 310 inclusive
24	3	89	315 or more
32	4		

CODE TABLE 5.   SYMBOL D_c—DIRECTION FROM WHICH CLOUDS ARE MOVING

Code figure	True direction	Code figure	True direction
0	No clouds, or calm	5	Southwest
1	Northeast	6	West
2	East	7	Northwest
3	Southeast	8	North
4	South	9	Unknown,* or variable

* It is important that a *correct* direction of clouds be sent whenever possible.

CODE TABLE 6.   SYMBOL a—BAROMETRIC TENDENCY
(Characteristic of tendency during 3-hour period ending at time of observation)*
SYMBOL a₃—BAROMETRIC TENDENCY
(Characteristic of tendency during 3-hour period ending 3 hours before obser-·
vation.)*

Code figure	Description	
0	Rising, then falling	
1	Rising, then steady, or rising; then rising more slowly	Barometer now higher than, or the same as, 3 hr. ago
2	Rising unsteadily, or unsteady	
3	Rising steadily, or steady	
4	Falling or steady, then rising; or rising, then rising more quickly	

CODE TABLE 6.—(*Continued*)

Code figure	Description	
5	Falling, then rising	
6	Falling, then steady; or falling, then falling more slowly	
7	Falling unsteadily, or unsteady	Barometer now lower
8	Falling steadily	than 3 hr. ago
9	Steady or rising, then falling; or falling, then falling more quickly	

*In this case "time of observation" means "time observation was actually taken" and NOT "reference time of observation."

CODE TABLE 7. SYMBOL pp

Conversion of barometric pressure differences from inches of mercury to millibars

Code figure	Inches of mercury	Millibars	Code figure	Inches of mercury	Millibars
00	0.000	0.0			
02	0.005	0.2	52	0.155	5.2
03	0.010	0.3	54	0.160	5.4
05	0.015	0.5	56	0.165	5.6
07	0.020	0.7	58	0.170	5.8
08	0.025	0.8	59	0.175	5.9
10	0.030	1.0	61	0.180	6.1
12	0.035	1.2	63	0.185	6.3
14	0.040	1.4	64	0.190	6.4
15	0.045	1.5	66	0.195	6.6
17	0.050	1.7	68	0.200	6.8
19	0.055	1.9	69	0.205	6.9
20	0.060	2.0	71	0.210	7.1
22	0.065	2.2	73	0.215	7.3
24	0.070	2.4	75	0.220	7.5
25	0.075	2.5	76	0.225	7.6
27	0.080	2.7	78	0.230	7.8
29	0.085	2.9	80	0.235	8.0
30	0.090	3.0	81	0.240	8.1
32	0.095	3.2	83	0.245	8.3
34	0.100	3.4	85	0.250	8.5
36	0.105	3.6	86	0.255	8.6
37	0.110	3.7	88	0.260	8.8
39	0.115	3.9	90	0.265	9.0
41	0.120	4.1	91	0.270	9.1
42	0.125	4.2	93	0.275	9.3
44	0.130	4.4	95	0.280	9.5
46	0.135	4.6	97	0.285	9.7
47	0.140	4.7	98	0.290	9.8
49	0.145	4.9		0.295	10.0
51	0.150	5.1		0.300	10.2

NOTES

1. The 3-hour period used in computing the tendency is the full 3 hours preceding the actual time of observation.

2. When the amount of the barometric tendency equals or exceeds 9.9 millibars, the group "99ppp" will be inserted in the message following the "6Dcapp" group.

CODE TABLE 8.   SYMBOL s_s—DEPTH OF SNOW
(On ground at time of observation)

Code figure	Depth of snow on ground, in.	Code figure	Depth of snow on ground, in.
0	None	5	5
1	1	6	6
2	2	7	7
3	3	8	8 or more
4	4	9	0.5 in. or less*

* Trace of snow or ice (amount present is too small to measure).

CODE TABLE 9.   SYMBOL R_t—TIME PRECIPITATION BEGAN OR ENDED

Code figure	Time began or ended	Code figure	Time began or ended
0	No precipitation	6	5–6 hr. ago
1	Less than 1 hr. ago	7	6–12 hr. ago
2	1–2 hr. ago	8	More than 12 hr. ago
3	2–3 hr. ago	9	Unknown
4	3–4 hr. ago		
5	4–5 hr. ago		

CODE TABLE 10.   SYMBOL RR—AMOUNT OF PRECIPITATION
(In 6-hr. period preceding observation)

Code figure	Amount, in.	Code figure	Amount, in.	Code figure	Amount, in.
00	None	07	0.07	97	0.97
01	0.01	08	0.08	98	0.98
02	0.02	09	0.09	99	Trace*
03	0.03	10	0.01	00	1.00†
04	0.04	11	0.11	01	1.01†
05	0.05	Etc.	Etc.	02	1.02†
06	0.06	96	0.96		

* A "trace" of precipitation is an amount generally considered too small to measure; actually it is less than 0.005 in.

† When the amount of precipitation is 1.00 inch or more, the number of whole inches is reported as a plain language word inserted immediately following the "7RRR$_t$s" group, and the hundredths of an inch are reported for "RR." For example: If the amount of precipitation is 2.67 inches, the groups are coded "767R$_t$s TWO; if 3.00 inches, "700R$_t$s THREE"; if 1.99 inches, "799R$_t$s ONE"; etc.

CODE TABLE 11. SYMBOL h_sh_s—HEIGHT ABOVE STATION OF THE LAYER OF
SIGNIFICANT CLOUD REPORTED BY N_s

Code figure	Height, ft.	Code figure	Height, ft.
00	Lower than 100	78	7800
01	100	79	7900
02	200	80	8000
03	300	81	9000
04	400	(82)	Not specified
05	500	83	10,000; 11,000; 12,000
06	600	84	13,000; 14,000; 15,000
07	700	85	16,000; 17,000; 18,000;
08	800		and 19,000
09	900	86	20,000; 21,000; 22,000
10	1000	87	23,000; 24,000; 25,000
11	1100	88	26,000; 27,000; 28,000;
Etc.	Etc.		and 29,000
		89	30,000 or higher

NOTE: The increment of increase for code figures 02 to 80, inclusive, is 100 feet. The values reported for code figures 02 to 80, inclusive, can be obtained by multiplying the code figure by 100; *e.g.*, code figure 78 multiplied by 100 equals 7800 feet.

CODE TABLE 12. SYMBOL S_pS_p—SPECIAL PHENOMENA—GENERAL DESCRIPTION*

00–39: Direction of maximum wind and special wind data

02 Maximum wind from the north northeast (ff)
04 Maximum wind from the northeast (ff)
06 Maximum wind from the east northeast (ff)
08 Maximum wind from the east (ff)
10 Maximum wind from the east southeast (ff)
12 Maximum wind from the southeast (ff)
14 Maximum wind from the south southeast (ff)
16 Maximum wind from the south (ff)
18 Maximum wind from the south southwest (ff)
20 Maximum wind from the southwest (ff)
22 Maximum wind from the west southwest (ff)
24 Maximum wind from the west (ff)
26 Maximum wind from the west northwest (ff)
28 Maximum wind from the northwest (ff)
30 Maximum wind from the north northwest (ff)
32 Maximum wind from the north (ff)
33 Direction of maximum wind unknown (D_mD_m)
34 Velocity of maximum wind unknown (ff)
35 Wind direction in past hour, or wind direction one hour ago (zz or D_mD_m)
36 Wind velocity in past hour (zz)
37 Time of highest wind (tt)
38 Pronounced shift in wind direction (tt, zz)
39 Wind velocity at time of observation (ff)

* NOTE: Detailed code used is shown in parentheses.

CODE TABLE 12.—(*Continued*)

40–49: Fog, smoke, haze, dust, sand, and blowing snow

40 Fog (D_sD_s, zz)
41 Fog began (tt, zz)
42 Fog ended (tt, zz)
43 Fog bank in distance (D_sD_s, zz)
44 Smoke (D_sD_s, zz)
45 Haze (D_sD_s, zz)
46 Blowing dust or sand (D_sD_s, zz)
47 Storm of blowing dust or sand (tt, zz)
48 Storm of drifting or blowing snow (tt, zz)

50–59: Clouds, ceiling, and cloud height

50 Direction of C_L *and* C_H clouds (each to 8 points in D_C code) (D_L and D_H)
51 Clouds, or direction of clouds, *from station* (zz or D_sD_s)
52 Direction of C_L clouds (to 16 points), or C_L clouds (D_mD_m or zz)
53 Direction of C_M clouds (to 16 points), or C_M clouds (D_mD_m or zz)
54 Direction of C_H clouds (to 16 points), or C_H clouds (D_mD_m or zz)
55 Ceiling (zz)
56 Height of lowest clouds above ground (in hundreds of feet) (nn)
57 Height of highest clouds above ground (in thousands of feet) (nn)
58 Height of "ceiling," if under 950 ft. (in tens of feet) (nn)
59 Tops of overcast (reported by pilot) in thousands of feet (nn)

60–69: Precipitation

60 Precipitation (D_sD_s, zz)
61 Precipitation began (tt, zz)
62 Precipitation ended (tt, zz)
63 Rain, or rain began (zz or tt)
64 Snow, or snow began (zz or tt)
65 Freezing rain, or freezing rain began (zz or tt)
66 Sleet, or sleet began (zz or tt)
67 Wet snow, or wet snow began (zz or tt)
68 Hail, or hail began (zz or tt)
69 Rain and snow mixed, or rain and snow mixed began (zz or tt)

70–79: Visibility, temperature, and pressure

70 Visibility (zz)
71 Reduced visibility (D_sD_s, zz)
72 Visibility in whole miles (nn)
73 Visibility in tens of feet (nn)
74 Vertical visibility (zz)
75 Water temperature in °F. (nn)
76 Record temperature (when "record" temperature occurs) in °F. (nn)
77 Surface "station pressure" in tenths and hundredths of an inch (nn)
78 Lowest sea level pressure in last 6 hr. (in tens and units of millibar) (nn)
79 Barometer, or time of lowest pressure (zz or tt)

80–89: Miscellaneous

80 Supplementary "present weather" at time of observation ("ww" code)
81 Frost (tt, zz)
82 Glaze (tt, zz)
83 State of sea, or period of sea or swell (S_sS_s, or K_pK_p)

CODE TABLE 12.—(*Continued*)

85   Depth of snow on ground (in inches) (nn)
86   Front passed station, or front (tt, zz)
87   Cold front passed station, or cold front (tt, zz)
88   Warm front passed station, or warm front (tt, zz)
89.   Direction and orientation of cloud shield (D_c and D_o)
90–99. Thunderstorms
90   Thunderstorm (D_sD_s, zz)
91   Thunder first heard at station (with precipitation at station) (tt, zz)
92   Thunder last heard at station (with precipitation at station) (tt, zz)
93   Thunder first heard (but without precipitation at station) (tt, zz)
94   Thunder last heard (but without precipitation at station) (tt, zz)
95   Direction of movement of thunderstorm (D_mD_m)
96   Distant lightning (D_sD_s, zz)
97   Distant thunderstorm (D_sD_s, zz)
98   Approaching thunderstorm (D_sD_s, zz)
99   Tornado (tt, zz)

CODE TABLE 13. SYMBOL s_Ps_P—SPECIAL PHENOMENA—DETAILED DESCRIPTION

This table has several "*parts*," each designated by the addition of a letter to the number. The table part actually used in a message depends upon the code figure used for "general" S_PS_P. In some cases code figures used for general S_PS_P may be used with "detailed" s_Ps_P figures from more than one table. No confusion can result in these cases, however, since the code table values which can be used for detailed s_Ps_P have only one meaning. The individual parts of Code Table 13 are as follows:

13*a*   Velocity (in miles per hour)..ff
13*b*   Numerical (in units of specific value)..................................nn
13*c*   Time (in time preceding observation)...................................tt
13*d*   Direction of Movement...D_mD_m
13*e*   Direction from Station...D_sD_s
13*f*   Variation...zz
13*g*   State of Sea...S_SS_S
13*h*   Period of Sea Swell...K_pK_p
13*i*   Direction of Swell and Cloud Movement..................D_L, D_H, and D_{CS}
13*j*   Orientation of Cloud Shield Table.......................................D_o

CODE TABLE 13*a*. VELOCITY
(Symbol ff = velocity in knots. 00 to 99)

Code figure	Velocity	Code figure	Velocity
00	Calm; or unknown	95	95
01	101*	96	96
02	102*	97	97
03	103*	98	98
04	104*	99	99†
Etc.	Etc.	Etc.	Etc.

* When wind velocity is more than 100 m.p.h. send *two* Special Phenomena groups. The second and third figures in both groups should be coded the same: the last two figures *in the first Special Phenomena group* should be coded 99 and in the *second Phenomena group* two figures should be coded to indicate the velocity in *excess* of 100 m.p.h.

† Or 100 m.p.h.

CODE TABLE 13*b*. NUMERICAL
(Symbol nn = units of specific value. 00 to 99)

Code figure	Value (depending on "General" Code figure used)
00	0, or less than 1 unit
01	1; 10; 100; or 1,000
02	2; 20; 200; or 2,000
Etc.	Etc.
12	12; 120; 1,200; or 12,000
13	13; 130; 1,300; or 13,000
Etc.	Etc.
98	98; 980; 9,800; or 98,000
99	99 or more; 990 or more; 9,900 or more; 99,000 or more

CODE TABLE 13*c*. TIME
(Symbol tt = units and tenths of hours *before* observation. 00 to 75)

Code figure	Hours and minutes *before* observation*	Code figure	Hours and minutes *before* observation*
00	At observation	25	2 hr. 30 min.
01	0 hr. 6 min.	26	2 hr. 36 min.
02	0 hr. 12 min.	27	2 hr. 42 min.
03	0 hr. 18 min.	28	2 hr. 48 min.
04	0 hr. 24 min.	29	2 hr. 54 min.
05	0 hr. 30 min.	30	3 hr. 0 min.
06	0 hr. 36 min.	31	3 hr. 6 min.
07	0 hr. 42 min.	Etc.	Etc.
08	0 hr. 48 min.	51	5 hr. 6 min.
09	0 hr. 54 min.	52	5 hr. 12 min.
		53	5 hr. 18 min.
10	1 hr. 0 min.	54	5 hr. 24 min.
11	1 hr. 6 min.	55	5 hr. 30 min.
12	1 hr. 12 min.		
13	1 hr. 18 min.	56	5 hr. 36 min.
14	1 hr. 24 min.	57	5 hr. 42 min.
		58	5 hr. 48 min.
15	1 hr. 30 min.	59	5 hr. 54 min.
16	1 hr. 36 min.	60	6 hr. 0 min.
17	1 hr. 42 min.		
18	1 hr. 48 min.	61	6–7 hr.
19	1 hr. 54 min.	62	7–8 hr.
		63	8–9 hr.
20	2 hr. 0 min.	64	9–10 hr.
21	2 hr. 6 min.	65	10–11 hr.
22	2 hr. 12 min.		
23	2 hr. 18 min.	66	11–12 hr.
24	2 hr. 24 min.	67	12–18 hr.

CODE TABLE 13c.—(*Continued*)

Code figure	Hours and minutes *before* observation*	Code figure	Hours and minutes *before* observation*
68	More than 18 hr.	72	Began and ended during observation †
69	Time unknown	73	Changed during observation† considerably
		74	Began after observation †
70	Began during observation †	75	Ended after observation †
71	Ended during observation †		

* "Before observation" means before the reference time of observation and is not necessarily the time before the observation was actually taken. The reference times of observation in the United States on August 1, 1942 (insofar as it affects this code table) were considered to be 0730 EST; 1330 EST; 1930 EST; and 0130 EST.

† Code figures 70 to 75, however, do not refer to reference time of observation; "during observation" and "after observation" here are understood to mean during or after *the precise time observation was actually being taken.*

CODE TABLES 13d, 13e. DIRECTION

(Symbol D_mD_m = direction of *movement.** 00 to 39. Symbol D_sD_s = direction *from station.*† 00 to 39)

Code figure	Direction	Code figure	Direction	Code figure	Direction
00	Calm†	18	SSW.	33	Variable
02	NNE.	20	SW.	34	Unknown
04	NE.	22	WSW.	35	In several directions
06	ENE.	24	W.	36	In several directions, but not at station
08	E.	26	WNW.	37	Over near-by water area
10	ESE.	28	NW.	38	Over near-by valleys
12	SE.	30	NNW.	39	Over near-by hills or mountains
14	SSE.	32	N.		
16	S.				

* Direction of movement is direction *from which* item is moving.
† For symbol D_sD_s code figure 00 means "at station."

CODE TABLE 13f. VARIATION

(Symbol zz = variation in phenomena. 70 to 99)

Code figure	Description
70	Began while observation was being taken
71	Began while observation was being taken
72	Began and ended while observation was being taken
73	Changed considerably while observation was being taken
74	Began *after* observation was taken
75	Ended *after* observation was taken
76	At station
77	At station, but not in distance
78	In all directions
79	In all directions, but not at station
80	Approaching station

CODE TABLE 13f.—(*Continued*)

Code figure	Description
81	Receding from station
82	Passing station in distance
83	Seen in distance
84	Reported in neighborhood, but not at station
85	Aloft, but not near ground
86	Near ground, but not aloft
87	Occasional; occasionally
88	Intermittent; intermittently
89	Frequent; frequently; at frequent intervals
90	Steady; steady in intensity; steadily; no appreciable change
91	Increasing; increasing in intensity; has increased
92	Decreasing in intensity; has decreased
93	Fluctuating; variable
94	Continuous; continuously
95	Very light; very weak; greatly below normal; very thin; very poor
96	Light; weak; below normal; thin; poor
97	Moderate; normal; average thickness; fair
98	Heavy; severe; thick; above normal; good
99	Very heavy; killing; very severe; dense; greatly above normal; very thick; very good

CODE TABLE 13g.   STATE OF SEA
(Symbol S_sS_s = state of sea.   00 to 09)

Code figure	Description of sea	Code figure	Description of sea
00	Calm, glassy	05	Rough
01	Calm, rippled	06	Very rough
02	Smooth	07	High
03	Slight	08	Very high
04	Moderate	09	Phenomenal*

* As might exist near the center of a hurricane.

CODE TABLE 13h.   PERIOD OF SEA SWELL
(Symbol K_pK_p = type of sea swell.   0 to 9)

Code figure	Period, sec.
11*	1
12	2
13	3
14	4
etc.	etc.

* The code figure gives the actual number of seconds plus ten.

CODE TABLE 13*i*. DIRECTION OF SWELL AND DIRECTION OF CLOUD MOVEMENT
Symbol D_L = direction of low clouds. 0 to 9. Symbol D_H = direction of high clouds. 0 to 9. Symbol D_{cs} = direction of cloud shield from station. 0 to 9.

Code figure	Direction	Code figure	Direction
0	No clouds (D_L, D_H) or calm	5	Southwest
1	Northeast	6	West
2	East	7	Northwest
3	Southeast	8	North
4	South	9	Unknown or variable

CODE TABLE 13*j*. ORIENTATION OF CLOUD SHIELD
(Symbol D_o = orientation of cloud shield)

Code figure	Orientation
0	No observation
1	NNE.–SSW., or reverse
2	NE.–SW., or reverse
3	ENE.–WSW., or reverse
4	E.–W., or reverse
5	ESE.–WNW., or reverse
6	SE.–NW., or reverse
7	SSE.–NNW., or reverse
8	S.–N., or reverse
9	Uncertain

The Station Model

The station model is a device used on the weather map to indicate as efficiently and completely as possible the observations made at a particular station. Figure 12-4 shows the model employed by the U.S. Weather Bureau and gives a description of each item, the International Code symbols representing them, and examples of an actual observation. Rarely does a particular station actually show all the observations indicated on this model, yet even in abbreviated form, a wealth of weather data is nevertheless shown.

As weather observations are received, whether by radio, teletype, or telephone, they are entered around the appropriate stations after being decoded. From this the weather map is analyzed and the forecasts developed. More attention will be given this topic later.

It is noticed on the station model, that some of the actual observations are entered in symbol rather than in numerical form. The items usually treated in this fashion are (1) present weather, ww, (2) forms of low, middle, and high clouds, respectively, C$_L$, C$_M$, C$_H$, (3) past weather, w, (4) total amount of clouds, N, and (5) barometric tendency or characteristic. Following the example of the station model, the code symbols utilized in the model for these items are reproduced, together with their international code number.

The pressure in millibars is always indicated on the model in the upper right corner. For convenience, the first 9 or 10 is omitted. Thus, 1014.3 millibars is indicated as 143; 998.6 millibars is indicated as 986. This is in accordance with the standard code form used in land station reports.

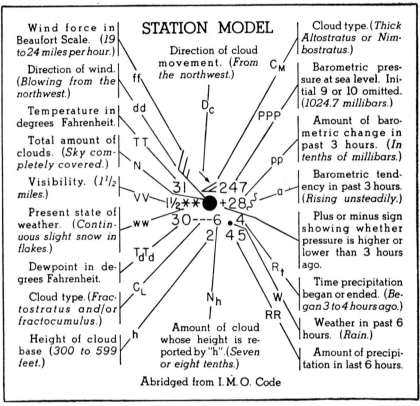

Fig. 12-4.—Station model.

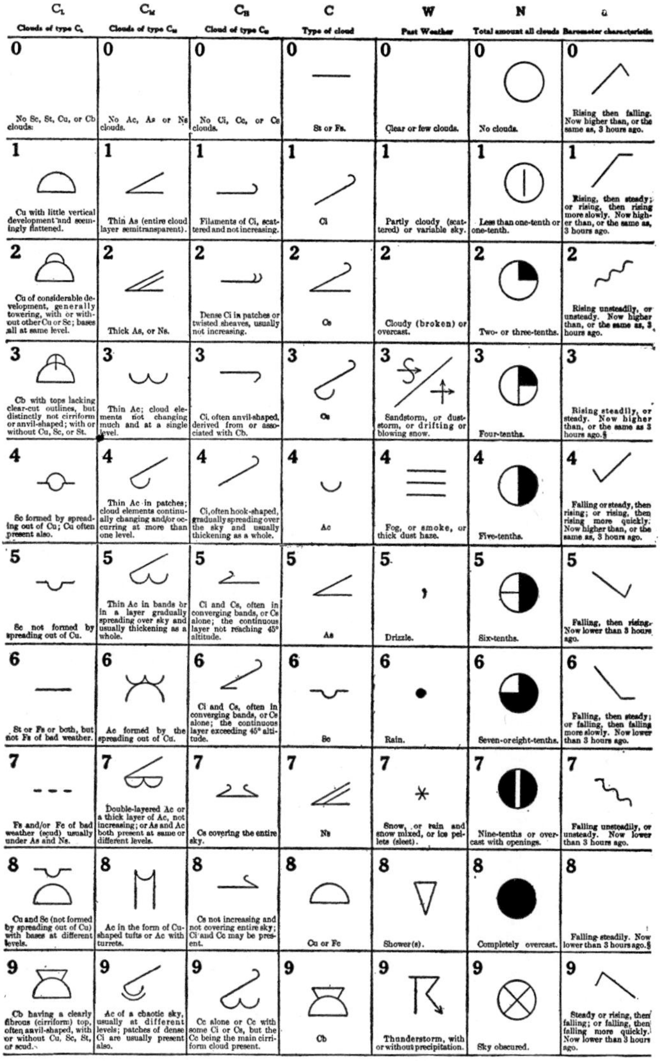

C_L	C_M	C_H	C	W	N	a
Clouds of type C_L	Clouds of type C_M	Cloud of type C_H	Type of cloud	Past Weather	Total amount all clouds	Barometer characteristic
0 No Sc, St, Cu, or Cb clouds.	**0** No Ac, As or Ns clouds.	**0** No Ci, Cc, or Cs clouds.	**0** St or Fs.	**0** Clear or few clouds.	**0** No clouds.	**0** Rising then falling. Now higher than, or the same as, 3 hours ago.
1 Cu with little vertical development and seemingly flattened.	**1** Thin As (entire cloud layer semitransparent).	**1** Filaments of Ci, scattered and not increasing.	**1** Ci	**1** Partly cloudy (scattered) or variable sky.	**1** Less than one-tenth or one-tenth.	**1** Rising, then steady; or rising, then rising more slowly. Now higher than, or the same as, 3 hours ago.
2 Cu of considerable development, generally towering, with or without other Cu or Sc; bases all at same level.	**2** Thick As, or Ns.	**2** Dense Ci in patches or twisted sheaves, usually not increasing.	**2** Cs	**2** Cloudy (broken) or overcast.	**2** Two- or three-tenths.	**2** Rising unsteadily, or unsteady. Now higher than, or the same as, 3 hours ago.
3 Cb with tops lacking distinctly clear-cut outlines, but not cirriform or anvil-shaped; with or without Cu, Sc, or St.	**3** Thin Ac; cloud elements not changing much and at a single level.	**3** Ci, often anvil-shaped, derived from or associated with Cb.	**3** Cc	**3** Sandstorm, or duststorm, or drifting or blowing snow.	**3** Four-tenths.	**3** Rising steadily, or steady. Now higher than, or the same as 3 hours ago.§
4 Sc formed by spreading out of Cu; Cu often present also.	**4** Thin Ac in patches; cloud elements continually changing and/or occurring at more than one level.	**4** Ci, often hook-shaped, gradually spreading over the sky and usually thickening as a whole.	**4** Ac	**4** Fog, or smoke, or thick dust haze.	**4** Five-tenths.	**4** Falling or steady, then rising; or rising, then rising more quickly. Now higher than, or the same as, 3 hours ago.
5 Sc not formed by spreading out of Cu.	**5** Thin Ac in bands or in a layer gradually spreading over sky and usually thickening as a whole.	**5** Ci and Cs, often in converging bands, or Cs alone; the continuous layer not reaching 45° altitude.	**5** As	**5** Drizzle.	**5** Six-tenths.	**5** Falling, then rising. Now lower than 3 hours ago.
6 St or Fs or both, but not Fs of bad weather.	**6** Ac formed by the spreading out of Cu.	**6** Ci and Cs, often in converging bands, or Cs alone; the continuous layer exceeding 45° altitude.	**6** Sc	**6** Rain.	**6** Seven-or eight-tenths.	**6** Falling, then steady; or falling, then falling more slowly. Now lower than 3 hours ago.
7 Fs and/or Fc of bad weather (scud) usually under As and Ns.	**7** Double-layered Ac or a thick layer of Ac, not increasing; or As and Ac both present at same or different levels.	**7** Cs covering the entire sky.	**7** Ns	**7** Snow, or rain and snow mixed, or ice pellets (sleet).	**7** Nine-tenths or overcast with openings.	**7** Falling unsteadily, or unsteady. Now lower than 3 hours ago.
8 Cu and Sc (not formed by spreading out of Cu) with bases at different levels.	**8** Ac in the form of Cu-shaped tufts or Ac with turrets.	**8** Cs not increasing and not covering entire sky; Ci and Cc may be present.	**8** Cu or Fc	**8** Shower(s).	**8** Completely overcast.	**8** Falling steadily. Now lower than 3 hours ago.§
9 Cb having a clearly fibrous (cirriform) top, often anvil-shaped, with or without Cu, Sc, St, or scud.	**9** Ac of a chaotic sky, usually at different levels; Ci are usually present also.	**9** Cs alone or Cc with some Ci or Cs, but the Cs being the main cirriform cloud present.	**9** Cb	**9** Thunderstorm, with or without precipitation.	**9** Sky obscured.	**9** Steady or rising, then falling; or falling, then falling more quickly. Now lower than 3 hours ago.

NOTE: 1 inch = 33.86395 millibars; 1 millibar = 0.02952993 inch; 1 millimeter = 0.039370 inch; 1 inch = 25.4005 millimeters; 1 millibar = 0.7500616 millimeter; 1 millimeter = 1.33322387 millibars.

FIG. 12-5a.—Explanation of symbols used on station model.

253

WW

Present weather

00	Cloud development NOT observed or NOT observable during past hour.§
01	Clouds generally dissolving or becoming less developed during past hour.§
02	State of sky on the whole unchanged during past hour.§
03	Clouds generally forming or developing during past hour.§
04	Visibility reduced by smoke.
05	Dry haze.
06	Widespread dust in suspension in the air, NOT raised by wind, at time of observation.
07	Dust or sand raised by wind, at time of ob.
08	Well developed dust devil(s) within past hr.
09	Dustorm or sandstorm within sight of or at station during past hour.
10	Light fog.
11	Patches of shallow fog at station, NOT deeper than 6 feet on land.
12	More or less continuous shallow fog at station, NOT deeper than 6 feet on land.
13	Lightning visible, no thunder heard.
14	Precipitation within sight, but NOT reaching the ground at station.
15	Precipitation within sight, reaching the ground, but distant from station.
16	Precipitation within sight, reaching the ground, near to but NOT at station.
17	Thunder heard, but no precipitation at the station.
18	Squall(s) within sight during past hour.
19	Funnel cloud(s) in sight during past hour.
20	Drizzle (NOT freezing and NOT falling as showers) during past hour, but NOT at time of ob.
21	Rain (NOT freezing and NOT falling as showers) during past hr., but NOT at time of ob.
22	Snow (NOT falling as showers) during past hour, but NOT at time of ob.
23	Rain and snow (NOT falling as showers) during past hour, but NOT at time of ob.
24	Freezing drizzle or freezing rain (NOT falling as showers) during past hour, but NOT at time of observation.
25	Showers of rain during past hour, but NOT at time of observation.
26	Showers of snow, or of rain and snow, during past hour, but NOT at time of observation.
27	Showers of hail, or of hail and rain, during past hour, but NOT at time of observation.
28	Fog during past hour, but NOT at time of ob.
29	Thunderstorm (with or without precipitation) during past hour, but NOT at time of ob.
30	Slight or moderate duststorm or sandstorm during past hour.
31	Slight or moderate duststorm or sandstorm, no appreciable change during past hour.
32	Slight or moderate duststorm or sandstorm, has increased during past hour.
33	Severe duststorm or sandstorm, has decreased during past hr.
34	Severe duststorm or sandstorm, no appreciable change during past hour.
35	Severe duststorm or sandstorm, has increased during past hour.
36	Slight or moderate drifting snow, generally low.
37	Heavy drifting snow, generally low.
38	Slight or moderate drifting snow, generally high.
39	Heavy drifting snow, generally high.
40	Fog at distance at time of ob., but NOT at station during past hour.
41	Fog in patches.
42	Fog, sky discernible, has become thinner during past hour.
43	Fog, sky NOT discernible, has become thinner during past hour.
44	Fog, sky discernible, no appreciable change during past hour.
45	Fog, sky NOT discernible, no appreciable change during past hour.
46	Fog, sky discernible, has begun or become thicker during past hr.
47	Fog, sky NOT discernible, has begun or become thicker during past hour.
48	Fog, depositing rime, sky discernible.
49	Fog, depositing rime, sky NOT discernible.

§ The symbol is not plotted for "ww" when "00" is reported. When "01, 02, or 03" is reported, the symbol is plotted on the station circle. Symbols are not plotted for "a," when "3 or 8" is reported.

FIG. 12-5b.—Explanation of symbols used on station model.—(Continued)

50	Intermittent drizzle (NOT freezing) slight at time of observation.
51	Continuous drizzle (NOT freezing) slight at time of observation.
52	Intermittent drizzle (NOT freezing) moderate at time of ob.
53	Continuous drizzle (NOT freezing), moderate at time of ob.
54	Intermittent drizzle (NOT freezing), thick at time of observation.
55	Continuous drizzle (NOT freezing), thick at time of observation.
56	Slight freezing drizzle.
57	Moderate or thick freezing drizzle.
58	Drizzle and rain, slight.
59	Drizzle and rain, moderate or heavy.
60	Intermittent rain (NOT freezing), slight at time of observation.
61	Continuous rain (NOT freezing), slight at time of observation.
62	Intermittent rain (NOT freezing), moderate at time of observation.
63	Continuous rain (NOT freezing), moderate at time of observation.
64	Intermittent rain (NOT freezing), heavy at time of observation.
65	Continuous rain (NOT freezing), heavy at time of observation.
66	Slight freezing rain.
67	Moderate or heavy freezing rain.
68	Rain or drizzle and snow, slight.
69	Rain or drizzle and snow, mod'te or heavy.
70	Intermittent fall of snow flakes, slight at time of observation.
71	Continuous fall of snowflakes, slight at time of observation.
72	Intermittent fall of snow flakes, moderate at time of observation.
73	Continuous fall of snowflakes, moderate at time of observation.
74	Intermittent fall of snow flakes, heavy at time of observation.
75	Continuous fall of snowflakes, heavy at time of observation.
76	Ice needles (with or without fog).
77	Granular snow (with or without fog).
78	Isolated starlike snow crystals (with or without fog).
79	Ice pellets (sleet, U. S. definition).
80	Slight rain shower(s).
81	Moderate or heavy rain shower(s).
82	Violent rain shower(s).
83	Slight shower(s) of rain and snow mixed.
84	Moderate or heavy shower(s) of rain and snow mixed.
85	Slight snow shower(s).
86	Moderate or heavy snow shower(s).
87	Slight shower(s) of soft or small hail with or without rain or rain and snow mixed.
88	Moderate or heavy shower(s) of soft or small hail with or without rain or rain and snow mixed.
89	Slight shower(s) of hail†, with or without rain or rain and snow mixed, not associated with thunder.
90	Moderate or heavy shower(s) of hail†, with or without rain or, rain and snow mixed, not associated with thunder.
91	Slight rain at time of ob.; thunderstorm during past hour, but NOT at time of observation.
92	Moderate or heavy rain at time of ob.; thunderstorm during past hour, but NOT at time of observation.
93	Slight snow or rain and snow mixed or hail†† at time of ob.; thunderstorm during past hour, but not at time of observation.
94	Mod. or heavy snow, or rain and snow mixed or hail†† at time of ob.; thunderstorm during past hour, but NOT at time of observation.
95	Slight or mod. thunderstorm without hail†† but with rain and/or snow at time of observation.
96	Slight or mod. thunderstorm, with hail†† at time of observation.
97	Heavy thunderstorm, without hail††, but with rain and/or snow at time of observation.
98	Thunderstorm combined with duststorm or sandstorm at time of ob.
99	Heavy thunderstorm with hail† at time of ob.

† Refers to "hail" only.   †† Refers to "soft hail," "small hail," and "hail."

Fig. 12-5c.—Explanation of symbols used on station model.—(Continued)

CLOUD FORMS ARRANGED IN ACCORDANCE WITH INTERNATIONAL CODE TABLES (TABLE XX, 13-15), AND STATION MODEL SYMBOLS[1]

Modifying Cloud Terms Are Included in Titles

Low Clouds

Cʟ 1

Fɪɢ. 12-6.—Cumulus humilis (cumulus of fair weather).

Cʟ 2

Fɪɢ. 12-7.—Cumulus congestus (heavy and swelling without anvil top).

[1] The cloud illustrations in this section have been furnished through the courtesy of the U.S. Weather Bureau.

C_L 3

FIG. 12-8.—Cumulonimbus calvus.

C_L 3

FIG. 12-9.—Cumulonimbus incus.

C_L 4

FIG. 12-10.—Stratocumulus vesperalis (formed by flattening of cumulus clouds).

CL 5

FIG. 12-11.—Stratocumulus translucidus (layer of stratocumulus).

CL 5

FIG. 12-12.—Stratocumulus opacus (layer of stratocumulus).

CL 5

FIG. 12-13.—Stratus (layer of stratus).

C∟ 6

− − −

FIG. 12-14.—Low broken clouds of bad weather, scud.

C∟ 7

FIG. 12-15.—Cumulus humilis and stratocumulus—above (fair weather cumulus and stratocumulus).

C∟ 8

FIG. 12-16.—Cumulus congestus and stratocumulus (heavy or swelling cumulus or cumulonimbus and stratocumulus).

CL 9

FIG. 12-17.—Cumulonimbus and fractocumulus—lower (heavy or swelling cumulus or cumulonimbus and low ragged clouds of bad weather).

MIDDLE CLOUDS

CM 1

FIG. 12-18.—Altostratus translucidus (typical thin altostratus).

CM 2

FIG. 12-19.—Altostratus opacus (typical thick altostratus).

CM 3

FIG. 12-20.—Altocumulus translucidus (altocumulus sheet at one level only).

CM 4

FIG. 12-21.—Altocumulus lenticularis (altocumulus in isolated patches and more or less lenticular in shape).

CM 4

FIG. 12-22.—Altocumulus patches—lenticular.

C_M 5

FIG. 12-23.—Altocumulus translucidus undulatus (altocumulus arranged in more or less parallel bands or an ordered layer advancing across the sky).

C_M 6

FIG. 12-24.—Altocumulus cumulogenitus (altocumulus formed by the spreading out of tops of cumulus).

C_M 7

FIG. 12-25.—Altocumulus duplicatus (altocumulus associated with altostratus or altostratus having an altocumulus character).

Cм 7

Fig. 12-26.—Altocumulus opacus (see description Fig. 12-25).

Cм 8

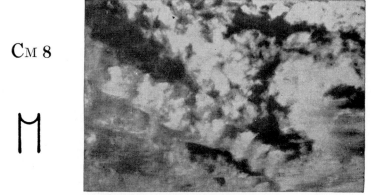

Fig. 12-27.—Altocumulus floccus (scattered cumuliform tufts).

Cм 8

Fig. 12-28.—Altocumulus castellatus (turreted altocumulus).

CM 9

FIG. 12-29.—Thundery altocumulus. (Chaotic sky appearance with altocumulus in several sheets at different levels, associated with fibrous cloud veils.)

HIGH CLOUDS

CH 1

FIG. 12-30.—Cirrus filosus (scarce delicate cirrus, not increasing, scattered and isolated)

CH 2

FIG. 12-31.—Cirrus filosus (abundant delicate cirrus but not forming a continuous layer).

Cн 3

Fig. 12-32.—Cirrus nothus (cirrus associated with anvil tops of cumulonimbus).

Cн 3

Fig. 12-33.—Cirrus densus (dense white cirrus).

Cн 4

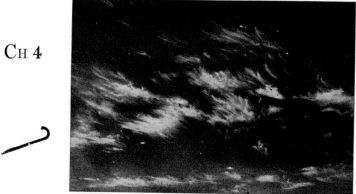

Fig. 12-34.—Cirrus uncinus (cirrus increasing, generally in the form of hooks ending in a point or a small tuft).

CH 5

FIG. 12-35.—Cirrus below 45° altitude. (Cirrus in bands, or cirrostratus, advancing over the sky, but not more than 45° above the horizon.)

CH 6

FIG. 12-36.—Cirrus above 45° altitude. (Cirrus, in bands, or cirrostratus, advancing over the sky, and more than 45° above the horizon.)

CH 7

FIG. 12-37.—Cirrostratus filosus (veil of cirrostratus covering the whole sky).

CH 8

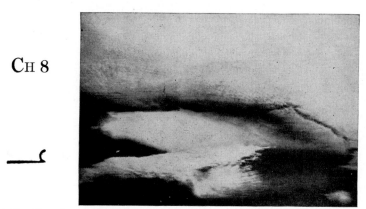

FIG. 12-38.—Cirrostratus (cirrostratus layer not increasing and not covering the whole sky).

CH 9

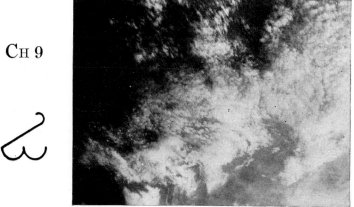

FIG. 12-39.—Cirrocumulus. (Cirrocumulus predominating, associated with small amounts of cirrus or cirrostratus.)

CHAPTER 13

AIR MASSES AND FRONTS

Nature of Air Masses

Modern weather theory treats of air masses and their properties, movements, and changes. An air mass is a large horizontally homogeneous or uniform body of air within the atmosphere as a whole. Its uniformity is principally one of *temperature* and *humidity*.

In size, air masses cover hundreds of thousands of square miles; vertically, they extend upward for thousands and tens of thousands of feet. There is no difficulty in conceiving of uniform ocean currents within the main ocean body. We can see them; ocean water is visible. The Gulf Stream is readily apparent by its movement, color, temperature, seaweed content, and so on.

Uniform bodies of air, or air masses, are not so obvious, but their presence is adequately shown by meteorological observations, particularly of their temperature and humidity. Although air masses are identified and their motion traced through instrumental rather than visual observation, their presence is often felt very noticeably by our senses. We are all aware of the oppressively hot, "sticky," summer heat waves. We are also aware of the dramatic end of such a hot weather spell, when, following a violent thunderstorm, a wave of cool dry air is experienced for several days. Clearly a large, hot, humid air body responsible for the heat wave was simply replaced by a cool dry air mass with its consequent relief for the heat sufferers.

The study of air-mass characteristics and behavior is known as "air-mass analysis" and is the basis of modern weather forecasting. A primary weather concern is to determine the conditions within the air mass, its direction of movement and the changes in its properties as it moves. The resulting properties of this moving air mass are the weather conditions that are experienced along its line of motion.

ORIGIN AND TYPES OF AIR MASSES.—Air masses derive their original properties from the surface over which they form. It will be remembered from an earlier discussion that the air is heated primarily by the process of conduction from the earth's surface. The humidity characteristics of an air mass are also determined directly by the nature of the surface beneath.

In considering the relatively large volume of air masses and the

261

poor powers of heat conduction that air possesses, it is apparent that such uniform bodies will not form too rapidly. A large volume of air must remain stagnant for some time over a particular portion of the earth, gradually acquiring its distinguishing temperature and humidity characteristics.

Air masses develop more commonly in some regions than in others, the areas of formation being known as "source regions." We may note, for example, that the common source regions for air masses affecting American weather are the Northern Pacific west of Canada; the northern interior of Canada; the North Atlantic east of Canada; the Pacific west of Southern California; the desert areas of Southwestern United States and northern Mexico; and the Gulf of Mexico and the Caribbean Sea.

It is noticed that the source regions tend to bound the belt of prevailing westerlies. One set of source regions exists along the northern boundary in the vicinity of the subpolar low-pressure circle, while the other set exists along and to the south of the horse latitudes. The basic difference between the air originating in the northern source regions and that in the southern is therefore one of temperature. A second difference is that of humidity.

Cold northern air masses are called "polar air masses," while the warm-air bodies originating in low latitudes are called "tropical air masses." Then, depending on whether they form over land or water, the air masses will be dry or humid, respectively. This leads to two subdivisions for the above air types. Dry polar air of continental origin is known as "polar continental air," and when of oceanic origin "polar maritime air." Similarly, tropical air is known as "tropical continental" and "tropical maritime air."

"Arctic" and "equatorial" air masses form in the far north and in equatorial regions, respectively. However, the effect of the former is not so direct as the polar and tropical air. We shall therefore omit further mention of arctic air since it does not affect the treatment of the subject.

Thus we see that, dependent on the primary or general pressure and wind conditions, large masses of air become stagnant over particular portions of the earth's surface. In so doing, the temperature and humidity properties of the underlying surfaces are acquired by the air. Table XXII summarizes the basic information concerning the five principal air masses.

The symbol w or k following the air-mass designation indicates whether the air is warmer or colder than the surface over which the air is passing. Thus cPk is polar continental air, colder than the underlying land or water.

MOVEMENT OF AIR MASSES.—The air must remain relatively motionless for air masses to form. Ultimately, the very factor that allows for their development, namely, the general air circulation, starts these masses in motion. Whole masses or large portions of them will then start moving away from the source region. In the case of polar air, tongues of cold air will lap southward transgressing the areas previously beyond their limits. Tropical air set in motion will conform to the primary air motion and overlap to the northward.

TABLE XXII. CLASSIFICATION OF AIR MASSES

Name of mass	Place of origin	Properties	Symbol
Polar continental	Subpolar continental areas	Low temperatures (increasing with southward movement) low humidity, remaining constant	cP
Polar maritime	Subpolar and arctic oceanic areas	Low temperatures, increasing with movement, higher humidity	mP
Tropical continental	Subtropical high-pressure land areas	High temperatures, low moisture content	cT
Tropical maritime	Southern borders of oceanic subtropical, high-pressure areas	Moderately high temperatures; high relative and specific humidity	mT
Equatorial	Equatorial and tropical seas	High temperature and humidity	E

As the polar air blows equatorward, it is strongly influenced by the earth's rotational force and is deflected to the west. In the same manner, the northward-moving tropical air is deflected to the east. Along the paths of these migrating air bodies, the weather conditions observed will depend on the properties of the air masses.

Clearly, areas entirely within the permanent boundaries of either the tropical or the polar air masses will experience more or less uniform weather conditions, dependent on their properties. But areas that are outside these permanent boundaries, in *the middle latitudes or westerlies belt*, will undergo continual changes resulting both from the passage of warm and cold air masses and from the effects of the meeting of tropical and polar air.

As a result of their motion, the basic properties of air masses are often strongly modified, the nature of the modification depending on the surface conditions beneath. The actual amount of change within a given body of air depends on (1) the type and conditions of the underlying surface and (2) the velocity of the air in passing over this surface. Consequently, continental polar air (cP) may undergo a transition to maritime polar (mP) air, after protracted motion over the sea. Continental tropical air (cT) behaves similarly. Remember, however, that even maritime tropical air (mT) is warm and also dry at high levels in the subtropical high-pressure belts (horse latitudes).

PROPERTIES OF WARM AND COLD AIR MASSES.—Conditions within moving air masses often depend very strongly on the temperature of the underlying surface. If a body of air is traversing a cold surface, it is usually termed a "warm air mass" and would have the symbol w attached. If the underlying surface is relatively warm, the air mass is considered a "cold air mass," with the symbol k attached.

Warm air masses are usually of tropical origin, moving toward higher latitudes, but they may be warm marine air bodies moving inland over colder land, or warm continental air moving offshore over colder sea surfaces. The effect of the cooler surface beneath is to cool the air slowly from the surface upward. This uniform cooling of the air by a large cool surface tends to produce stratified conditions within the air, with an absence of vertical air motion or turbulence. Consequently, any clouds that exist will be of the stratiform type. Any precipitation existing will be of the drizzle or light rain variety. The absence of turbulence produces poor visibility in warm air masses owing to the settling of dust and other foreign particles in the vertically calm air. Fog will be more common in such air as a result of the surface cooling.

Cold air masses may arise from polar air moving toward lower latitudes or from cold marine air moving over warmer land, or relatively cold continental air traversing warmer sea areas. In the passage over warmer surfaces, convection and turbulence develop rapidly in the cold air. Clouds of the cumuliform type tend to form, with precipitation, if present, being heavy or showery. Visibility is usually good to excellent in such air owing to the general stirring and overturning inherent in convectional turbulence.

Conservative Properties of Air Masses

Our knowledge of the existence and nature of air masses would be of less value if there were not some method of tracing their motion. To do this we must use some property of air masses that remains fairly constant regardless of the common modifications experienced through turbulence and other causes in the course of traveling over different surfaces. Temperature, relative humidity, pressure, cloudiness, and other weather features already studied, vary too widely for the purpose of positively identifying air masses from day to day. There are, however, three characteristics of air masses that serve as excellent "tags" in keeping track of the flow of air: (1) the potential temperature, (2) the equivalent potential temperature, and (3) the specific humidity. No treatment of air masses in the light of modern knowledge should omit at least a brief explanation of these important "conservative" properties.

POTENTIAL TEMPERATURE.—Potential temperature is the temperature of a quantity of air at a standard pressure—the pressure of 1,000 millibars. A small quantity or parcel of air may have to be raised or lowered in the atmosphere until this pressure is reached. If the unit of air is considered to expand or contract adiabatically during this raising or lowering, its temperature at the 1,000-millibar level would be the potential temperature. As long as the air remains unsaturated during the adiabatic process, this temperature value is a constant for a particular unit of air. Let us consider an example: Assume the atmospheric pressure at a given time to be 1,000 millibars at an altitude of 1,500 feet; assume also, that the temperature of a unit of air, measured at an altitude of 500 feet, is 60°F. If this air is now raised 1,000 feet, until the pressure is 1,000 millibars, it will cool at the dry adiabatic rate (5.5°F. per 1,000 feet), and become 54.5°. Should the air rise another 1,000 feet, its temperature will then be 49°F. If brought back to the 1,500-foot 1,000-millibar level, the temperature will be 54.5°. For this particular unit of air, 54.5° is thus the potential temperature. Regardless of any change in position experienced by the air, it will always have this temperature, if brought adiabatically to a pressure of 1,000 millibars, provided the air remains unsaturated.

However, the potential temperature of a given sample of air may be increased, if, in rising, the air becomes saturated and continues cooling at the saturated adiabatic rate. Let us assume, for example, that in the foregoing case the air rises another 1,000 feet after cooling to a temperature of 49° at 2,500 feet, but that it becomes saturated with resulting condensation and precipitation above this 2,500-foot level. The temperature at 3,500 feet will be only 3.2° cooler (the saturated adiabatic rate), or will have a temperature of 45.8°. If we now allow the air to return to the 1,000-millibar level at 1,500 feet, warming at the dry adiabatic rate as it descends, it will warm by 11°, thereby reaching a new potential temperature of 56.8°, not 54.5°. Had the air risen still farther after becoming saturated, its potential temperature would have increased still more.

The explanation of potential temperature may be aided by reference to a simple graphic statement of the problem, as shown in Fig. 13-1. Point *A* represents a unit of air with a temperature of 60°F. at the 500-foot level. Rising and cooling at the dry adiabatic rate to point *B*, where the pressure is 1,000 millibars at the 1,500-foot level, the potential temperature is shown to be 54.5°. Further rising and cooling to point C reduces the temperature to 49°, but upon descending to B, the original potential temperature is reached. In fact any mass of air ascending or descending along the line ABC would have the potential temperature of 54.5°, shown at C. Thus, ABC is a line of constant potential temperature.

If, in rising above 2,500 feet, the air cools according to the saturated adiabatic rate, its temperature will be 45.8°, shown at D. The line CD represents the saturated adiabatic curve. Now, in descending, the air warming at the dry adiabatic rate, reaches the new potential temperature, 56.8°, at point E.

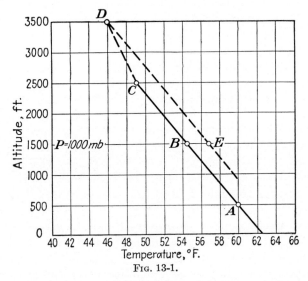

Fig. 13-1.

EQUIVALENT POTENTIAL TEMPERATURE.—We have just seen that the potential temperature is fairly constant for a given air mass, provided no condensation occurs; otherwise this property may vary. To overcome this defect of potential temperature, the more conservative concept of equivalent potential temperature has been developed. This is arrived at in the following manner: Consider a unit of air to be raised, cooling at the dry adiabatic rate until condensation begins; we then continue the uplift of the air at the saturated adiabatic rate, until all the moisture had condensed with the air absorbing the latent heat of condensation; the air is then returned to the 1,000-millibar level, warming at the dry adiabatic rate all the way. The temperature at this level is the equivalent potential temperature and is clearly a more constant air-mass property. This feature can be calculated easily for a given unit of air, for it is seen to be the temperature of a unit of air at standard pressure with the total latent heat of condensation added.

In Fig. 13-2, line *AB* represents air rising and cooling at the dry adiabatic rate, until the level at *B* is reached. Then, cooling occurs according to the saturated adiabatic rate until condensation is complete, which we assume to be at level *C*. Upon descending, the air, which now contains the liberated heat of condensation, warms at the dry adiabatic rate to *D*, which temperature is the equivalent potential temperature. The line *ABC* has a constant equivalent potential temperature, regardless of humidity conditions.

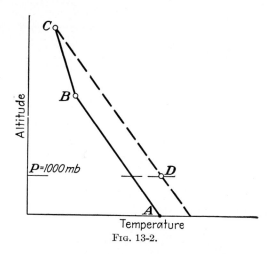

Fig. 13-2.

SPECIFIC HUMIDITY.—Specific humidity is another conservative air-mass property which was considered in an earlier chapter. The application of specific humidity and potential temperature to the analysis of air-mass conditions forms the basis of a method of analysis known as "isentropic analysis." The *mixing ratio* has come into wider use in analysis of upper air conditions than specific humidity.

Fronts

In considering air masses it was observed that the weather properties within are relatively uniform. But, when air masses differing in temperature meet in the course of air movement, a sharp transition in weather conditions (temperature, pressure, wind, etc.) occurs across their boundaries. If one were traveling northward in a warm or tropical air mass, a slight but steady temperature decrease would be encountered. Then on crossing into the colder polar air to the north a sudden sharp drop in temperature would result. Thus the uniform slow change in weather conditions gives way to an abrupt discontinuous change in leaving an air-mass boundary. This leads to the term "line of discontinuity," applied to the limiting line of an air mass. The term "front" is synonymous with line of discontinuity and has pretty much replaced it.

More specifically, *fronts* are the boundaries of, or separations between, air masses.

It should be remembered that air masses have a large vertical as well as horizontal extent. Hence the surface separating adjacent air masses vertically is known as the "frontal surface." The ground front is therefore the line formed by the intersection of the frontal surface with the ground.

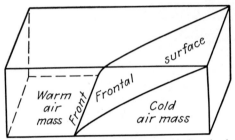

FIG. 13-3.—Three-dimensional characteristics of a front.

These three-dimensional aspects should always be considered and kept in mind when dealing with air masses and fronts. Most of the weather charts and maps that will be encountered, either in this text or elsewhere, will be surface maps showing the horizontal distribution of air masses, fronts, isobars, etc. The vertical extension of the sloping frontal surface should not be forgotten in viewing such charts.

General Frontal Characteristics

Although fronts differ as to type, as explained in the following section, they have many weather properties common to all. As pointed out

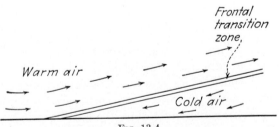

FIG. 13-4.

earlier, when cold and warm air masses meet, the cold air wedges beneath the warmer air, which in turn rises over the sloping upper surface of the cold mass. Figure 13-4 shows a vertical cross section through adjacent warm and cold air masses and indicates, again, this condition.

The slope of the upper surface of the cold air is actually very gentle, varying from 1:100 to 1:500 with different air masses. By slope is meant the ratio of vertical rise to horizontal distance. Thus, a slope of 1:100 indicates a vertical change of 1 unit for each 100 horizontal units; *e.g.*, a slope of 1 mile vertically over a horizontal ground distance of 100 miles. However, this slope is always greatly exaggerated in diagrams for explanatory purposes.

Although treated as such, the frontal surface is not actually a mathematical surface. In reality, a transition zone exists between the two different air masses. The frontal transition zone may vary from a few hundred to a few thousand feet, depending on the contrast in properties between the air masses. The greater the temperature and humidity contrast, the less is the mixing of the air bodies and the thinner is the transition zone. Owing to the gentle slope of the frontal surface, the transition area, even though of small thickness, will cover many miles when intersecting the horizontal ground surface.

1. TEMPERATURE.—The temperature conditions across a front may vary through wide ranges and may take place very abruptly, or more or less slowly. Air masses that have strong temperature contrasts will exhibit very abrupt changes across the frontal zone, not only in temperature but in the dependent weather conditions as well. In addition, the frontal transition zone will be relatively thin when temperature conditions between the air masses differ markedly.

Further, it follows from this and our previous discussion of temperature that an inversion exists along a vertical line through the front. The temperature in the cold wedge of air will decrease with altitude until the front is reached. Then there will be a rise in temperature in the transition zone, the abruptness and amount depending on the temperature difference between the two masses. With continued increase in altitude the temperature will again fall in the warm mass.

2. PRESSURE.—A pronounced difference in pressure gradient occurs between adjacent points on either side of the front. The nature of this pressure discontinuity depends on the basic temperature and resulting density difference between the air bodies. This pressure gradient discontinuity across fronts is clearly shown by the isobars. Within an air mass, isobars are always smoothly curving lines. But, when crossing air-mass boundaries or fronts, they bend sharply in order to conform to this abrupt change in the pressure gradient.

Figure 13-5 shows a front separating a polar from a tropical air mass. The atmospheric pressure at the earth's surface is shown by isobars with .the pressure being lowest at the northern end of the map. The pressure at point 1 in the cold polar air is higher than at the adjacent point 2 in the warm air. The pressure decreases north of point 1 in

the polar air, whereas it becomes increasingly higher to the south.   Thus,
the 1,002-millibars isobar cannot continue directly across the front but
must bend sharply to the north on encountering the polar air in order to
remain on points with pressure readings of 1,002 millibars.   Hence
isobars always bend toward the lower pressure when crossing fronts, and

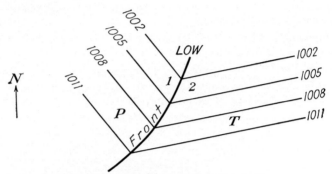

Fig. 13-5.—The kink in isobars at a front.

the wedge formed by this bending points toward higher pressures.   Note
that the pressure increases in a direction perpendicular to the front, so
that a front always lies in a trough of low pressure.

3. Wind.—It will be recalled that wind, in response to the pressure
gradient and the deflecting forces, blows with a slight angle to the isobars
and crosses them from higher to lower pressure.   It is clear then, that to

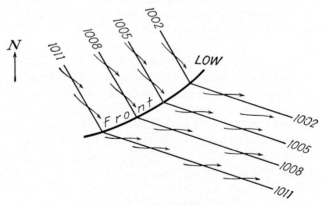

Fig. 13-6.—The wind shift at a front.

obey this rule, an abrupt wind shift must take place at fronts.   This is
shown more graphically by adding wind arrows to the case considered
above, as in Fig. 13-6.

We see in this case that the wind in the tropical air blows from the
southwest while the wind immediately across the front, in the polar air, is

northwesterly. Long before the true identity of air masses and fronts was recognized, these lines of abruptly shifting winds were observed. They were known simply as "wind shift lines."

4. CLOUDS AND PRECIPITATION.—Fronts exhibit characteristic cloudiness and precipitation. These result from the adiabatic cooling of the warm air as it ascends the sloping frontal surface. The exact nature of the clouds and precipitation depends on the moisture content of the air and the slope of the front. Clouds of frontal origin thus extend for hundreds of miles because the warm air ascends along the entire extent of the frontal surface. The heavy low clouds formed in the rising and cooling warm air may yield precipitation. It should be noted that the main cloud body forms in the air above the cold wedge, and the resulting

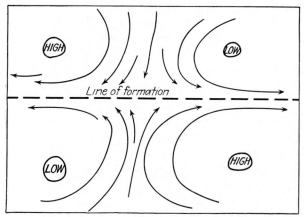

FIG. 13-7.—Pressure and wind conditions conducive to frontogenesis.

precipitation originates in clouds in the warm air. Clouds in the cold air mass owe their development to local heating and are usually of the cumulus type except for nimbostratus formed beneath the rain-producing clouds. More specific cloud-front relationships are discussed in the following section.

FORMATION OF FRONTS.—In many if not most cases, existing fronts form through the motion and meeting of air masses whose original properties are contrasting. Frequently, however, fronts may form where none existed or may have been suspected previously. The process of formation of a front is known as "frontogenesis." Should the air motion in a particular area be such, as a result of the pressure systems, as to cause air of different temperatures to be brought together, continuation of this process may cause a front to develop along the line of meeting of the different air bodies.

Figure 13-7 shows a pressure distribution with the resulting wind motion most conducive to the formation of a temperature discontinuity between warm air brought in from the south and cold air flowing in from the north. This is for the Northern Hemisphere.

Technically, this is known as a "deformation field," for there is a contraction along a north-south axis and an expansion along an east-west axis as a result of the wind motion induced by the pressure arrangement. A careful study of pressure, wind, and temperature conditions often warns of future frontal development.

"Frontolysis" is the process in which a front dissolves as the contrasting conditions causing the discontinuity between the air masses disappears.

Types of Fronts

Depending on the motion of the air masses involved, several different types of fronts, each having particular properties, develop. These

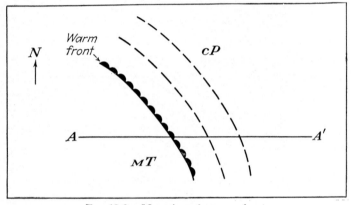

Fig. 13-8.—Map view of a warm front.

fronts will be treated individually: "warm fronts," "cold fronts," "stationary fronts," and "occluded fronts."

1. WARM FRONTS.—A warm front is defined as a front along which warm air replaces cold air. Thus, if a cold and a warm air mass are adjacent, they will be separated by a front. Should the direction of motion of the air masses be such that the warm air progressively passes over ground surface previously covered by the cold air, the front becomes a warm front. On printed weather maps, the warm front is commonly indicated by black semicircles drawn on the side of the front toward which it is moving and thus pointing in the direction of the cold air. On the working copy of a weather map, it is drawn as a solid red line.

As shown in Fig. 13-8, we have a warm front separating continental polar from maritime tropical air. This front is moving in the direction of the cold air, later positions of the front being indicated by the dashed lines.

Stations east and northeast of this front will therefore experience a sequence of weather conditions. The weather prevailing in the cold air will undergo a more or less sudden transition as the front passes. These changes will follow the principles developed in the previous section regarding the temperature, pressure, wind, and cloud relationship to the fronts. Following the warm-front passage, the weather conditions of a tropical air mass will then prevail. A study of the weather map indicates just what conditions exist in the respective air masses.

The characteristic cloudiness and precipitation associated with a warm front will now be examined further. To do this we consider not only the horizontal air-mass distribution but the third-dimensional or vertical picture as well. In Fig. 13-9 we have a vertical cross section running west to east through the preceding warm front, along AA'. As shown on this vertical section, the warm front is perhaps best defined as the receding or trailing edge of a cold-air wedge.

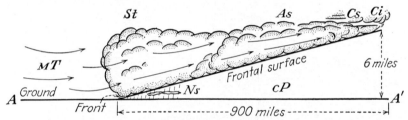

Fig. 13-9.—Cross section of a warm front showing typical cloud deck formed in the rising warm air.

The cold polar air sloping away from a warm front must always slope upward in the direction of motion of the front, here from west to east. Thus the warm tropical air ascends the frontal surface as a continuous sheet all along the warm front. When the rising air cools to the dew point, an extensive cloud sheet will form in the warm air and will blanket the frontal surface up to a distance of 1,000 miles ahead of the front, extending along its entire length.

With a warm front having an average slope of 1:150, or of 1 mile vertically for every 150 miles of horizontal distance, the high clouds forming in the warm air at heights around 6 miles will be 900 miles ahead of an approaching warm front. Consequently, as the warm front approaches, the cloud cover usually shows a typical sequence of cirrus, cirrostratus, altostratus, stratus, and associated nimbostratus. The relatively thick cloud sheet overlying the warm frontal surface near its tapering end usually yields steady precipitation which may extend over a long distance ahead of the front.

We see now that our earlier explanation of the formation of the above cloud system was nothing more than the consideration of a warm front.

As the warm front passes the observer, the heavy stratus-type clouds and any existing precipitation give place to clearing or partially clearing skies in the warm air.

2. COLD FRONTS.—Cold fronts are defined as fronts along which cold air replaces warm air. Figure 13-10 shows a surface map with cold and warm air masses separated by a cold front. The black wedges are

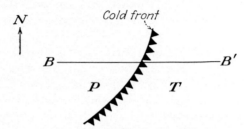

FIG. 13-10.—Map view of a cold front.

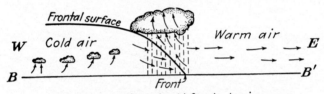

(a)-Cross-section of cold front, showing typical weather characteristics

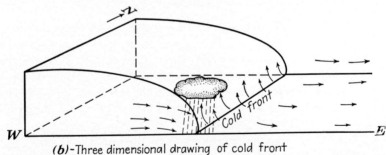

(b)-Three dimensional drawing of cold front

FIG. 13-11.—a, cross-sectional view and b, three-dimensional view of a cold front.

standard cold-front symbols and are always shown on the side toward which the front is moving; or they point into the warm air. The cold front is represented by a solid blue line on the working map. Here the air masses and front are moving from left to right, or west to east.

In this case the frontal surface will slope downward in the direction of motion as shown in the cross section along BB' through the cold front (Fig. 13-11). The cold front is therefore the advancing or leading edge of a steep cold wedge of air.

It is noticed that the cold frontal surface steepens considerably as it approaches the ground. This is a consequence of the motion of the cold air in the same direction as the slope of the front. The air motion near the ground is retarded from the effect of friction, while the free air at higher altitudes has a higher velocity than the lower. This tends to push the front forward at higher altitudes at a faster rate than the front at the ground, causing it to become much steeper than the warm front considered previously. The steepness of the front will clearly depend on its velocity. With a low rate of motion, the slope of the cold front will become very gentle and approach that of a warm front. With higher velocities the lower part of the frontal surface begins to buckle and steepen.

In most cases the cold air advances faster than the warm air ahead. Consequently, the warm air immediately preceding the front will be forced violently upward along the steep cold-front surface. The rapid vertical uplift of the warm air results in rapid cooling in the air column. This yields clouds of the cumulus and cumulonimbus types, with frequent precipitation in the form of showers.

Depending on the steepness of the front and the temperature conditions in the warm air, the resulting clouds and showers develop as severe thunderstorms with extremely turbulent air conditions, which extend all along the front. Before the cold front was recognized as such, the term "line squall" was applied to this long line of squally thundershowers. The precipitation, although very heavy, will usually cover but a narrow zone along the cold front.

For moderately sloping fronts the area of cloudiness and precipitation will be greater, but the intensity of any precipitation will be less.

It follows from the foregoing discussion that the storms associated with relief after a summer heat wave are of the cold-front type. Actually the thunderstorms have not brought about cooler weather. The colder air brought in the thundershowers which are merely incidental to the drop in temperature as a cold front ends a heat wave. Local showers within a warm air mass yield no appreciable relief from the heat.

As the cool air traverses the surface previously warmed by the tropical air, local heating within the cold mass yields local rising air columns, whose summits are capped by typical fair-weather cumulus clouds. The bases of these clouds, representing the height of the dew point of the rising air, are nearly on a level plane that stretches away into the distance.

3. STATIONARY FRONTS.—Suppose that we consider two air masses, a cold and a warm, separated by a front. Will this front be a cold or warm front? The answer of course is that the identity of the front depends on its behavior. If the front is progressively displaced in the

direction of the warm air it will be a cold front; if in the direction of the cold air, it will be a warm front.   But if the air masses are not in motion, the front will be stationary and is called a "stationary front," which is represented on weather charts by a combination of the warm- and cold-front symbols.   No new cross section of the stationary front is

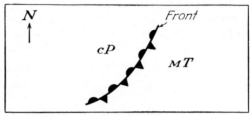

FIG. 13-12.—Map view of a stationary front.

shown for it resembles in vertical section the picture of the warm front. The weather conditions are similar to those of a warm front.

Should the cold air develop a movement toward the warm, the frontal surface, which will be sloping downward in the direction of motion, will buckle and steepen near the ground, and develop cold-front characteristics.   Or, if a cold front slows, it will assume characteristics of the stationary and warm fronts.

4. OCCLUDED FRONTS.—Occluded fronts are those formed by the merging of cold and warm fronts.   If a cold front overtakes a warm, the

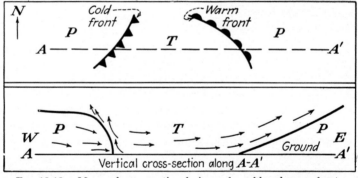

FIG. 13-13.—Map and cross-sectional views of a cold and warm front.

result is an occluded front.   It was stated above that the cold air with its bounding cold front moves faster than the warm air that may be ahead.   If we have three air masses, a cold, a warm, and a cold in succession moving from west to east, two fronts will exist (Fig. 13-13).

As a consequence of its higher velocity, the advancing cold front will overtake the warm front ahead.   This results in the occluded front shown in Fig. 13-14, which is represented by a combination of warm-

and cold-front symbols pointing in the direction of motion of the front. When drawn on a map, the occluded front is shown by a solid purple line.

But what has happened to the warm air? Where has it gone? It has been squeezed upward by the meeting of the cold- and the warm-front surfaces and no longer shows itself at the ground. To see it, we

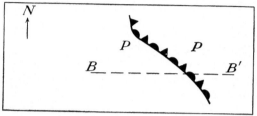

Fig. 13-14.—Map view of an occluded front. The warm *T* air, being forced aloft, does not show at the surface.

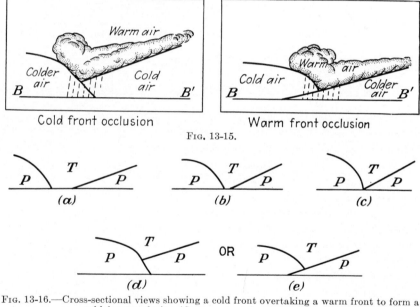

must examine the vertical air section across the front. Two possible cross sections may exist (Fig. 13-15). Exactly what has taken place to result in these cross sections is shown in Fig. 13-16, *a, b, c, d, e,* which trace the movement of the fronts as the advancing cold overtakes the slower warm front.

The type of occlusion (warm- or cold-front type) that results, depends on which of the polar air masses is the colder. If the air following the cold front is colder, the cold-front occlusion occurs; if the cold wedge preceding the warm front is the colder, the warm-front occlusion forms.

In either case, as the occluded front approaches, the cloud system with resulting precipitation will be very similar to that of the warm front, for the shape of the tapering wedge has not been altered prior to the front itself. As the front itself passes, the clouds and precipitation will be of the cold-front type.

From a knowledge of local weather conditions alone it is often impossible to distinguish between the approach of a warm and an occluded front. The weather conditions at the zone of occlusion, where cold and warm fronts meet, are seriously affected. However, the conditions out ahead of the occlusion, overlying the warm frontal surface, are "unaware"

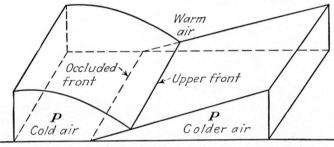

Fig. 13-17.—Three-dimensional view of a warm-front occlusion.

of the changes associated with the occlusion and consequently show no indications of any occlusion.

UPPER FRONTS.—Although they are of primary importance in aviation, our treatment of fronts should include a brief examination of upper fronts, for they represent a significant weather feature. As the name implies, upper fronts are those which exist in the upper air but whose effects on the weather may often be experienced at the ground. Most upper fronts occur in connection with, and as the direct result of, occlusions.

In the occlusion process, a cold front overtakes a warm one and, depending on the relative temperatures of the respective cold air masses involved, one of the fronts is forced up over the surface of the other. The front remaining at the ground, we defined above, as the occluded front. *The front that is forced aloft is the upper front.*

In the case of the warm-front occlusion, the cold front ascends the warm frontal surface and becomes an upper cold front. In the cold-front type of occlusion, the warm front being forced over the cold becomes an upper warm front. Figures 13-18, *a* and *b* indicate this relationship. On working maps, upper cold fronts are shown by broken blue lines; upper warm fronts by broken red lines. On printed maps the symbols

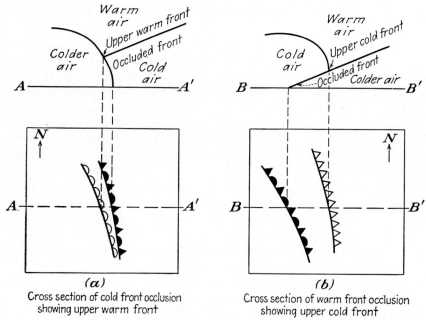

(a)
Cross section of cold front occlusion
showing upper warm front

(b)
Cross section of warm front occlusion
showing upper cold front

Fig. 13-18.

TYPE OF FRONT	ON WORKING MAP COPY	ON PRINTED MAPS
Warm front	Red line	
Cold front	Blue line	
Stationary front	Red and blue line	
Occluded front	Purple line	
Upper warm front	Broken red line	
Upper cold front	Broken blue line	
Formation of a front	F.G.	← Frontogenesis →
Dissipation of a front	F.L.	← Frontolysis →

Fig. 13-19.—Summary of frontal symbols appearing on working and printed weather maps.

are the same as those for surface fronts, with the exception that they are not in black.

Upper fronts may not always be drawn on normal surface weather maps. Notice, however, that the upper warm front lies much closer to the occluded front than does the upper cold front. It is clear that, owing to the relative steepness of the cold front, the rising warm front, in the occlusion process, has a large vertical component of motion. When the cold front rises over the warm, as shown in *b*, a large horizontal component of motion exists, owing to the much more gentle slope of the warm frontal surface.

World Air Masses and Fronts

We have now considered the general weather features of air masses and fronts. It might be well at this time to examine the important principal air masses and associated frontal zones of the world, since they are so important in determining the weather conditions experienced. A brief mention was made, above, of the main air-mass types. The generalized maps shown in Figs. 13-20 and 13-21 present the average world air mass and frontal positions for the periods stated thereon.

ARCTIC AIR (A).—Arctic air originates farther north than polar air, over the Arctic icecap and the Greenland icecap. It is distinguished from the polar continental air by lower temperatures, although this distinction may often be absent, in which case no definite frontal zone occurs between these air masses. On occasions arctic fronts do exist in the far North Atlantic and Pacific, with polar maritime air existing to the southward. For the most part, the weather of the middle latitudes is rarely influenced by arctic air.

POLAR CONTINENTAL AIR (cP).—Polar continental air is characteristically cold and dry. In the winter it originates over the cold, often frozen areas of central Asia and Canada. During the summer these cold-air bodies become more restricted as their sources necessarily retreat farther northward.

In the winter, the great polar air mass of Asiatic origin overflows to the south and eastward. The air moving southward travels with the northeast Indian monsoon, spreading cold air over the Indian Ocean and even reaching the South Pacific. The air traveling eastward continues into the North Pacific Ocean, where it plays a dominant role in shaping the weather, not only of the Pacific but of western North America, as well.

When in the source region, polar continental air is very stable and clear, since the cold surface beneath prevents convection. The temperature in such air often increases with increase in altitude, yielding an inversion. This results essentially from the pronounced cooling of the surface air. After leaving the source region, the nature and amount of modification depend on the underlying surface conditions. Winter continental polar air suffers little change while crossing cold land surfaces.

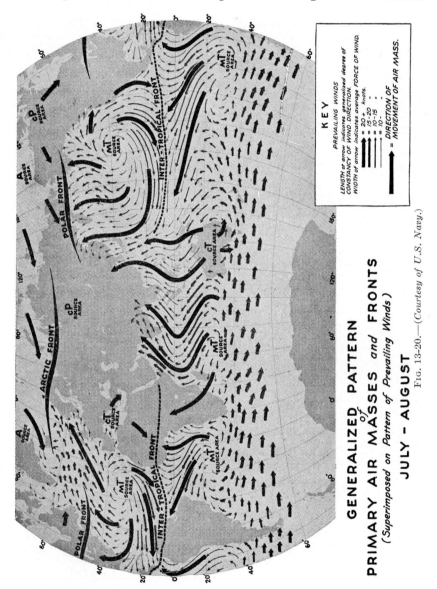

FIG. 13–20.—(*Courtesy of U.S. Navy.*)

Upon reaching warmer land areas, local surface heating causes the formation of cumulus clouds which may become heavy and join to form stratocumulus.

When this air of winter origin advances over sea surfaces, arctic sea smoke or steam fog may form in the low levels of the air masses, if the water is warm.   With the evaporation of sea water into it, the dry

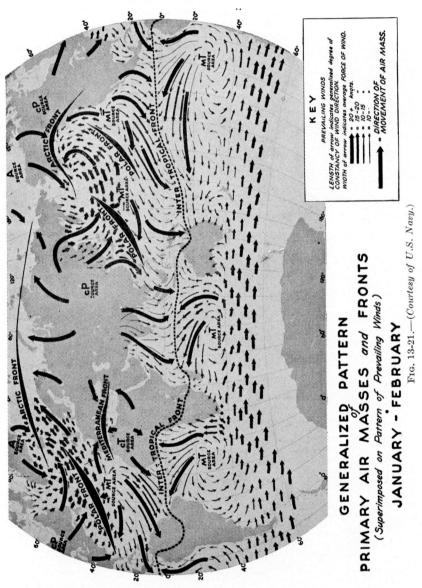

Fig. 13-21.—*(Courtesy of U.S. Navy.)*

polar continental air mass undergoes modification to polar maritime air. Over cold water surfaces this air remains stable but tends to develop clouds of the stratus type, yielding drizzle and light rain.   Fog may occur with or without the formation of the stratus sheet. Over warmer ocean waters, convectional-type clouds tend to form, with associated showers.

In the summer season, polar continental air is not nearly so prominent, remaining in higher middle latitudes for the most part. Modifications of the air in summer are very similar to conditions observed in winter air of the same origin.

POLAR MARITIME AIR (mP).—Polar maritime air is for the most part polar continental air that has remained over the sea surface a sufficient length of time to absorb relatively large quantities of moisture. Since air masses ultimately move eastward, owing to rotational forces, the eastern sections of the oceans are characteristically overlain by polar maritime air. The western portion of the oceans may be influenced by polar continental air, or polar continental air acquiring maritime characteristics. When moving over warmer surfaces, whether water or land, this air mass tends to yield cumulus-type clouds and associated showers, as a result of convection. When crossing colder surfaces, stratus clouds, fog, and often drizzle may result.

TROPICAL CONTINENTAL AIR (cT).—In its source region, tropical continental air is warm and very dry. This air is limited in occurrence, originating over desert areas of North Africa, where it affects Mediterranean weather, and over the deserts of Southwestern United States and northern Mexico. Continental tropical air, being dry and warm, has a high moisture capacity and a low relative humidity, and will therefore absorb moisture rapidly when traversing water areas. It is thus modified rapidly to tropical maritime air.

TROPICAL MARITIME AIR (mT).—Tropical maritime air originates in the subtropical high-pressure zones of the oceans (Azores and Pacific highs in the Northern Hemisphere). The weather here, as considered previously in connection with the horse latitudes, is mostly calm and clear. As maritime tropical air moves outward from its source, with either the westerlies or trade-wind circulation, its properties are modified. When this air moves with the westerlies, colder water surfaces are encountered. The uniform chilling of the air mass tends to produce fog and stratus clouds and occasionally light rain. With the retreat of the polar air masses in summer, the tropical maritime air extends farther northward than in winter. The northward surge of warm humid air, upon meeting cold arctic ocean currents, is responsible for the prevalent summer fogs of the North Atlantic and North Pacific oceans. In moving equatorward with the trades, maritime tropical air becomes warmer and more humid. For the most part, clear skies with scattered cumulus clouds prevail in this air in the poleward portion of the trade-wind belt. The closer the approach to the doldrums, the greater is the tendency for the formation of convection-type clouds, with associated clouds and thunderstorms.

The maritime tropical air, moving eastward or westward from the source regions, encounters shore currents of varying temperatures and coastal zones of varying slopes. Consequently, California coastal fog develops when warm moist tropical air from the Pacific high moves across the colder California current (and the cold coast, in the winter). Upon ascending the steep slopes of the coast ranges that border both California and Chile, heavy precipitation results. If cooler land masses are approached, fog and stratus-type clouds tend to form. If warm land exists to leeward, cumulus and cumulonimbus clouds with associated showers and thundershowers are common.

EQUATORIAL AIR (E).—Equatorial air plays a prominent part in weather conditions over equatorial and tropical seas. When air becomes stagnant in equatorial areas, properties of high temperature and humidity are acquired. Cumulus clouds predominate in such air with frequent thunderstorms.

When equatorial air crosses land areas, the effect of solar heating of the ground is to cause surface air temperatures to be highest in the afternoon. Consequently, towering cumulus and cumulonimbus clouds with resulting showers are most common in that part of the day. However, over ocean areas, as explained previously in considering thunderstorms, the lapse rate tends to increase during the night and finally provides the atmospheric instability necessary for thundershowers. Owing to the high absolute humidity of hot equatorial air, any precipitation therein is usually very heavy.

Equatorial air is encountered in great quantities in the vicinity of the doldrums in the Southwest Pacific. On occasions when equatorial air is carried to relatively high latitudes, it may be the source of dense fog, should cold currents be encountered.

ARCTIC FRONTS.—Strong air-mass contrasts are occasionally produced when arctic air meets relatively warmer maritime air. Typical frontal weather disturbances then develop. Their effects are usually beyond the sphere of our normal activities, so that we shall omit further discussion of this situation.

POLAR FRONTS.—Polar fronts are the boundaries of polar air outbreaks. The polar front advances as the polar air advances, and retreats accordingly. Thus, in winter time polar fronts advance with the polar air masses to much lower latitudes than in summer. An examination of the world air-mass maps shows clearly the northeast-southwest trend of the polar front during the winter. This becomes more nearly east-west during the summer. For the most part the transgressions and regressions of the polar fronts are characteristic of the middle latitudes. This accounts for the great variability of weather conditions in this zone, for invasions of widely differing air masses of either polar or tropical origin are continually recurring. Note these polar fronts well. We shall give them much greater attention in the following chapter, when their significance will become still more apparent.

INTERTROPICAL FRONTS.—The exact nature and behavior of intertropical fronts are topics that require further research and explanation. These fronts form as a result of the meeting and convergence of the trade winds of both hemispheres in tropical regions. Clearly then, the position of this boundary must also shift seasonally and geographically in accordance with the migration of the doldrums. The intertropical front of the Atlantic is therefore always north of the equator.

When the sun is on or near the equator (during the equinoctial periods), temperature conditions in the air masses on either side of the front are very nearly uniform. However, near the middle or end of summer or winter, temperature contrasts reach a maximum, for the temperature differences between the two hemispheres are then most pronounced.

It should be noted that in all of the foregoing discussion, the word "tend" has always been used in describing air-mass conditions. The changes and modifications are always potential ones. The fact that an air mass is highly heated and very humid will not directly cause showers or even cloud formations. For this to occur, adiabatic expansion of the air is necessary, which may result from further local heating or the encountering of fronts or topographic deformities. If the air traverses a cooler surface, condensation takes a different form, as described. We emphasize again the importance of the surface conditions over which the air travels.

PRESSURE-JUMP LINES.—Cold fronts are often preceded by squall lines that may show more violent weather conditions than those associated with the front. Very recent research has shown that these squall lines are invariably associated with abrupt increases in pressure which are considered to result from the passage of a wave on an inversion surface aloft. The wave is believed to be generated by the pressure of a cold front on an inversion surface preceding the steeply sloping front. These pressure-jump lines have become important elements in modern observations and forecasts.

CHAPTER 14

DEVELOPMENT AND STRUCTURE OF CYCLONES

The weather of the middle latitudes is intricately associated not only with air masses and their motion, but also with cyclones and anticyclones, studied in a previous lesson. It will be recalled that these low- and high-pressure areas move approximately eastward in the belt of the prevailing westerlies, between horse latitudes and subpolar low. An approaching low brings with it a host of weather changes, mostly bad. We shall consequently be concerned here mainly with the study of the low-pressure area.

Considerably more information about the weather conditions in a low or cyclone is gained when it is considered in the light of modern weather knowledge of air masses and fronts. The application of this knowledge explains the origin, growth, and typical weather conditions of a cyclone. Such a knowledge is requisite for the purpose of interpreting and forecasting the weather. Let us therefore proceed to the study of the cyclone in relation to air masses, noting its origin, development, and structure.

The Polar-front Theory or Wave Theory of Cyclones

The modern weather theory of cyclones, air masses, and fronts had its inception in Bergen, Norway. The great Norwegian meteorologist, Bjerknes, was one of the leaders of this famous Bergen school of meteorologists and is one of the principal founders of the newer concepts. Certain American universities advanced these ideas still further. This was accomplished in two ways: (1) by sending American scientists to Norway to study the new developments and (2) by actually inviting the more eminent Norwegian specialists to come to the United States to engage in their research and teaching in American universities. The results have been most successful.

THE POLAR FRONT.—We have seen that large relatively uniform masses of cold air overlie the polar areas of the earth. The southern limit of this polar air is by no means a regular one. It is irregular and in constant fluctuating motion advancing southward or receding to the north. Nor is this polar-air boundary a perfectly continuous one around the earth since the cold polar air forms in more or less distinct source regions.

The natural name for the mobile southernmost limit or boundary of this polar air is the "polar front"—the front of the polar air. The polar front may have warm- or cold-front characteristics depending on its direction of motion.

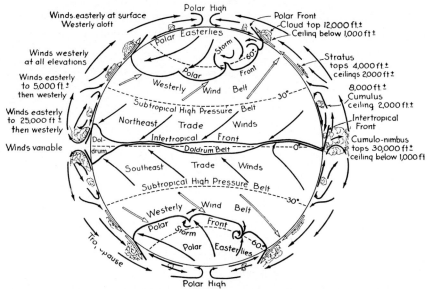

Winds easterly at surface
Westerly aloft

Polar High

Polar Front
Cloud top 12,000 ft.±
Ceiling below 1,000 ft±

Winds westerly at all elevations

Polar Easterlies

Storm

60°

Winds easterly to 5,000 ft ±
then westerly

Polar Front

Westerly Wind Belt

30°

Stratus tops 4,000 ft.±
ceilings 2,000 ft±

8,000 ft.±
Cumulus
ceiling 2,000 ft±

Winds easterly to 25,000 ft ±
then westerly

Subtropical High Pressure Belt

Northeast Trade Winds

Intertropical Front

Winds variable

Dol-
drum

Intertropical Front

Doldrum Belt

0°

Cumulo-nimbus tops 30,000 ft.±
ceiling below 1,000 ft

Southeast Trade Winds

Subtropical High Pressure Belt

30°

Westerly Wind Belt

Polar Front

Storm

Polar Easterlies

60°

Tropopause

Polar High

FIG. 14-1.—Relation of the polar front to the ideal atmospheric circulation. (*Courtesy of U.S. Navy.*)

This polar-front or polar-air boundary is particularly significant. Along it cyclones or low-pressure areas form and develop. Remember that, as the polar air moves southward from arctic regions into the middle latitudes or westerlies belt, there is often at the same time a mass of warm tropical air moving northward, toward the polar front.

The cyclone develops along this front as a result of the interaction between the warm humid tropical air on one side of the front and the cold polar air on the other.

We may further consider the polar front to be the southern limit of the polar easterlies, or the line along

N

Polar front

FIG. 14-2.

which the cold polar winds from the north meet the warm prevailing westerlies that originate in much lower latitudes. This relationship of the polar front to the general atmospheric circulation is shown in Fig. 14-1.

Figure 14-2 indicates the polar front at this stage of meeting. The arrows show the wind motion in the respective air masses, the cold southward moving air being deflected westward and the warm northward moving air being deflected eastward.

Recall again the cross-sectional or three-dimensional view of this front, with the air masses it separates. As shown in Fig. 14-1, the cold air is wedged under the warm air, which in turn flows up over the cold, when it meets the polar front. To help clarify this picture still further, the three-dimensional drawing of the same situation (Fig. 14-3), is given.

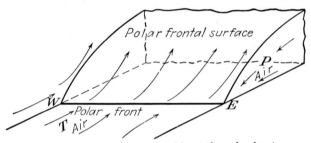

FIG. 14-3.—Air-mass relationship at the polar front.

Development of the Cyclone

INITIAL STAGE.—Under the conditions necessary for a low or cyclone to form, we have a mass of cold polar air moving generally southward and forcing its way into, and wedging beneath, the warm tropical air that is blowing in a northerly direction. A very strong and marked contrast of energy exists between the two air masses separated by the front. Heat is an important form of energy. Hence the tropical air has much more energy than the polar. Whenever two such masses meet or oppose each other, something usually happens. In the case of the polar front it is the low-pressure area that "happens."

As the cold air advances farther and farther southward into the warm, it gradually slows, with increasing distance from the source region. The polar front or southern boundary of this invading cold air tends to maintain itself as a smoothly curving line, any relatively small part being practically straight. In the winter time the polar front reaches a latitude much farther south than in the summer, extending frequently to 30° or 35°N. in winter, with the average summer position being about 45° to 50°N.

Regardless of the reason, the forward movement of the polar front slowly weakens. Almost any one of a host of causes may then interrupt or stop this advance at some point. Perhaps as a huge slowing cold mass swings southward over the ocean, it encounters a mountainous island. The cold air in the vicinity of this island no longer has the energy to continue on uninterruptedly. It is slowed still more or is stopped entirely. The advancing air on either side of the obstruction may continue farther and leave a northward tongue of warm air protruding into the cold, resembling a wave (Fig. 14-4).

This wave, forming on the polar front, represents the earliest stage of the cyclone. However, just as some infants never survive their birth, so do some cyclones also fail to develop after this initial stage. We shall

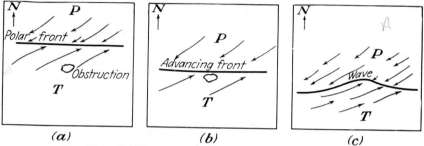

(a)   *(b)*   *(c)*

Fig. 14-4.—Initial stages in the development of a cyclone wave.

assume that the cyclone is destined to continue. In such a case, as soon as the northward bulge forms on the slowing polar front, the warm energetic air (tropical) immediately forces itself still farther into the wave, widening and deepening this "beach head."

Figure 14-5 is an attempt to give a three-dimensional picture of the incipient low in this stage. Notice that the warm air in the vicinity of the wave does not now begin to rise over the polar frontal surface until it has penetrated the area of the warm tongue.

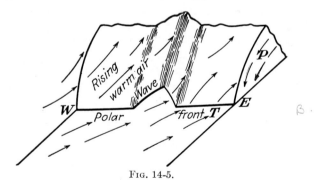

Fig. 14-5.

STAGE 2.—After the initial stage the cold air continues to force itself southward around the warm-air bulge, as the warm tropical air proceeds to enlarge the wave rapidly. *As a consequence of the forces resulting from the rotation of the earth, the wave moves generally eastward as it continues to grow in size.*

While the cold air to the west of the wave continues southward and slows still further, two things happen: (1) The piling up of this cold air forms an area relatively high in pressure.   (2) The air, as it slows, loses its deflection to the southwest and starts curving eastward as a result of the pressure gradient extending out from the center of the dense cold-

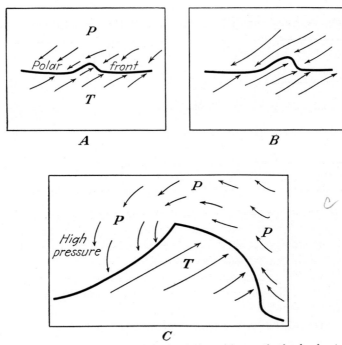

Fig. 14-6.—Development of cyclonic circulation with growth of polar-front wave.

air mass immediately west of the wave.   The development so far is shown in the diagrams in Fig. 14-6.

The movement of the warm air in the bulge and of the cold air surrounding the bulge is of such a nature that eastward of the "high,"

Fig. 14-7.—A low-pressure center forms at the apex of the polar-front wave.

pressure becomes lowest at the apex or tip of the wave.   This slight "low" at the apex *forms immediately after the formation of the wave;* later air motion further strengthens and adds to the formation of the low.

Let us also note the atmospheric pressure pattern about the wave as shown by the configuration of the isobars as the wave develops. Before distortion of the polar front, the isobars are more or less uniform and straight in the respective air masses (Fig. 14-8*A*). As the warm tongue of air is forced northward into the cold mass, the isobar that is intercepted by the wave is bent on both sides of the wave upon crossing the front (Fig. 14-8*B*). This is in accordance with the principles of fronts and isobars seen in the last lesson, for the pressure, as explained, has already become lowest at the apex of the wave. Continued growth of the wave results in a definite low center (Fig. 14-8*C*).

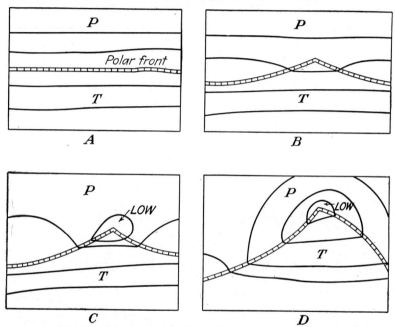

Fig. 14-8.—Development of the isobar pattern about a low.

Further deepening of the low, with the development of the wind circulation shown in Fig. 14-6, yields an isobar pattern shown in Fig. 14-8*D*. The process so far described may take place in a matter of 12 to 24 hours, and sometimes a bit longer.

STAGE 3.—THE MATURE CYCLONE.—Continued development of the factors described results in the fully developed or mature cyclone. The typical well-formed cyclone is pictured in Fig. 14-9, with two vertical cross sections showing the vertical air conditions on lines north and south of the center, respectively. This cross-sectional or third-dimensional view is necessary in order to understand properly the distribution of clouds and precipitation within the low.

We note that there are several basic differences between the old picture of the cyclone, given in Chap. 10, on Winds, and the new picture viewed in the light of modern weather theory. There is not quite the continuous circulation of a single air mass about the center. The mature cyclone or low is composed of at least two more or less well-defined masses of air, a cold and a warm. As seen on the map view of the cyclone, most of the air experienced at the ground in the low is cold

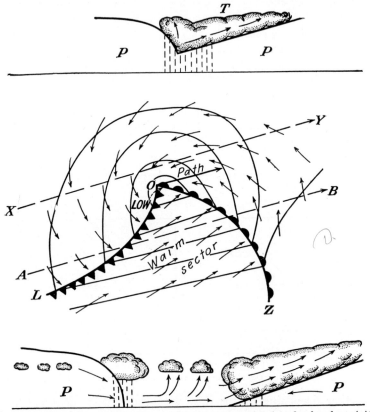

FIG. 14-9.—A mature low-pressure area with cross sections showing cloud and precipitation conditions north and south of the center.

or polar. The warm tongue of air extending into polar air in the southern part of the low is known as the "warm sector." As a result of this warm sector in the cyclone, the isobars about the mature low will show pronounced kinks when crossing either side of this warm zone. This differs also from the older picture showing smooth circular isobars in the low. Isobars in the warm sector of a well-developed cyclone are usually straight and parallel.

As a consequence of the two air masses present, with their distinct differences of temperature, pressure, and direction of movement, a pronounced wind shift occurs in crossing into the warm sector from the polar air on either side. No such abrupt wind shift was stressed on the earlier cyclonic illustration.

Since the cyclone with its attendant conditions moves easterly, it is clear that the line *OZ* along the original and now distorted polar front will be a line along which warm air will replace cold air. This is therefore a warm front and *has been a warm front ever since the wave first formed.* Similarly, the line *OL is and has been a cold front.*

The marine weather map sequence of January 17 to 19, 1930 (Figs. 10-5 to 10-7) omits any illustration of air mass or frontal conditions. However, the isobar and wind pattern on these charts clearly demonstrates the distribution of frontal zones within many of the cyclonic areas.

Refer to the map of January 17. The intense low in the central North Atlantic offers a good example. A pronounced kink in the isobars exists along a line extending from the center of the low approximately southward just east of the 60° meridian. To the west of this kink the winds are from the northwest; to the east, the winds are from the southwest. This wind-shift line is clearly the cold front of the cyclone. Extending northeastward from this "cold front," the isobars are nearly straight and parallel, with winds prevailing from the southwest, marking the warm sector zone. Another wind shift, this time from southwest to southeast, occurs in the forward or eastern section of the low. The isobars bend again along this wind-shift line, although the abruptness of the bend is not quite so pronounced. This represents the warm front. Similar conditions can be developed for other cyclones on this and the succeeding charts.

The vertical cross sections through the cyclone show the typical cloudiness and precipitation picture (Fig. 14-9). It is seen that basic areas of clouds and precipitation are those associated with the ascent of the warm air over the warm and cold fronts. These conditions are given in detail in the previous chapter. We note that as a consequence of the uniform and extended cloud sheet lying above the gently sloping warm front, the precipitation covers a large area but is rather steady and mild.

Among the earliest local indications of an approaching low, or depression, are the cirrus clouds thickening into the cirrostratus that lie on the outer fringe of the advancing warm-front cloud deck. If at all possible, this should be related to pressure and wind conditions before any positive prediction is made. The precipitation falling through the cold air from the stratus clouds above the warm front frequently saturates the cold air and causes low clouds and fog to form. This greatly reduces both ceiling and visibility of the air preceding the warm front.

The warm sector is characterized by horizontally moving warm air.

Vertically rising air is a local feature, resulting from overheating or topography. The clouds in the warm sector will therefore be of the cumulus type—either cumulus or altocumulus. Should the cumulus form in heavy bands, they become stratocumulus. Pronounced vertical movement of local air columns will form cumulonimbus clouds, yielding local thunderstorms so frequent in the warm sector in spring and summer.

The cloudiness and precipitation at the cold front are very different from that at the warm front. Owing to the greater steepness of the cold front, the cloud band formed by the forced uplift of the warm air over the advancing front is much narrower in extent and in area covered.

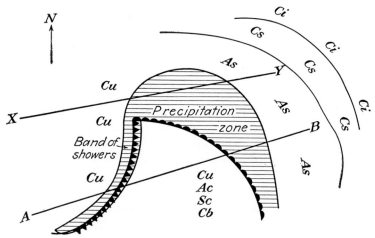

Fig. 14-10.—Typical cloud and precipitation zones of a mature low.

At the same time the more violent uprush of air over the steep cold front forms thick cumulus and cumulonimbus cloud types yielding precipitation of great intensity in the form of showers and thundershowers. Since this precipitation is usually not nearly so widespread as that of the warm front, its duration is thus much shorter. The cold-front portion of the cyclone was long known as the "squall line," or "line of clearing showers," before the nature of the front itself was understood. The approach of the cold front in a low is often marked by a long ominous band of rolling black clouds with associated severe winds and precipitation approaching from the west. After the passage of the cold front, the observer is situated in the relatively cool dry-air mass following the front. Local convection caused by the passage of the cool air over the previously warmed ground surface causes thin flat fair-weather cumulus to form, very typical of the fair post-cold frontal weather.

We should note here that "secondary cold fronts" frequently form in a low following the passage of the first or primary cold front. The leading portion of the cold air following the warm sector is often so modified in passing over the previously warmed surface that it develops characteristics different from the main cold-air mass. This gives rise to the secondary cold front, which separates the main mass from the modified mass and is also distinguished by a temperature, pressure, and wind discontinuity. Secondary-front weather conditions are usually weaker than those of the primary front. This front also extends outward from the low-pressure center but is farther to the west.

To avoid confusion on Fig. 14-9, the areas and types of cloudiness and precipitation are shown in Fig. 14-10, where only the fronts are drawn.

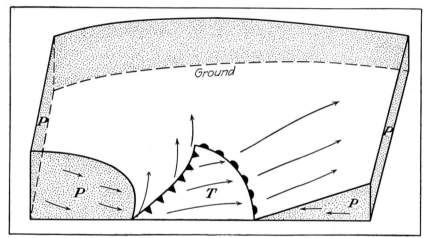

Fig. 14-11.

Along the path of the storm represented by the cross section *XY* on Figs. 14-9 and 14-10, it is noted that no front nor warm sector is encountered north of the cyclone center as a result of the warm air rising over the fronts which here are above the ground.

The three-dimensional diagram (Fig. 14-11) is given in an attempt to clarify further the air mass and frontal picture of the mature cyclone.

SUMMARY OF WEATHER CONDITIONS ALONG PATH *AB* OF TYPICAL MATURE CYCLONE (see Fig. 14-9, page 292)

Preceding an Approaching Warm Front:

1. Temperature.—Steady or rises slightly as front nears.
2. Relative Humidity.—Increases steadily as front approaches.
3. Pressure.—Falling steadily.
4. Winds.—From south to southeast.
5. Clouds.—Cirrus or cirrostratus at great distance from front, thickening to altostratus and then to stratus and nimbostratus near front.

6. Precipitation.—Rain or snow within a zone 200 to 300 miles ahead of front.

As Warm Front Passes Observer:

1. Temperature.—Rises.
2. Relative Humidity.—Increases rather rapidly.
3. Pressure.—Becomes steady (may fall very slowly).
4. Winds.—Become variable, shifting abruptly to south or southwest.
5. Clouds.—Stratus or nimbostratus give way to clouds of cumulus type.
6. Precipitation.—Rain or snow ceasing as front passes.

In Warm Sector:

1. Temperature.—Steady but definitely higher than in air preceding warm front.
2. Relative Humidity.—High.
3. Pressure.—Steady.
4. Winds.—South to southwest.
5. Clouds.—Cumulus, altocumulus, or clear skies. In the winter at sea, broken to overcast conditions usually prevail in the warm sector.
6. Precipitation.—Only local showers, generally fair.

As Cold Front Passes:

1. Temperature.—Abrupt drop.
2. Relative Humidity.—Increases as front passes and then falls rapidly.
3. Pressure.—Rises.
4. Winds.—Gusty, west to northwest.
5. Clouds.—Cumulus or cumulonimbus.
6. Precipitation.—Showers, squalls, or thunderstorms.

After Cold Front Has Passed:

1. Temperature.—Falls rapidly.
2. Relative Humidity.—Decreases rapidly.
3. Pressure.—Increases (more or less rapidly).
4. Winds.—Northwest.
5. Clouds.—Cumulus or fractocumulus (wind broken).
6. Precipitation.—Clearing behind front.

WEATHER CONDITIONS ALONG PATH *XY* OF MATURE CYCLONE.— The trend of weather conditions north of the center of the low, such as along path *XY*, is similar to that south of it. There is one notable exception. No fronts, and consequently no warm sector conditions, are experienced. The fronts north of the center exist aloft, above the observer. Nevertheless, they still exert their influence on clouds and precipitation. Refer to the earlier cross section (Fig. 14-9) along path *XY* of the low.

The surface winds will back continuously around to northwest or north, instead of exhibiting the two abrupt shifts of the warm and cold fronts experienced south of the center.

Owing to the absence of the warm sector, the warm-front rains will give place directly to the cold-front showers followed by clearing. The barometer will not exhibit the period of steadiness observed in the warm sector, where the isobars were parallel to the cyclone motion.

If the path of the low is taken too far north of the center, it can be seen from the diagrams that no precipitation will be experienced—only a protracted period of cloudiness.

STAGE 4. THE OCCLUDED CYCLONE. We have noted that the low-pressure or cyclone area consists of two principal air masses: a cold air mass and a tongue of warm air projecting into the cold. The warm-and cold-air boundary or discon-

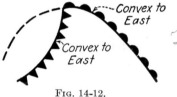

FIG. 14-12.

tinuity in the eastern or forward part of the low has become a warm front, owing to the direction of motion of the low. For the same reason, the western section of the warm- and cold-air boundary has become a cold front.

Recall that cold fronts move faster than warm fronts. A glance at the typical cyclone diagram shows that the air masses on either side of the cold front are moving approximately in the same direction, or roughly, eastward, with the front. But the cold air ahead of the warm front tends to oppose the motion of the front and slow its rate of travel.

Further, the cold front moves faster at its northern end, where it joins the warm front, than it does at the southern end. It is this difference in the speed of the fronts that causes the cyclone wave to lose its symmetry, with both sides of the wave becoming convex to the eastward (Fig. 14-12).

Continued development of the mature cyclone results in the faster moving cold front catching up to the warm front ahead. The overtaking of the warm by the cold front takes place first near the apex or point of the wave. Ultimately the warm sector is completely squeezed aloft as the cold and warm fronts merge. This is the process of "occlusion," and the cyclone in this stage is said to be an "occluded" cyclone.

The weather disturbances within the cyclone reach their greatest intensity at the occluded stage when the fronts have merged. Immediately thereafter, however, the occluded front begins to decay, and as it does so, the cyclone weakens and dies, as the occluded front dissolves with the mixing of the cold air masses on either side.

During the occlusion process, the most violent atmospheric disturbances occur in the zone extending from the point of occlusion, to a distance 50 to 100 miles northward.   This fact is of particular importance in aviation.   The diagrams in Fig. 14-13 show the successive stages of development from the inception of the cyclone wave, through the final occlusion.

Chapter 13 described the weather conditions of the occluded fronts and showed the cross-sectional views of the different stages of occlusion.

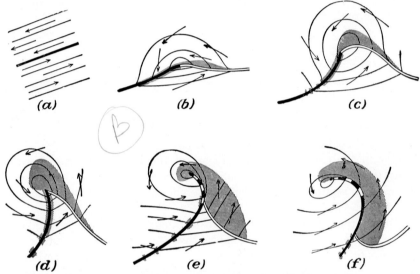

(a)   (b)   (c)

(d)   (e)   (f)

Fig. 14-13.—Life history of a cyclone from inception to occlusion.

The complete life cycle of a wave cyclone from its inception along the polar front to the final stage after occlusion usually covers from 5 to 7 days.

Cyclonic Development in the Southern Hemisphere

The development of a cyclone in the Southern Hemisphere follows the same pattern as in the Northern.   However, the polar air comes from the south and the tropical air from the north in this case.   Hence the apex of the wave points southward rather than northward.

Paths and Movement of Cyclones

The directions and velocities of motion of different cyclones may vary widely, depending on surrounding pressure, temperature, air circulation, and upper-air conditions.   We have mentioned that cyclones have an average rate of motion varying from 20 to 30 miles per hour; or from 480 to 720 miles per day. The lower velocities prevail during late spring, summer, and early autumn, when atmospheric circulation in general is rather sluggish. This velocity then increases, with the higher rates prevailing during the winter period. Cyclonic activity as a whole is far more active during the cold part of the year in either hemisphere, when the vigorous polar front encroaches toward tropical latitudes, causing the production of numerous and active cyclonic waves.

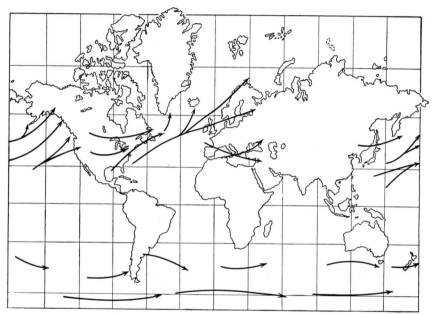

Fig. 14-14.—Generalized world-cyclone paths.

Cyclones, on the average, follow certain well-defined paths or tracks. The determination of speed and path of a particular cyclone are problems to be considered under Weather Interpretation. However, we may note here an important observational fact: *Cyclones tend to move parallel to the isobars in their warm sectors.* Thus, the path of an individual cyclone with a definite warm sector can often be determined by noting the isobar pattern in this zone. Figure 14-14 illustrates the average world cyclone tracks.

Secondaries and Cyclone Families

SECONDARIES.—Frequently, during the late mature or the occluded stage of a cyclone, a small new low develops on the fringes of the original depression. This usually occurs in either the southeastern or the southwestern quadrants, along the warm or the cold front, respectively.   The new cyclone is known as a "secondary."   A secondary cyclone sometimes matures very rapidly, often at the expense of the primary, or as the latter becomes extinct.   After occlusion, the secondary may follow along in the track of the primary cyclone, or it may move in a new path.   Whatever the case, the weather conditions in the area affected by the development of the new depression alter very rapidly.   Care should be given to any tendency for the development of a secondary after a cyclone matures.

CYCLONE FAMILIES.—So far, we have considered the development of a wave cyclone along a relatively small section of a polar front.   However, with each outbreak of polar air into the middle latitudes, there usually develops not one but a series of waves along the polar front, each wave forming its own cyclonic disturbance.   Each wave westward along

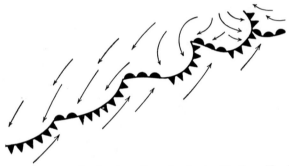

FIG. 14-15.—A cyclone family along the polar front—Northern Hemisphere.

the polar front is at a successively earlier stage in development.   The polar-front boundary of the advancing cold air extends roughly as a northeast-southwest line.   The earliest wave forms near the northeastern end of the original front and, as this wave develops into a true cyclone, the polar air to the west continues moving southward.   As it does so, further reaction between the advancing polar air and the warmer prevailing westerlies leads to the development of newer waves.   Anywhere from two or three to five cyclones may thus form along a particular polar front.   These waves then move east or northeastward, so that the polar front has local characteristics of warm, cold, or occluded fronts.   Figure 14-15 illustrates a family of wave disturbances.   Following the passage of one cyclone family, another outbreak of polar air may occur, and with it a new system of disturbances.

Examples of Cyclone Motion and Development

The accompanying U.S. Navy weather maps illustrate three weather sequences for the North Atlantic, the North Pacific, and the South Pacific oceans. respectively.   These maps are printed in accordance with the standard weather symbols studied previously. Areas of moderate precipitation, such as those associated with warm or occluded fronts, are shown by closely spaced, slanting lines. Areas of heavy or showery precipitation along cold fronts are indicated by widely spaced lines crossing the cold fronts. These sequences all show very clearly the development of cyclone families, with the formation of young disturbances, as those to the east become mature or occluded.

NORTH ATLANTIC SEQUENCE, FEBRUARY 14 TO 19, 1945.—This series illustrates the life history of a family of disturbances formed along the polar front during a particular outbreak of polar air. The strong high-pressure area prevailing at approximately 30°N. on all the maps of the series is the subtropical high-pressure belt for the Atlantic. On some of the maps, this high-pressure zone is distinctly infringed upon as a result of the advancing polar frontal activity (see Figs. 14-16 to 14-21).

The map of the fourteenth shows an occluded low governing most of the weather of the North Atlantic, with a rapidly intensifying disturbance moving offshore from the American seaboard. A small secondary wave is apparent midway between the two lows and has already developed sufficiently to yield precipitation along the warm front. Another wave disturbance has formed near the Spanish peninsula, causing precipitation along Portugal and adjacent waters. On the fifteenth the three disturbances on the Atlantic polar front have continued to move northeastward (parallel to the warm sector isobars). The cyclone in the western Atlantic has grown considerably in intensity, as regards pressure gradient, winds, and precipitation. The small secondary wave in mid-Atlantic is also doing nicely. Note the long uniform extension of the polar front to the southwest. We can undoubtedly expect further activity along this section.

The map for the sixteenth shows continuation of the movement and process described above. The original easternmost cyclone is now almost dissipated over the British Isles. To the southwest, our secondary cyclone is in the occlusion process and exhibits large areas of precipitation in the frontal zones. The strong low, originally observed along the east coast, has entered the occlusion stage, having grown in size and influence. And behold, a new wave has been born on its southwestern flank, as we expected!

On the seventeenth, the parent cyclone, just described, dominates nearly all the Atlantic and surrounding coastal areas, with a second offspring having formed still farther to the southwest.

The maps for the eighteenth and nineteenth trace the further progress and dissipation of this cyclone family, with a new polar front appearing in the west, as the older one gradually loses its prominence in the eastern and central Atlantic.

NORTH PACIFIC SEQUENCE, DECEMBER 18 TO 22, 1938.—In this sequence, we see another series of cyclone waves developing along an outbreak of polar air in the North Pacific. As the polar front itself moves southeastward, the waves travel northeastward, along the main front. Again we note that the new cyclones form to the southwest of the earlier ones, with the polar front extending from northeast to southwest. Precipitation symbols have been omitted from this series (see Figs. 14-22 to 14-26).

The map for the twentieth is particularly illustrative of a cyclone family. We see here four cyclone waves on the polar front in various stages of development. The earliest one, now along the Alaskan coast, has become completely occluded and is rapidly dissipating. The two waves to the southwest are in different stages of occlusion, while the last is still youthful in appearance.

Continued development has resulted in the weather configuration shown on the map of December 22, where we note a southwestward extension of the polar front. The formation of a new wave may be anticipated along this portion, while a further outbreak of polar air can be expected in the northwest.

SOUTH PACIFIC SEQUENCE, FEBRUARY 2 TO 4, 1941.—We emphasize again that frontal activity in southern latitudes is neither so vigorous nor so widespread as in northern latitudes. The map of February 2 (Fig. 14-27) shows two cold fronts. The front extending from New Zealand to Australia separates the subtropical high in this area, into two divisions or cells of high pressure. Figures 14-28 and 14-29 show the development of two waves on this front, with attendant cyclonic conditions. By February 4 the earlier wave has begun the occlusion process, as the wave to the west reaches maturity. Note also on this map, the early phase of a new wave which has begun formation on the cold front farther east. The wind circulation in connection with these wave cyclones is again typical of that studied previously.

RELATION OF CYCLONES TO THE JET STREAM.—Current research indicates a close connection between the position and movement of the jet stream and the polar front. There are also strong indications of a genetic relationship between the jet stream and cyclone development. Further, the jet stream seems to exert a definite steering control over cyclonic paths, and in the forecasting of cyclonic motion, the use of wind data from upper-air charts is of great value.

NORTH ATLANTIC WEATHER MAP SERIES SHOWING
CYCLONE MOTION AND DEVELOPMENT
Figs. 14–16 to 14–21. *(Courtesy of U.S. Navy.)*

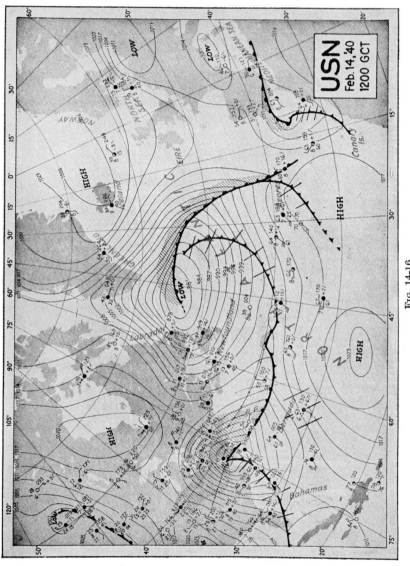

Fig. 14-16.

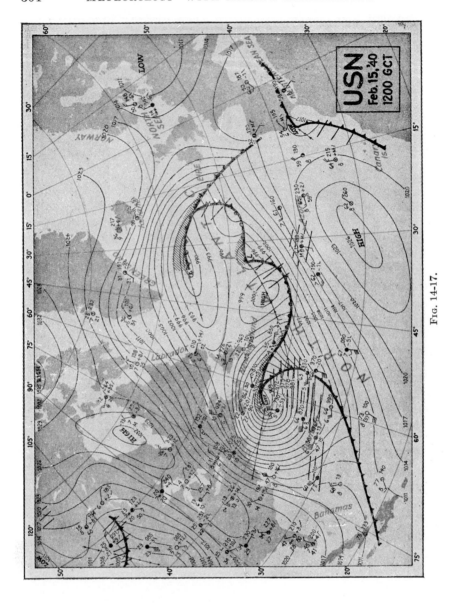

Fig. 14-17.

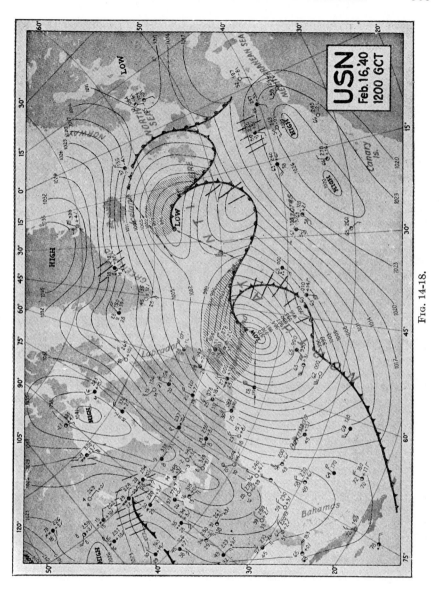

FIG. 14-18.

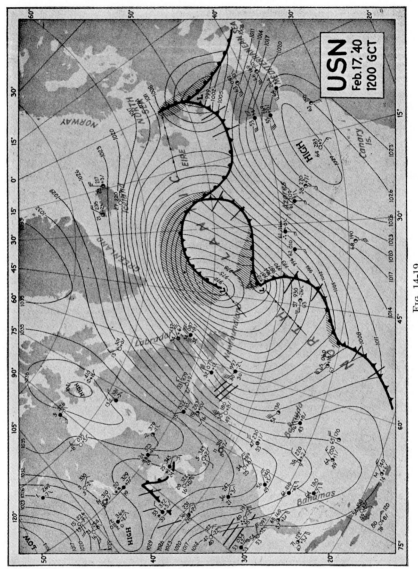

Fig. 14-19.

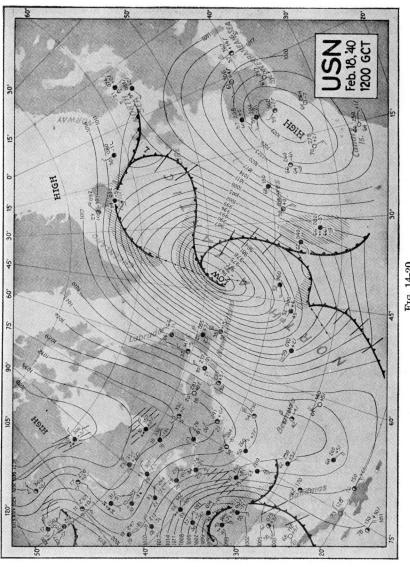

FIG. 14-20.

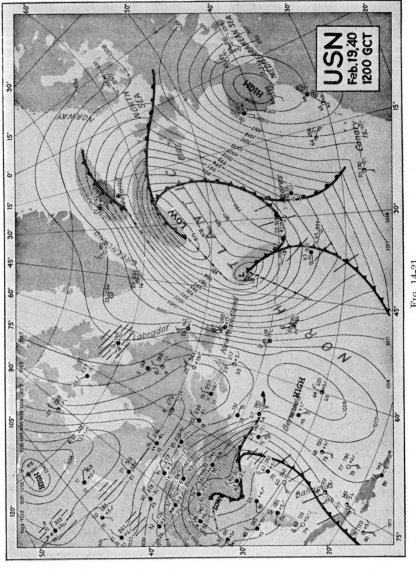

Fig. 14-21.

NORTH PACIFIC WEATHER MAP SERIES
Figs. 14–22 to 14–26. (*Courtesy of U.S. Navy.*)

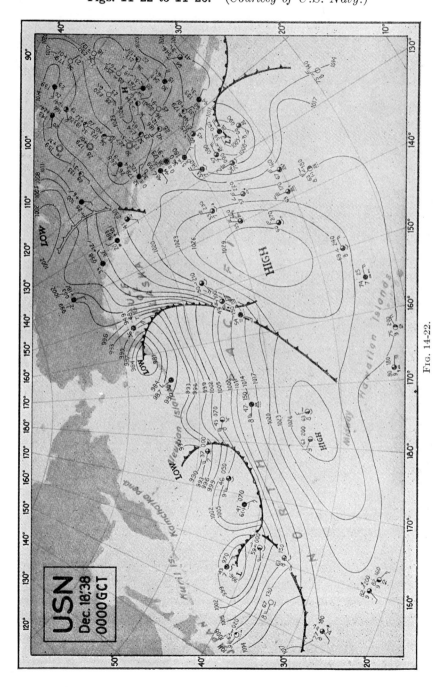

Fig. 14-22.

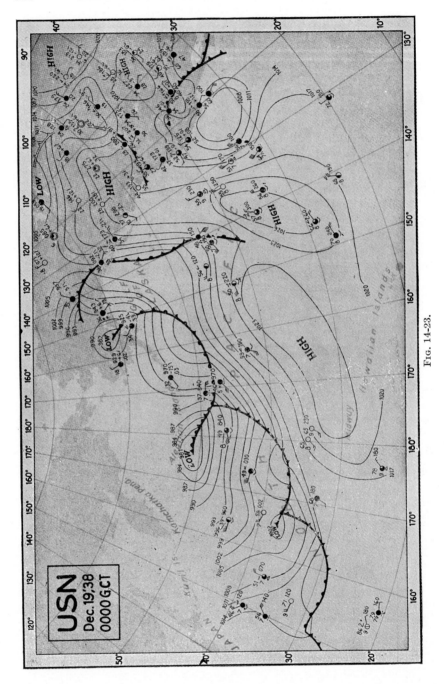

FIG. 14-23.

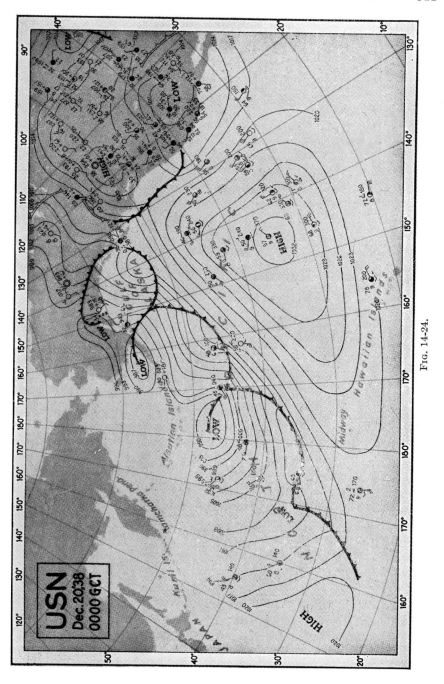

Fig. 14·24.

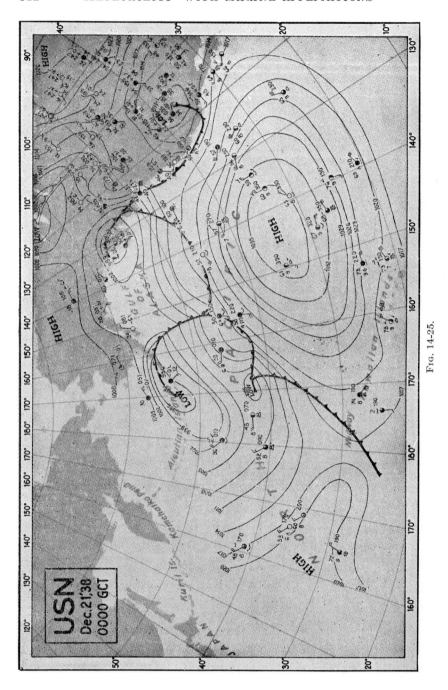

Fig. 14-25.

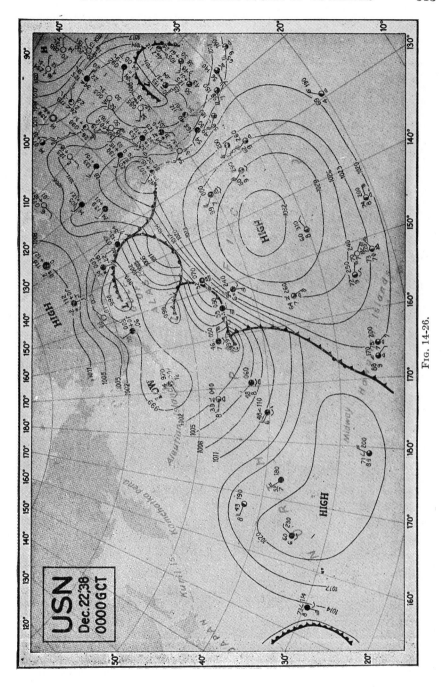

FIG. 14-26.

SOUTH PACIFIC WEATHER MAP SERIES
Figs. **14–27** to **14–29.**   (*Courtesy of U.S. Navy.*)

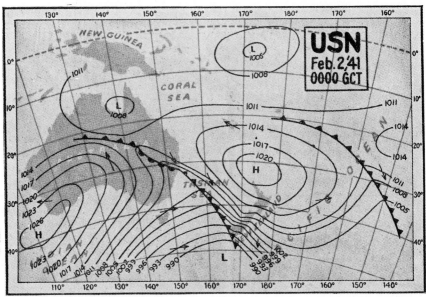

FIG. 14-27.

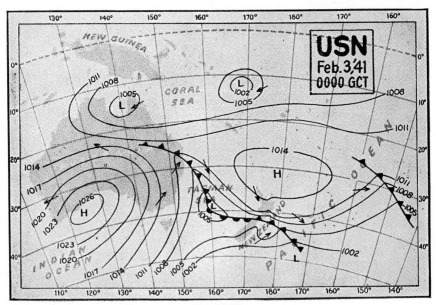

FIG. 14-28.

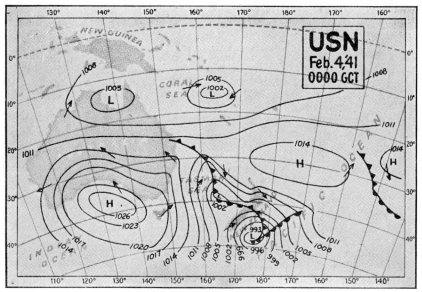

FIG. 14·29.

CHAPTER 15

WEATHER ANALYSIS AND INTERPRETATION

A forecaster's life is not a happy one. So numerous and complex are the factors that determine the behavior of the weather, that forecasts are frequently prepared that never come to pass. Although complete, accurate, modern forecasting requires a thorough groundwork in physics, mathematics, and meteorology, we can study here only some of the basic techniques and problems.

Regardless of the quantity of theoretical knowledge that may be had, experience is equally important in prognosticating the weather. This experience can be gained only by observing weather conditions and by preparing and studying weather maps. A fundamental axiom in forecasting is that *weather conditions in the middle latitudes move generally eastward*. Thus, a study of successive weather maps, tracing the movement of the weather, is essential to the problem of forecasting. No two weather map situations are exactly alike, but there are frequently very close resemblances. Hence, in the interpretation of a map, the knowledge of earlier, similar conditions, and their results is of great value.

Errors in anticipating weather conditions may not necessarily be ascribed to poor interpretation. Often, changes in atmospheric conditions develop that alter expected weather. Yet these changes may not have been indicated by the observation data available.

We may separate the steps necessary to forecasting, into four broad stages:

1. The taking of accurate observations, together with their coding and transmission
2. The plotting of the weather map
3. The analysis of the weather map
4. The interpretation of the analyzed map

Plotting the Weather Map

We have already considered the methods of observing and coding weather data. We have considered, too, the common technique of plotting the weather map. It will be remembered that, after decoding, the weather information for a given station is entered in a prescribed form in conformance with the station model. The circle in the center

316

of the model, indicating the state of the sky, represents the actual location of the station, since the other information covers a relatively large area on the map.

The station model illustrated previously is a complete model. Even land stations do not usually include all this information, but use the model in an abbreviated form, although the data used are still in the proper designated position.

When drawn for marine weather conditions, the central circle must correspond to the latitude and longitude of the reporting vessel. Consequently, while models for land stations remain fixed in location, marine station models appear at different locations on successive maps. This disadvantage cannot be helped.

The marine weather observer and the nonprofessional meteorologist will rarely plot station observations as completely as those plotted in regular weather offices. In any case, however, maps plotted at sea should, if at all possible, contain at least the following:

1. Atmospheric pressure
2. Wind direction and force
3. Temperature
4. State of the sky

The type of clouds and the nature of any existing precipitation are of almost equal importance, but reports on these conditions may not always be readily available.

Figure 15-1 illustrates the plotting of these weather elements according to data received mostly from ships in the North Atlantic. This map itself is a reduced and somewhat abbreviated copy of the regular radio marine weather map. The Weather Bureau will supply blank copies on request to ships desirous of preparing daily weather maps.

The numerals below the permanent land and island stations are the index numbers of each. Remember that these constitute the first three symbols of fixed station weather reports. Pressure is here recorded in millibars, in the accepted form of omitting the first 9 or 10. Thus, as in the lower left corner of the map, 155 is 1,015.5 millibars; 172 is 1,017.2 millibars, etc.

Weather conditions over given areas, even the relatively large area embraced by the above observations, are but a part of the considerably greater world weather pattern. As a result of the movement of air masses and associated fronts, in addition to the existing wind circulation, one must be aware of the weather over a considerably greater area, in order to anticipate or prognosticate weather conditions for a small area. Further, since "weather" moves generally eastward, a knowledge of the state of the atmosphere over a large region to the west, is absolutely essential for an accurate forecast. Consequently, a weather map of the

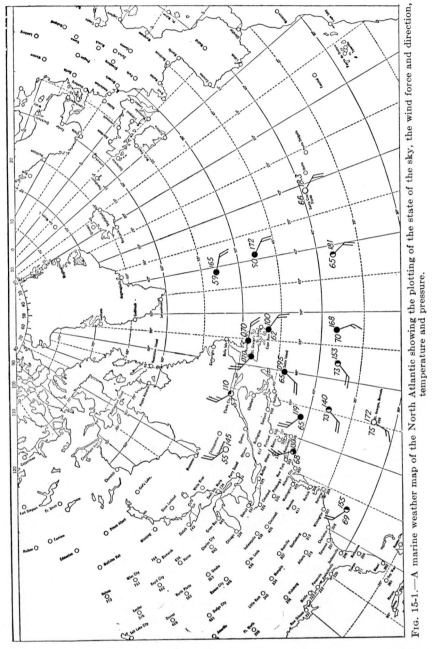

FIG. 15-1.—A marine weather map of the North Atlantic showing the plotting of the state of the sky, the wind force and direction, temperature and pressure.

North Atlantic necessarily includes a large portion of North America and Europe.

Owing to the synopsis of weather conditions presented by weather maps, they are commonly called "synoptic charts." In addition to the plotting of actual station conditions, the areas covered by precipitation are indicated by shading in some manner.

Weather Map Analysis

The analyzed weather map is often said to present, both directly and indirectly, more information than any other chart in existence. Such a map, after being plotted, is a maze of apparently disorganized facts. Potentially, it has an important story to tell. The process of weather map analysis consists of organizing the information on it into a logical meteorological picture.

We can divide the procedure into three basic steps:

1. Frontal analysis
2. Isobaric or pressure analysis
3. Analysis of air-mass conditions

In accordance with the scope of this book, special attention will be given to the first two steps. We shall mention only briefly the problems of analysis and interpretation of air-mass conditions. The reason for this is twofold: (1) A detailed study of air masses requires more observational data than are usually available for the marine or lay forecaster. (2) The problem involves a technical study of atmospheric conditions beyond our present scope. Each of these three steps can of course be refined or subdivided further. For a more complete treatment of the analysis and interpretation of air masses as applied to weather conditions, the interested reader is referred to the many advanced texts covering this subject, some of which are recommended in the Bibliography.

In all weather analysis it is of prime importance to consider the weather map or maps previous to the one at hand. Obviously, conditions on the new map must tally with those of the previous ones. This also simplifies analysis, since the analyst thus obtains a knowledge of how conditions ought to appear on the new map. If no previous maps are available, the first one may be more difficult to prepare.

Frontal Analysis

Fronts, being the boundaries of air masses, clearly have a pronounced influence on weather changes. The distinguishing of the existing fronts on a weather map not only indicates the air-mass boundaries, but also aids greatly in the identification of the position of the different air masses themselves. In Chap. 13 on Air Masses and Fronts, a study was made of the more obvious weather differences on opposite sides of a front.

It follows then, if we can determine the position of a line on either side of which more or less marked weather differences exist, that the line is probably a front.

The important criteria employed in the location of fronts may be enumerated as follows:

1. Temperature differences
2. Wind shifts
3. Humidity differences
4. Clouds and precipitation conditions
5. Pressure and isobaric conditions

As many of these factors as possible should be utilized in frontal analysis.

1. TEMPERATURE CONDITIONS.—We have noted that temperature conditions are the essential feature of air masses. The determination of the temperature difference or discontinuity between air masses is very useful in establishing the location of a front. However, the surface air temperatures are often strongly affected by local heating and cooling, in addition to topography and other factors. The true temperature discontinuity is best shown in the upper air, away from the influence of surface conditions. Marine air temperatures are also more indicative of the true discontinuity than those over land.

Further, the air bodies separated by the front may have very nearly the same temperatures. In such cases, this factor may be unreliable; in any case, it should be supplemented by other criteria.

2. WIND SHIFTS.—The wind shift or wind discontinuity on either side of a front is normally one of the best criteria in locating it. There is nearly always some degree of shifting of the wind associated with fronts. This usually shows quite clearly on the synoptic weather chart and enables the proper placing of the front.

On occasions, abrupt wind shifts may occur without an attending front. A pronounced wedge or ridge of high pressure will cause such a shift along the axis of the ridge, in order for the wind to conform to the isobars. A further empirical rule is of great value in distinguishing such cases. Consideration of the relationship between winds and fronts developed in the past two chapters shows that in the Northern Hemisphere, *if one places his back to the wind, any associated front will be on the left.* Hence, as a result of the clockwise wind circulation about a high, this rule places the front in a direction opposite to the axis of the high-pressure ridge, where the wind shift occurs.

It is apparent that the direction of the wind is of greater significance than its velocity, for this purpose. However, there may also exist a marked difference in velocity on opposite sides of the front, particularly in the case of an advancing cold, "blustering," polar air mass. This property is also of value in frontal analysis.

3. Humidity Differences.—Dew-point observations are usually the only direct humidity observations shown on the synoptic chart. A careful examination of dew-point differences along the position of a suspected front often aids materially in analysis. At times these differences may be the only definite indication of the presence of a front. Remember that the dew point of a given air mass remains quite constant, barring gain or loss of water vapor.

4. Clouds and Precipitation Conditions.—The relationship between areas of cloudiness and precipitation is often well defined, when these conditions are of frontal origin. The association of the types and areas of clouds, with the fronts responsible, has been explained in the

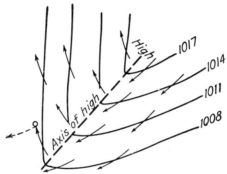

Fig. 15-2.—The use of the left-hand rule in locating fronts shows the above to be a high-pressure axis rather than a front. An observer at "0" places the front in the direction shown by the broken arrow.

chapters of fronts and cyclone development. This knowledge can be used only if these factors are included in the report. They are nearly always available on land station reports but may be omitted from ship reports. If cloud and precipitation data are recorded on the weather map, a study of their type and distribution is often an excellent guide to the type and location of existing fronts. Thus a narrow band of heavy cumulus or cumulonimbus clouds, especially if associated with storms, may indicate a cold front. A warm front has its own sequence of clouds and precipitation, as studied earlier. This information, together with wind observations, may clearly mark warm-or cold-front positions.

5. Pressure and Isobaric Conditions.—Normally, any existing fronts are located before the drawing of the isobars. However, an examination of pressure conditions is still of value since some pressure change characterizes nearly all fronts. The pressure tendency, given in the supplemental section of a weather report, is very useful. Thus, the position of a front may be determined by the fact that a negative tendency

(falling pressure) exists on one side, while a positive tendency (rising pressure) exists on the other. Fronts lie in pressure troughs!

Then there is the angular bend in the isobars where they cross a front. Regardless of how much an isobar bends, it always does so sharply. After the position of the front is located roughly, the drawing of the isobars in the vicinity of it will locate it more accurately.

ILLUSTRATIONS OF SIMPLE FRONTAL ANALYSIS.—At times, conditions may be such that a front will stand out like the proverbial sore thumb.

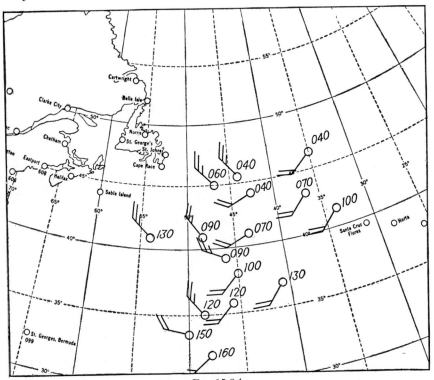

FIG. 15-3A.

At other times, the determination of existing fronts may require a much closer examination of the plotted weather map. The more knowledge and experience the analyst can apply, the more easily and accurately will the fronts be located.

Figure 15-3A, shows ship reports of pressure and wind plotted on a small portion of the marine radio weather map. A rapid survey indicates that two distinct wind streams are present: one from the northwest and one from the southwest. It seems clear that a front probably lies between the two air masses distinguished by the different wind directions. An examination of the pressure reports shows that the isobars would make a very sharp bend at the position of the suspected front.   Figure 15-3*B* illustrates the result of this survey, with the front being drawn so as to have northwest winds on one side and southwest on the other.   Note that, if the observer places his back to the wind, the front is to the left in accordance with the rule.   Note also that, if isobars were drawn, those to the right of the front would have a northeast-southwest trend, whereas those to the left would have northwest or north-northwest to southeast trend, marking a definite sharp angle at the front.

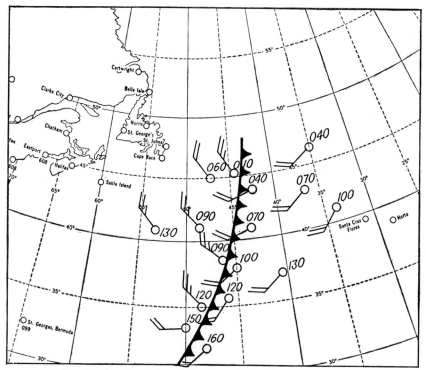

FIG. 15-3*B*.—Frontal analysis of conditions shown on Fig. 15-3*A*.

In consideration of the direction of the two air masses present, from the cold northwest and warm southwest, respectively, the front is considered to be cold, despite the absence of temperature reports.   Since both air masses are moving generally eastward, the front will clearly move in the same direction, or toward the warmer (tropical) air.   From our knowledge of the cyclone structure we can conceive of the air mass from the southwest as being part of the warm sector of a cyclone.

Figure 15-4*A* illustrates an example of reports where wind, temperature, and state of the sky are given.   A study of these reports indicates the presence of a front running approximately northwest-southeast, through the island of Horta.   One group of reports shows temperatures in the low sixties, with clear to partly cloudy conditions and southwest winds.   The other group shows southerly winds with temperatures in the fifties and overcast conditions.   This leads us to place the front in the position shown on Fig. 15-4*B*.   A consideration of temperatures and directions of motion leads to the assumption that it is a warm front, which might well be the eastern boundary of a cyclone warm sector.

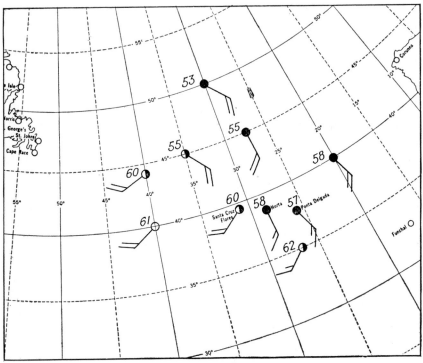

FIG. 15-4*A*.

Figure 15-5*A* is slightly more complicated than the other illustrations. Here we have reports on wind, temperature, clouds, and present weather conditions.   It is noticed that three sets of wind systems prevail: a southeasterly set, a southwesterly set, and a west-to-northwesterly set. The ships with northwesterly winds on the 30th and 35th meridians show thundershowers and intermittent heavy rains, respectively.   The temperatures at these ships are lower than those to the east.   Three other ships, to the west, also show low temperatures but have fair-weather cumulus clouds.   Apparently we have here a cold air mass, with the line of showers marking the cold-front boundary.

South of latitude 50°, the cold northwest air is separated from the relatively cold southeast air by a sector of warm air from the southwest. North of latitude 50°, the cold air masses are adjacent to each other, with heavy rains or showers prevailing in both. The rain in the southeast air, south of 50° is moderate, and out ahead of the rain altostratus clouds prevail. Here we have indications of a warm front. From a consideration of wind direction, clouds, and precipitation it seems that a front exists between the southwest and southeast air and extends

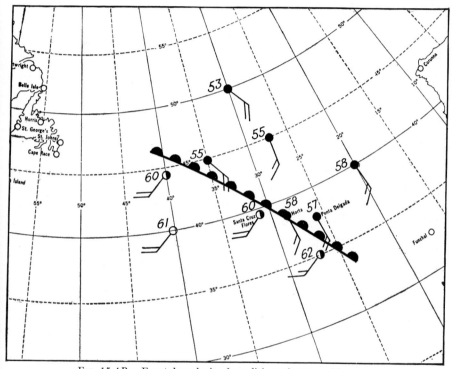

Fig. 15-4*B*.—Frontal analysis of conditions shown on Fig. 15-4*A*.

south-southeast from 50°N. 27°W. Northwestward from this point, the warm front joins the previously determined cold front, yielding an occluded front separating two cold air masses.

Figure 15-5*B* shows the completed frontal analysis. Note that an east-west line, north of 50°, crosses but one front or wind-shift line. South of 50°, both cold and warm fronts are encountered, with associated wind and temperature changes.

If no fronts can be located on a plotted weather map, there is not necessarily cause for alarm. Only one air mass may exist in the area covered by the observations. In such a case, the weather is determined by conditions within the air mass and will show no effect of frontal disturbances.

On the basis of wind, pressure, and sky conditions the reader may attempt to place the fronts on the weather maps (Figs. 10-5 to 10-7) in Chap. 10. Further experience and benefit will be derived from such practice.

Isobaric Analysis

Isobaric analysis is necessary (1) to indicate the distribution of high- and low-pressure areas, with their relation to existing air masses

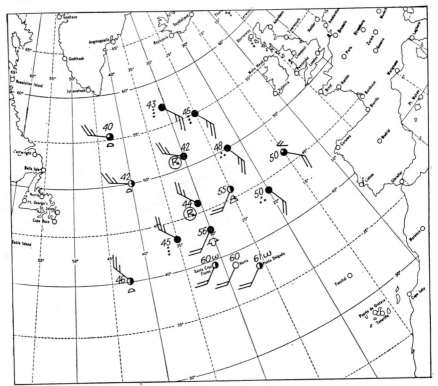

Fig. 15-5A.

and fronts, and (2) to show the nature of the pressure gradient in different areas, which aids greatly in determining the future movement of weather conditions. The difficulty in drawing isobars lies mainly in the inadequate number of observations available. Consequently, their positions must usually be estimated. Remember that isobars are drawn only for every 3 or 4 millibars, depending on the number of observations available.

Another source of difficulty lies in the errors in plotted pressure observations. These errors may arise from a number of causes, such as instrumental, observational, transmissional, plotting, or coding. To simplify the process of drawing isobars, a number of empirical rules have to be developed. These rules and their explanations follow.

Before studying these rules, recall the generalities drawn from our consideration of isobars in Chap. 7 on Atmospheric Pressure.

Isobars are always closed curved lines. No loose or dangling ends can exist on a map. An isobar may not close up within the confines

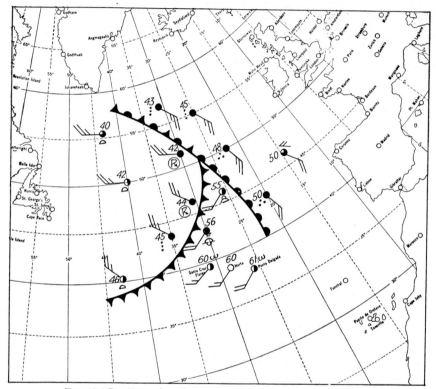

FIG. 15-5*B*.—Frontal analysis of conditions shown on Fig. 15-5*A*.

of a map but is terminated at the map border. Obviously, isobars may never cross each other or meet at a right angle, with one coming to a dead end. All this is equally true of topographic contour lines for much the same reason.

RULES FOR DRAWING ISOBARS.—1. *Smooth isobars with simple patterns are more usual than irregular isobars, or complicated patterns.* Minor irregularities that are not common to other isobars are probably due to errors, such as those listed above. The isobars should then be smoothed or "faired" to eliminate minor wiggles and bends.

If pressure observations on a weather map are followed faithfully, results shown in Fig. 15-6A might develop. The smoothed isobars are shown in Fig. 15-6B.

If systematic irregularities exist, as indicated by several isobars, the condition shown is probably real. Note the sharp bend of the isobars in the eastern and southwestern sections of the low. This is common to the whole pressure pattern. Our knowledge of fronts leads to the

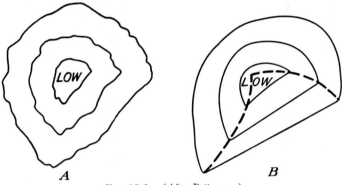

A   *B*

FIG. 15-6.—(*After Petterssen.*)

supposition that these kinks represent the warm and cold fronts of a cyclone.

At points *A* and *B* in Fig. 15-7, we note two apparent anomalies in the isobars. These may be the result of an error, or they may indicate the beginning of a secondary low-pressure center. Rule 2 aids us in this case.

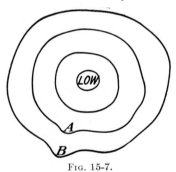

FIG. 15-7.

2. *The direction of the isobars should conform to the proper relationship with wind directions; the spacing of the isobars should agree with the pressure gradient and dependent wind velocity.* As a result of deflection, recall that the wind blows along the isobars with but a slight inward drift, from higher to lower pressures. At sea, with normal wind velocities, the acute angle between wind direction and the isobars is about 15°. Thus, the isobars should be drawn "down wind," keeping this approximate relationship. The wind should not cross the isobars at, or nearly at, right angles.

Assume that, in accordance with the pressure readings, the isobars are drawn. In Fig. 15-8A the wind reports do not agree with the isobars at points *D* and *E*. Either the wind or the pressure reports are in error here, for the wind crosses the isobars nearly perpendicularly. Wind reports are usually more dependable than pressure reports at sea.   Thus, in accordance with rule 1, we fair the isobars as shown by the broken line, noting that wind directions and isobars now agree.

In Fig. 15-8*B* we see that, despite the irregularity, the isobars *do* conform to the wind direction, with the wind having slight drift across

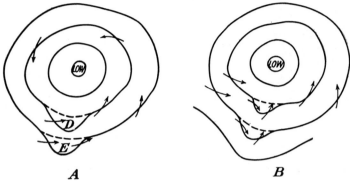

A   *B*

Fig. 15-8.

them from higher to lower pressures.   If we smooth the isobars as shown by the broken line, the wind either crosses them at a large angle or blows from lower to higher pressure.   Such a situation may represent the beginning of a secondary low, which must then be watched closely on succeeding maps for further development, since a major cyclonic dis-

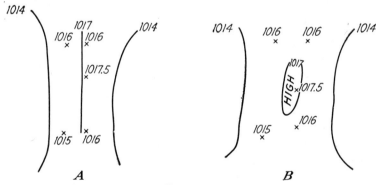

A   *B*

Fig. 15-9.

turbance often develops from original pressure and wind irregularities of this type.

Where the pressure gradient is steep, with relatively high wind velocities, the isobars should be closer together than on other parts of the map where lower velocities prevail.   Care should be taken in drawing the map to see that the isobars conform to this principle.

3. *All pressure observations on one side of an isobar must be higher in value than the isobar, and all readings on the other side must be lower.* In accordance with our knowledge of isobars, it is clear that they may not have higher and lower pressure readings on the same side. Thus, in Fig. 15-9*A*, the 1,017 isobar cannot stand alone. An examination of the surrounding observations shows that it actu-

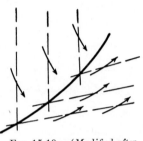

Fig. 15-10.—(*Modified after Petterssen.*)

ally encloses a small ridge or dome of high pressure, as in Fig. 15-9*B*. Now the area within the 1,017 isobar is all higher in pressure, while the outer area is lower.

4. *Isobars crossing fronts should be drawn with sharp bends, the kinks pointing to higher pressures; this brings out the pressure gradient discontinuity.* According to Petterssen's technique, the isobars on either side of a front should be continued across it as a straight line. A line drawn connecting the points of intersection of the isobars thus serves as a further accurate method of locating the front. This is illustrated in Fig. 15-10.

Figure 15-11*a* illustrates isobars drawn without careful attention

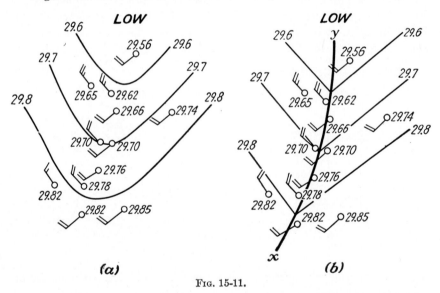

(*a*)

(*b*)

Fig. 15-11.

to the wind direction along the axis of the low. The application of rules 2 (wind direction) and 4 gives the more correct picture shown in Fig. 15-11*b*, with the front in the position *x-y*. Pressure observations are here given in inches and tenths.

5. *Isobars should be drawn first where the pattern is apparently simplest and most easily seen.* Accordingly, the analysis is best started where the number of reports is the densest. On marine maps, the drawing of isobars should start at coastal regions where the reports may be more numerous than over the sea and where they will probably be more accurate. The isobars should then be extended seaward. They should also be drawn first in one air mass and then in another, starting if possible with the pressure centers. After analysis is complete within each air mass, the isobars should be continued and linked across the fronts.

6. *Isobars, when drawn, should show a logical agreement with the preceding map.* Since weather conditions move, and often change as they move, the isobars on a new map should agree with the expected movements and changes of the pressure areas on the previous map. If the pressure centers show an erratic path of movement, it is probable that the new map is wrongly analyzed, provided the earlier map is correct. This may not always be the case. The earlier map may be shown to have been incorrect on the basis of the new one.

A very interesting and unusual, though by no means unique, example of the application of frontal and isobaric analysis to the problem of navigation at sea was given in a letter by Chief Officer Duggan, of the Canadian M. V. Ary Larsen to the Hydrographic Office. Part of this follows:

"We left Belgium bound for Hampton Roads in ballast. The weather was very bad, and for three days after leaving St. Catherines we saw nothing by which we could fix our position. Our leeway was purely guesswork, and at times we estimated about five points. Our reckoning was bound to be faulty, as we had nothing to check by, and the course the ship was steering was, to say the least, wild. On the fourth day the second officer and the Captain had fixed a position by dead reckoning, and I, in the meantime, had done Rugby's weather, which showed that a very deep depression was to the west of Ireland (it took no map to show that we were in it) with a very marked cold front. I plotted our barometer reading in our assumed position, but it seemed to be a great deal out. However, I ignored it, and reckoned the possible time the cold front would meet us. I argued that either our position was wrong or that the barometer was sadly in error. Further, I argued that if we were on the isobar our barometer gave, the cold front should pass over us in about an hour, whereas if we were in the D.R. position, it would not meet us for about two hours. In approximately one hour there was a heavy downpour of rain, the wind increased to about force 10 and shifted violently and suddenly to the northwest. Later that afternoon the sky cleared and we were able to get a good fix, which found the D.R. position some 60 miles in error, and proving that the ship was on the isobar indicated by the barometer.   I am not going to say that the position of the ship can be accurately fixed by means of a weather map and isobars, but it could, with a good barometer, be a good check against such errors as large as these, and which can happen in the winter time in ships such as these which carry very little ballast, and which are at the mercy of the elements, literally and absolutely."

Analysis of Air Masses

After the fronts and isobars have been drawn, attention is then given to an examination of the air masses present.   Many of the recorded observations are employed in this process.   The data of particular importance include temperature, movement, dew point, clouds, and present weather conditions.

1. By means of the study of the above data and reference to preceding charts, the source or origin, and hence the type, of air mass may be determined.

2. The existing characteristics of the air mass are determined from a consideration of the cloud and present weather conditions.   Clouds of the cumulus or vertical development type, and associated showers, indicate convection and instable conditions within the mass.   Fog and stratus clouds, with or without light rain or drizzle, indicate stable air conditions, with a lack of pronounced vertical movement.

3. Modifications of the air mass may be estimated by noting the conditions of the underlying surfaces, over and toward which the air mass is moving.   The temperature of the lower layer of air may be noticeably affected by the surface temperature beneath and cause surface air to become either warmer or colder.   If the air becomes colder, as a result of a colder surface beneath, the lapse rate will tend to decrease, increasing the stability of the air.   Heating of the surface air, while the upper air temperature remains fairly constant, will increase the lapse rate and thus increase the tendency toward instability.

Continental air moving out across sea areas tends to develop a higher humidity through increasing the water content by evaporation.

4. As explained earlier, the air-mass boundaries are indicated by the discontinuities in weather conditions prevailing at the fronts.   A band of clouds of the cirrostratus-altostratus sequence is indicative of an approaching front, although it may be beyond the confines of the particular map.

Once again it is emphasized that air-mass conditions on a map must exist in logical sequence with conditions exhibited on previous maps. We have considered here mainly a descriptive or qualitative treatment of air masses.   More exacting quantitative studies of air masses and their motion, involving relations between *specific humidity* and *potential temperature*, known as "isentropic analysis" are used by the professional weather man. Discussions of this important and relatively new phase of analysis may be found in more advanced texts, some of which are listed in the Bibliography.

Examples of Complete Map Analysis

We shall examine now the complete analysis of two surface weather maps of the United States, noting the application of the principles and techniques studied heretofore. A set of land maps has been chosen for this purpose, rather than marine maps. This allows for a more complete illustration of the methods of analysis, owing to the completeness and the greater number of reports available. The analyses are those of B. C. Haynes of the U.S. Weather Bureau.

Figures 15-12 and 15-13 are the unanalyzed surface maps of the United States for 1930 EST, April 17, 1940, and 0130 EST, April 18, 1940. After examination of these maps, the written analysis should be studied carefully, with continual reference to the maps. Figures 15-14 and 15-15 are the same maps with the results of the analyses included.

The reader is invited to attempt his own analysis of the unanalyzed maps for 0730 EST and 1330 EST, of April 18, 1940 (Figs. 15-16 and 15-17). The results can then be compared to the correctly analyzed maps shown in Figs. 15-18 and 15-19. No written analyses are given for this second set.

ANALYSIS OF THE SURFACE WEATHER MAP FOR 1930 EST, WEDNESDAY, APRIL 17, 1940

Frontal Analysis

"Examining the map we find the lowest pressure in western Indiana where a station reports the pressure of 998.0 millibars. The wind at this station is southwest force 4; therefore, the lowest pressure is to the west of this station. At this point let us begin the frontal analysis. It will be noted that the general wind pattern over Kentucky, Tennessee, and the Southeastern States is from south to southwest. It will be further noted that the winds over Illinois, Missouri, Kansas, and the Central Plains States are generally northwest to north. On this map the front is sharp enough to be found almost exclusively by use of winds. However, other indications must also be used since in some cases with low-wind velocities or in thunderstorm areas the winds may not be representative of the true direction of movement of the air mass.

"Beginning at the station in western Indiana which has a pressure of 998.0, we trace the front to the west of this station. The next station to the west shows a north wind force 5, overcast, and a temperature of 37°, dew point 36°, with a +2.4 millibars pressure tendency. On the

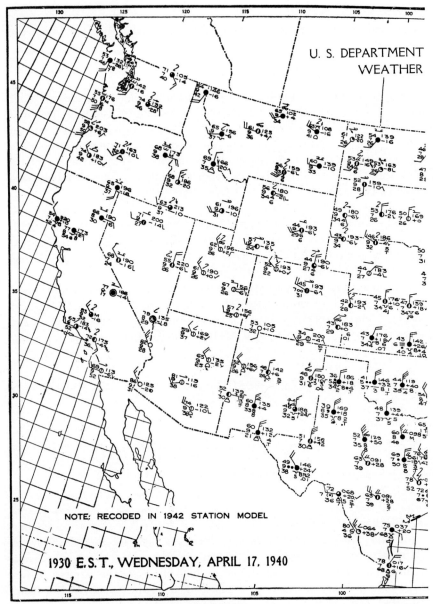

FIG. 15-12.

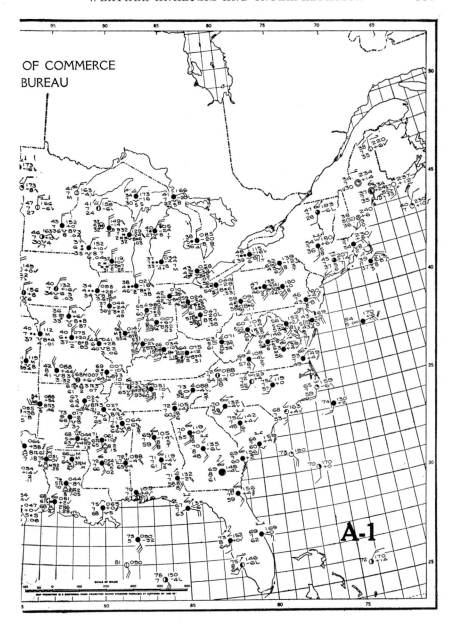

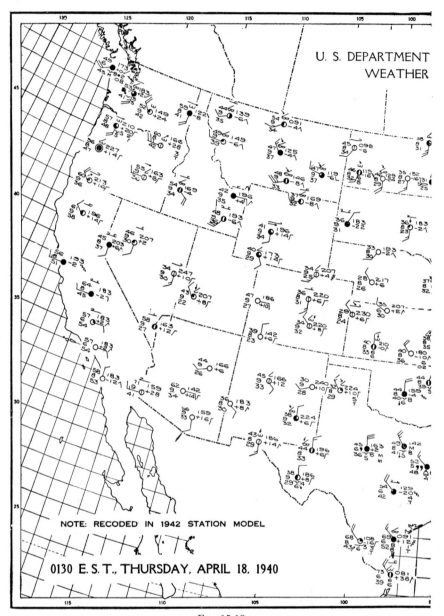

FIG. 15-13.

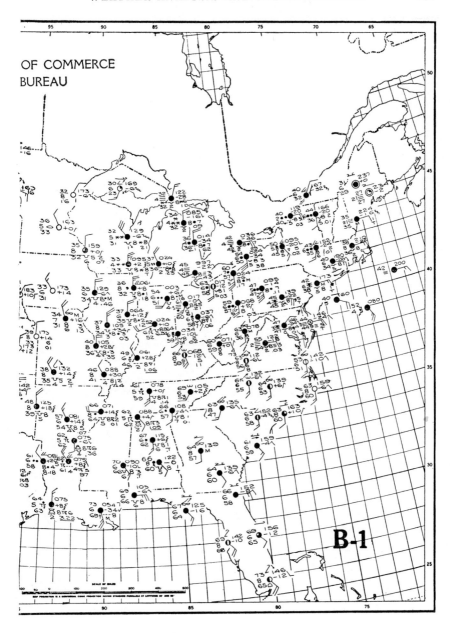

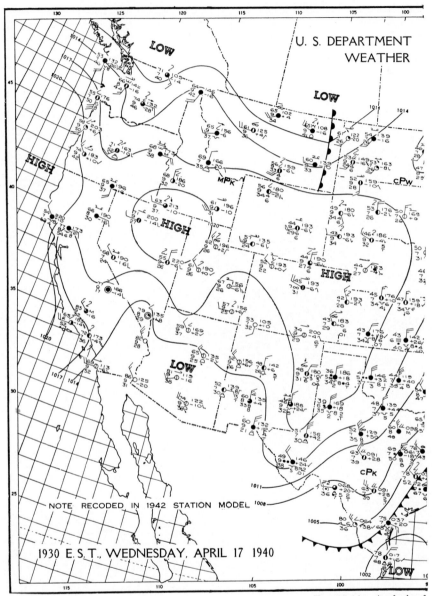

FIG. 15-14.—Analysis of

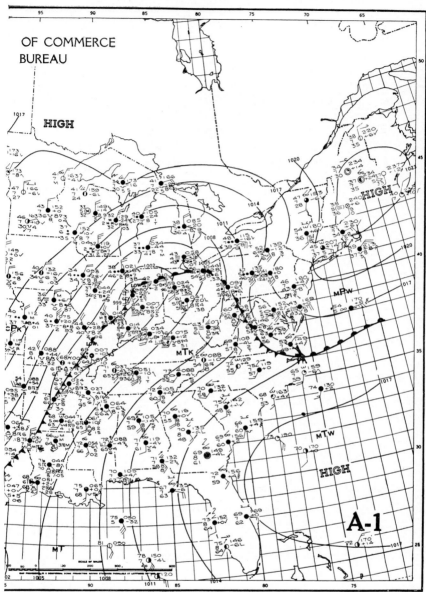

map shown in Fig. 15-12.

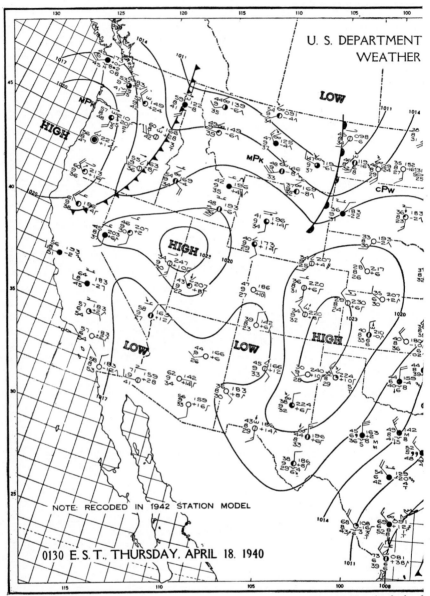

U. S. DEPARTMENT
WEATHER

NOTE: RECODED IN 1942 STATION MODEL

0130 E. S. T., THURSDAY, APRIL 18. 1940

FIG. 15-15.—Analysis of

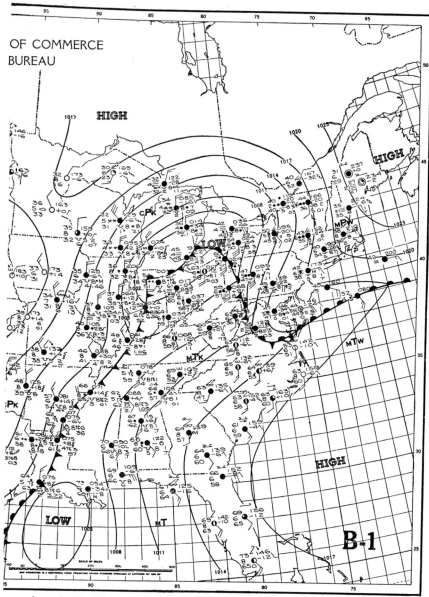

map shown in Fig. 15-13.

other hand the station in western Indiana with a pressure of 998.0 millibars has a temperature of 65°, dew point 60°, with a falling pressure tendency of −2.2 millibars. Between these two stations we have a good example of the temperature, dew point, and pressure-tendency differences, as well as a decided wind shift across the front. Following southwestward from this point we observe a station in eastern Illinois with a northwest wind force 4, pressure 1,001.4 millibars, temperature 56°, dew point 53°, and a pressure tendency of +1.6 millibars with a characteristic of falling then rising. Immediately to the southeast of this station another station reports temperature 66°, dew point 62°, pressure 1,001.4 millibars, wind southwest force 4, and a tendency of −0.2 millibars. Here again we have a temperature difference, a dew-point difference, and a pressure-tendency difference, in addition to the wind shift to aid us in locating the front. Since the station in eastern Illinois shows a kink in the pressure-tendency characteristic and, also, since the temperature is still high, we will place the front just to the southeast of this station.

"Again following toward the southwest we see stations in southeastern Missouri reporting wind discontinuities, temperature differences, and pressure-tendency differences. Therefore, we may continue to draw the front down through southeastern Missouri and through central Arkansas between the stations reporting westerly or northwesterly winds and the stations reporting southerly or southwesterly winds.

"Entering Louisiana, we see that the most northwestern station in Louisiana is reporting north wind force 4 and cumulonimbus clouds. The pressure tendency reported at this station is 0 but shows a kink. Stations to the west report strong positive-pressure tendencies and stations to the east zero or small negative tendencies. The front may then be drawn through this station and continued toward the southwest through eastern Texas, following between the station with the pressure of 1,003.4 and northwest force 2 wind and station with a pressure of 1,004.7 and southeast force 2 wind. Although at this point a temperature difference no longer exists, there is still some indication of a dew-point difference. The western station has a dew point of 52° and the eastern station 67°. The front may then be continued based mostly on dew point and consideration of the wind direction. The front will then be placed between a station in southern and western Texas having a pressure of 1,006.4, northwest force 5 wind, dew point 36°, and the station on the coast with the east-southeast force 3 wind and dew point of 68°. The front may be dropped in northern Mexico where data are lacking.

"Picking up the front again at the low-pressure center in western Indiana and looking eastward, we observe that through southern Michigan and northern Ohio there is again a good wind discontinuity. Temperature and dew-point differences may also be used over this section of the map to find the front. From a point just west of the station with pressure 998.0 in western Indiana the front may be drawn east-north-eastward to between stations with a pressure of 1,004.4 in northern Ohio and a pressure 1,005.8 in southern Michigan. The northernmost station reports a wind of east-northeast force 3, overcast, rain and fog, temperature and dew point both 43°. The southern station reports rain within the last hour, wind south force 4, temperature 56°, and dew point 54°. Pressure is generally falling in this area and tendency differences across this front will not be observed. This may also indicate that the front in this position is stationary.

"Following southeastward from this point in northeastern Ohio the front becomes more obscure. However, there still remain fairly good temperature and dew-point differences across the front. The station in western Pennsylvania reports a south-southeast wind force 3, overcast, rain in the last hour and temperature 59°, dew point 58°, while a station in central Pennsylvania reports temperature 47°, dew point 46°, and continuous light rain. The front may be placed through the station in western Pennsylvania which reports rain in the last hour, and continued southeastward between the station in West Virginia with a temperature of 60°, dew point 56°, and the station in central Virginia with a temperature of 59°, dew point 53°, and an east-northeast force 3 wind. From this point on, the wind discontinuity shows clearly the location of the front, and the front may be extended into the Atlantic between the stations in eastern Virginia and northern North Carolina. The front then passes off the coast at latitude 36°N. between the station with a pressure of 1,014.9 and the station in North Carolina with a pressure 1,015.9. The northern station reports temperature 53°, dew point 49°, and wind northeast force 3, while the station to the south has a temperature of 65°, dew point 59°, wind south-southwest force 4. In this section of the map the cloud condition is also an indicator of front location. To the south of the front broken or overcast high clouds are observed, while to the north middle clouds and low clouds are observed as a continuous overcast.

"Shifting our attention now to the western part of the map, we observe in eastern Montana another wind shift and temperature discontinuity. The highest temperatures are to the west and the lowest temperatures to the east. No precipitation is observed, however, so that the front we may locate here can be considered as a weak front. It may be drawn between the station with the pressure of 1,010.8 millibars in northern Montana and the station with a pressure of 1,012.2 millibars in northern North Dakota. Here there is a temperature difference, a wind discontinuity, and a dew-point difference also. Following southward the front may be located between the station in southeastern Montana with a temperature of 60°, dew point 33°, and a west wind at force 3, and the station in southwestern North Dakota with the temperature 53°, dew point 24°, and the wind southwest force 3. Farther to the south this front becomes more indistinct, and it may be dropped near the border of Wyoming and Montana."

REVIEW.—"From the point in western Indiana just west of the station with a pressure of 998.0 and following southwestward, we locate a *cold front* because the air to the west and north has a lower temperature than air to the southeast of this front, and because the directions of the winds indicate that the cold air is moving toward the front, thus displacing the warm air and making this front a *cold front*.

"From the center of low pressure in western Indiana and eastward the front appears to be stationary, since there is very little pressure-tendency difference across the front. It may be drawn for a short distance from the center as a *warm front*, indicating a wave action in the vicinity of the center of low pressure, and from the point in western Pennsylvania to the coast as a *stationary front*.

"The front in western Montana is advancing eastward, as is shown by the wind in the cold air in advance of the front. Therefore, since the warm air is following and is replacing the cold air this front may be designated as a *warm front*."

Isobaric Analysis

"The isobaric analysis on this weather map is relatively simple. If we begin with the 1,008-millibar isobar at the Gulf Coast, it follows northward between stations having pressures higher than 1,008 millibars and stations having pressures lower than 1,008 millibars, and may be drawn through southeastern Mississippi, northwestern Alabama, eastern Tennessee, along the border of Kentucky and Virginia, through West Virginia. It intersects the front in western Pennsylvania. Here we make a slight kink in the isobar and continue northward curving the isobar cyclonically through northern Michigan, through Lake Michigan into northwestern Illinois, then southwestward through Missouri, northwestern Arkansas, southeastern Oklahoma, and through central Texas. The 1,005-millibar isobar may now be drawn in the same way beginning at the Gulf Coast and continuing around, intersecting the front in northern Ohio and following north and west of the frontal system, and ending in northern Mexico. The first closed isobar in the system is the 1,002-millibar isobar. This intersects the front in western Ohio and again in Arkansas. The second closed isobar is the 999-millibar isobar, which may be drawn around the station with the pressure of 998.0.

"The 1,011 and 1,014 isobars may then be drawn around this system. Other 1,011- and 1,014-millibar isobars are found in northern Montana. These may be drawn extending from the Canadian border and North Dakota into the Pacific Ocean. Continuing with the 1,017 and 1,020 isobars we find a closed 1,020-millibar isobar, or high-pressure center, in northeastern Nevada, and another closed high-pressure isobar of 1,023 centered off the coast of Maine.

REVIEW.—"We find a low-pressure center of 998.0 millibars in western Indiana. We also find two high-pressure centers on the map, one in northeastern Nevada of 1,020 millibars and the other of 1,023 millibars off the coast of Maine. Low pressure is indicated to the north of Montana and high pressure is indicated off the coast of Florida and Georgia, and also off the California and Oregon coasts. A weak anticyclonic system is also located in northeastern Colorado."

Air-mass Analysis

"From an examination of the finished isobaric and frontal analysis we must decide upon the types of air masses which are covering the various sections of the map.

"In the Southeastern United States the wind and pressure gradient indicates the movement of an air mass from the Gulf of Mexico northward across the Southeastern States. The high temperatures and high dew points in this air mass indicate an air mass of tropical maritime origin. This is a late afternoon map so we should expect any unstable characteristics of an air mass to be shown by clouds and weather. There is great variability of the weather within this air mass to the south and to the east of the main frontal system. It can be seen for the most part that the weather is of an unstable air-mass type with thunderstorms, showers, and cumulus and cumulonimbus clouds present at a number of stations. We may therefore conclude that this air mass is an unstable tropical maritime type. It may be labeled mTk. Looking now to the north of the front along the Atlantic Coast we see that winds and the pressure gradient indicate an onshore movement of the air from the Atlantic Ocean. Temperatures and dew points are fairly low, and fog and low clouds are present within the air mass. These are all signs of a stable maritime polar type of air. Continuous light rain is occurring at a few stations but this is due to overrunning of the maritime tropical air which moves aloft at the frontal surface. We may therefore conclude that the underlying air mass is stable. It may be labeled mPw. Looking to the west of the main cold front we see northerly winds, low temperatures, and low dew points. Stratocumulus clouds are prevalent within this air mass and a few stations are reporting clouds of the cumulus type. Examining the temperature gradient from north to south, we see

that the air mass definitely is being warmed up by its southward movement. This warming in the lower levels produces instability. The air
mass may be labeled cPk.

"Over the Dakotas, since no cumulus clouds are shown in the air
which is moving from south to north, we may conclude that this air mass
is a stable type of polar continental air. It may be labeled cPw. In
the Far West over the Montana, Idaho, Washington, and Oregon region
the winds are westerly, and temperatures are relatively high. On the
east side of the Rockies the dew points are relatively low. We may
therefore conclude that this air mass is of maritime polar origin which
has had a trajectory over the Rocky Mountains and which has had
moisture removed by precipitation on the westward side of the mountains.
This air mass is now undergoing a down-slope motion, thus giving a wide
temperature dew-point difference. Temperatures are still warmer than
the cPw to the east of the warm front. We may conclude that this dry
air mass is overrunning the cPw air, but the lift is sufficient only to
produce a small amount of cloudiness in advance of the warm front.

REVIEW.—"We may place a symbol mPw north of the main frontal
system in the Atlantic Ocean at latitude 39°N.; we may place a symbol
mTk over Kentucky or southern Ohio. We also may place a symbol cPk
over Missouri, the symbol cPw over North Dakota, and the symbol
mPk over Idaho."

ANALYSIS OF THE SURFACE WEATHER MAP FOR 0130 EST, THURSDAY, APRIL 18, 1940

Frontal Analysis

"The analysis of this map should be started only after carefully
reviewing the previous weather map for 1930 EST, April 17, 1940. With
this map constantly before us we may now examine the data for the
0130 EST chart. Examining the pressures in the eastern part of the
United States to determine the center of low pressure and also looking
at the wind circulation, we note that the lowest pressure is in the vicinity
of Lake Huron and Lake Erie. The lowest pressure reported is 999.7.
It also reports a west-southwest force 2 wind, temperature 45°, dew point
45°, and foggy, so we know that the real center is actually to the north of
this station. However, the next station to the north reports a north wind
of force 4, temperature 36°, dew point 36°, light rain, pressure 1,001.4
millibars, so that actually the center may be placed slightly to the northeast of the station with a pressure of 999.7 millibars. At this point we
may then begin to locate the cold front which we had on the previous
map. This station, which on the previous map showed an east-northeast
wind, has had a change of wind direction. However, the temperature

and dew point show little change. This means that the pressure center has probably moved to the south of this station and that the station has remained in the cold air. The cold front then may be drawn just to the east of this station and continued toward the southwest. Pressures remain relatively low in northern Indiana. Pressure-tendency differences between stations having northerly winds and those having southerly winds are relatively small. Therefore, a slight wave may be indicated on the front, with its crest just to the northwest of the station in northern Indiana with the pressure of 1,000.3 millibars, temperature 54°, dew point 51°, continuous light rain, wind southwest force 4. The cold front then continues at a slight angle and in a more southerly direction to just east of the station in central Indiana with the pressure of 1,002.4, wind west-southwest force 4, temperature 52°, dew point 52°, and a thunderstorm with rain in progress. The front then continues southwestward to east of the station with the pressure of 1,006.1, temperature 49°, dew point 46°, pressure tendency +28, and a shower occurring. From this point on, the front may be located easily by temperature differences and by wind discontinuity. It is drawn between stations reporting northerly winds and stations reporting winds with southerly components. The front passes off the coast in western Louisiana just east of the station with the north, force 3 wind, temperature 64°, dew point 63°, the pressure of 1,007.5 millibars, with thunderstorm in progress at the time of the observation.

"From the low-pressure center located near the southern tip of Lake Huron the warm-front portion of the front may be found mainly by temperature differences. It may be placed between the station in western New York reporting a south force 5 wind, temperature 60°, dew point 57°, and light rain, and the station to the northeast with the temperature 54°, dew point 50°, and light rain. The front may be continued southward through central Virginia between the stations with easterly or northeasterly winds and the stations with southerly winds. The front passes off the coast in southern Virginia. In this section it will again be observed that the clouds of the high or middle type are broken or scattered in the air to the south of the front, while the clouds to the north are of the low type with most stations reporting fog, drizzle, or light rain.

"Looking now to the western portion of the United States, in eastern Montana we see that the warm front has advanced slightly to the east. At the time of this map temperature differences are now not so apparent. The wind shifts however still prevail and a good tendency difference across the front is beginning to appear with pressures falling rapidly over North Dakota and South Dakota, and falling very slightly over eastern Montana and northern Wyoming. The front may then be

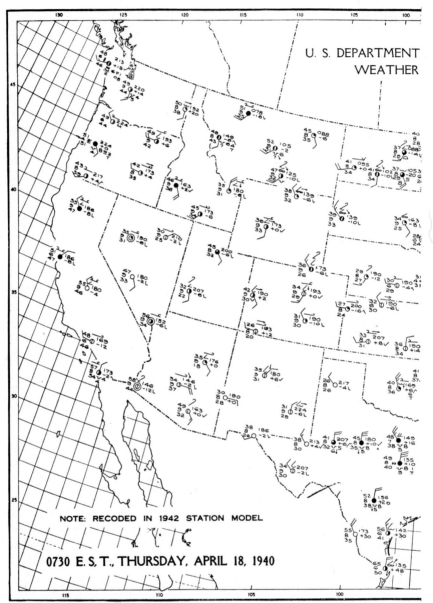

FIG. 15-16.

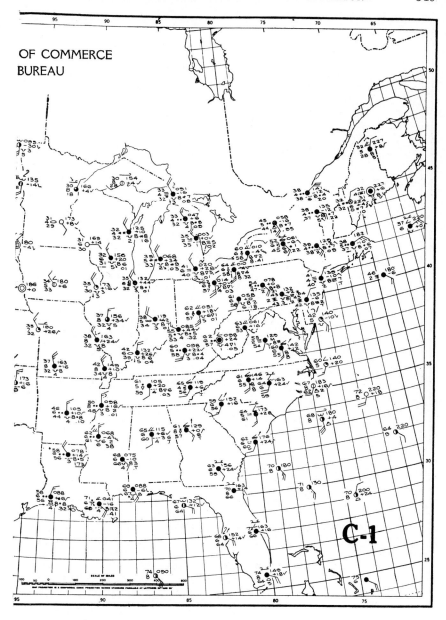

OF COMMERCE
BUREAU

C-1

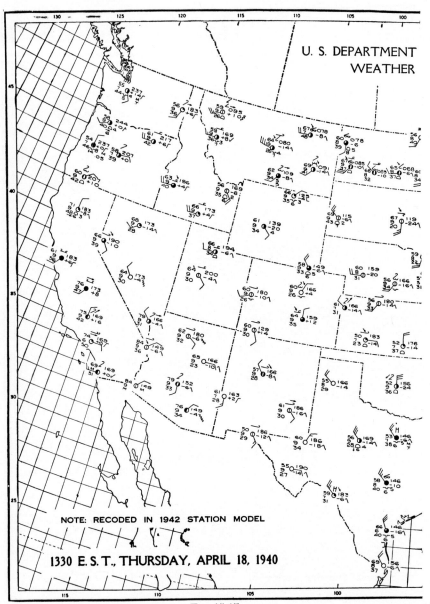

Fɪɢ. 15-17.

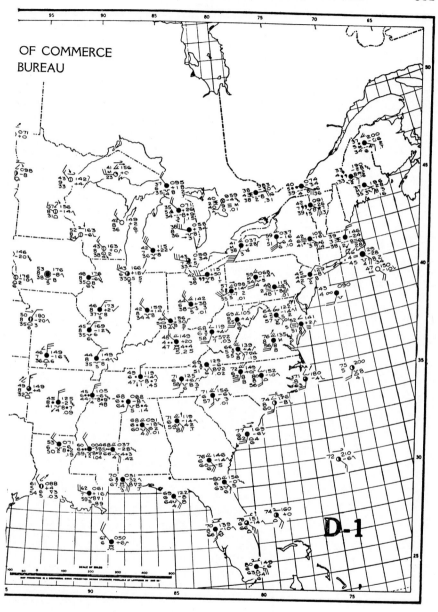

OF COMMERCE
BUREAU

D-1

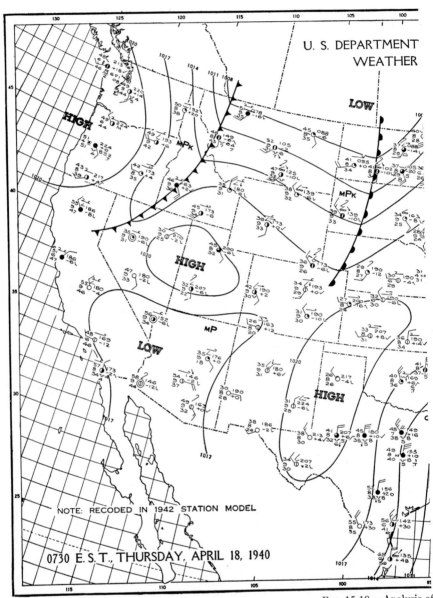

NOTE: RECODED IN 1942 STATION MODEL

0730 E. S. T., THURSDAY, APRIL 18, 1940

FIG. 15-18.—Analysis of

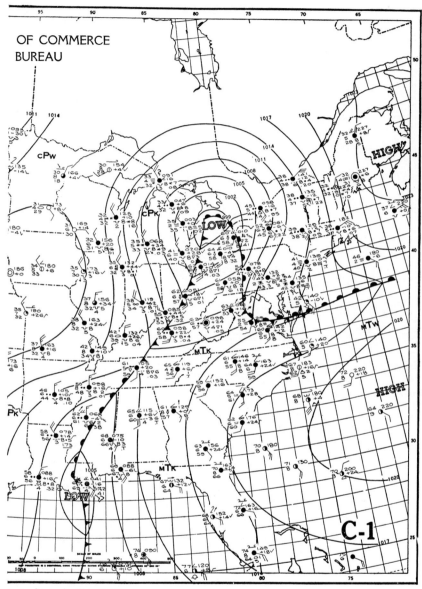

map shown in Fig. 15-16.

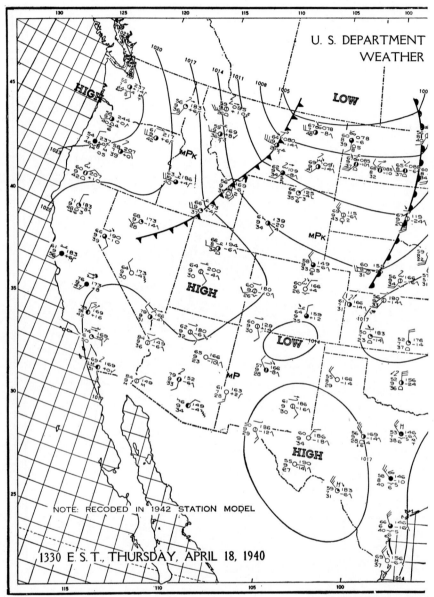

U. S. DEPARTMENT
WEATHER

NOTE: RECODED IN 1942 STATION MODEL

1330 E. S. T., THURSDAY, APRIL 18, 1940

FIG. 15-19.—Analysis of

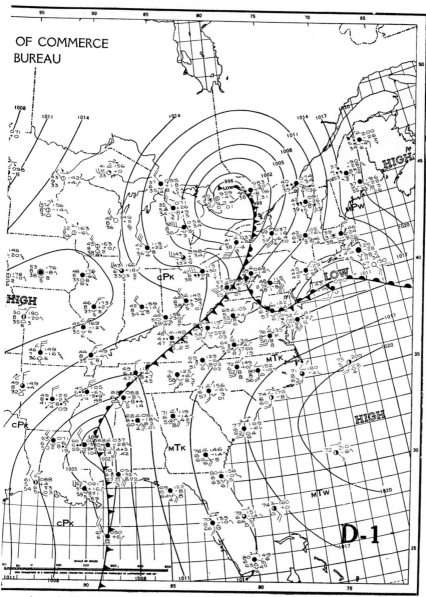

map shown in Fig. 15-17.

placed at the border of North Dakota and Montana and carried into northwestern Wyoming. Farther to the west we observe another tendency difference and a wind shift with fairly large pressure rises over Washington and Oregon. Temperatures have fallen at coastal stations since the last map. Along the line between the strong *pressure rises* and the *pressure falls* we may locate a cold front which has moved in from the Pacific since the last map."

Isobaric Analysis

"We begin the isobaric analysis on this map with the 1,014-millibar isobar. Beginning along the Gulf Coast of Florida this isobar may be completed in the same manner as in the previous map. Make sure that the wind is blowing in the same direction all along the isobar. If we are drawing the isobar in the direction of the wind, a sharp bend to the left is made when it intersects the front.

"On this map the essential pressure features are the closed 1,002-millibar isobar around the main center of low pressure near Lake Huron; the low-pressure center indicated along the Louisiana coast; the closed 1,023-millibar isobar in southeastern Colorado; and the closed 1,023-millibar isobar in eastern Nevada and western Utah. There is a high-pressure area indicated off the coast of Oregon. There are two high-pressure areas indicated off the east coast of the United States, one to the north of the front and the second to the south of the front. A weak trough of low pressure is also seen over Arizona and southeastern southern California. This low pressure trough is not connected with any fronts."

Weather Forecasting

We have already considered a wealth of facts and principles applicable to weather forecasting. For example, it can now be predicted with certainty that the temperature will normally increase toward mid-afternoon and decrease toward early morning. Our study of the inverse temperature and relative humidity relationship leads to an anticipation of decreasing relative humidity as the temperature rises, and an increase toward evening and early morning when temperatures fall. This routine may of course be upset by the passage of a front, introducing a new air mass with new properties.

We have noted the variations of wind direction to be expected, depending on the paths of lows or highs past our ship or station. We have considered also, the changes in cloud forms and states of the sky as different types of fronts come and go, together with the nature of the precipitation attending these fronts. We have studied the basic features of air masses, and the principal air masses that affect weather conditions, in addition to some of the changes suffered by these air masses in transit.

A combination of all these conditions has been considered in connection with the weather structure of the middle latitude cyclone. Further, we have learned the weather patterns and associated features of the violent tropical cyclones that beset the seas in certain areas and at certain seasons of the year. The guiding, general wind circulation of the atmosphere, on which all the above conditions are superposed, has also been examined in detail. These weather factors have not only been studied in their relation to each other, but the physical causes for their variations have been noted as well.

FORECASTING FROM WEATHER MAPS.—The technique of analyzing and forming a logical pattern of the plotted weather map has just been studied. How now, do we forecast weather? We do so by marshaling all our knowledge and with it attacking the analyzed weather map. We know now the basic axiom, that weather conditions in the middle latitudes move generally eastward. Apparently, all that is necessary is to estimate what conditions will pass over the zone of our ship or station, and thus obtain the required forecast. But this does not always work. Weather does not move due east, and conditions change even as the weather progresses.

The following is the general procedure employed in forecasting from synoptic charts:

1. Estimate the movement and changes in highs, lows, and other pressure configurations.

2. Estimate the movement and changes of fronts and associated frontal conditions.

3. Estimate the changes in air-mass conditions shown on the latest map.

Remember that the forecasting process requires a thorough examination of previous weather maps, as well as of the current one. From this examination, an attempt is made to project these conditions into the future and determine the probable appearance of succeeding weather maps, thereby showing the weather conditions 12 to 36 hours later. Thus, forecasting is the estimation of future weather conditions from a study of past and present conditions. The forecast must therefore be in logical conformance with these conditions.

Criteria for Estimating Weather-map Changes.—We shall now consider briefly some of the criteria that are useful in estimating future weather conditions in accordance with the three basic steps given above. It is emphasized again that complete scientific forecasting by means of modern weather theory is beyond the scope or purpose of this book. Those rules which are more or less applicable to maps that may be drawn either at sea or by the nonprofessional will be given.

1. Cyclones that exhibit warm sectors usually move in *fairly straight*

paths, *parallel* to the isobars in the warm sector.   Let us repeat that the isobars themselves are normally straight and parallel to each other in this sector.   Also, the amount or rate of movement of the low is proportional to the wind velocity of the warm air.

2. Cyclone movement tends to slow when the path becomes curved; if after curvature the path straightens, an increase in velocity may be expected.

3. A decrease in the forward movement of a cyclone often indicates a change of direction to follow.   The surrounding pressure systems should then be examined to determine the possible new path of the low.

4. In connection with rule 3, it is important to note that a stagnant or slowly moving high, preceding the cyclone, has a pronounced effect on the latter's movement.   Since the low cannot move through the high or anticyclone, it must move around it.   Since anticyclones in the Northern Hemisphere have a clockwise circulation, the western side of the high, toward which the low approaches, will exhibit winds moving to the north and thence to the east.   The cyclone will therefore follow the circulation of the high, moving around it by way of north (south in the Southern Hemisphere).   The cyclone may slow and become stationary itself, if for any reason it cannot move around the high.

5. Cyclones tend to move with the same speed as the warm front, and therefore slower than the cold front.

6. Cyclones and anticyclones with relatively pronounced low or high (deep) pressure centers, respectively, tend to move slower than shallow-pressure systems.

7. As the occlusion process proceeds during the life of a cyclone, the isobars will become more circular, and the wind discontinuity across the occluded front will become less and less pronounced.

8. During and after the occlusion the cyclone slowly "fills"; that is, the pressure slowly rises in the center.

9. Barring any conditions on the weather map to indicate otherwise, it may be expected that lows and highs will continue to move with practically the same velocity and direction that they have exhibited for the past 12 hours.

10. The movement of fronts depends on the wind to their rear. They move, with very nearly the velocity and direction of the *wind component perpendicular* to the front.   In this regard, it is not the surface wind that should be considered, but the free movement of the air that exists at an altitude of 1,500 feet.   If no upper air data are available, the velocity of the surface wind may be doubled.

11. Cold fronts, as we have mentioned many times, move faster than warm fronts and may be expected to overtake preceding warm fronts and cause occlusion.

12. Occluded front velocities depend on whether they are cold or warm front occlusions. Thus, a cold-front occlusion moves faster than a warm-front occlusion.

The association of the facts and principles studied heretofore, with the foregoing rules and their combined application to the weather map, will be a valuable asset in attempting the determination of future weather conditions.

FORECASTING FROM LOCAL INDICATIONS.—It is only in recent years that the mariner has had the aid of radio bulletins to provide synopses and forecasts of weather conditions at sea. As a result many, if not most, mariners have developed a so-called "weather sense." Actually, they are simply drawing conclusions after noting certain observational conditions with their results, during a period of years at sea. We have now studied the scientific basis for many of these conclusions.

However, the making of the true "weather man" requires more than the general knowledge so far acquired. But from this general knowledge of weather conditions and the factors underlying their changes, one can, by observation, make local predictions for short periods, the accuracy of which will increase with practice. Fairly accurate forecasts may be developed for 12 hours in advance of the observations. At times, the forecast may be safely extended for 24 hours, but this is definitely the limit in the middle latitudes.

The process of forecasting from local observations consists essentially of relating one's observations to the general pattern of weather. Thus, by knowing this relation of observed conditions to the moving weather pattern, a particular set of observations indicates what part of this pattern is in the observer's vicinity, and therefore what part is likely to approach with its associated weather.

At the very outset of this book, we stressed the fact that clouds and wind direction were the most important local features to be observed for the purpose of weather determination. The behavior of the barometer may further clarify the picture. It might be well to consider a few examples.

Observations of the wind direction enable the placing of the direction of the low-pressure center. When the wind sets in from northeast or southeast, a low is approaching. Observations of the barometer may confirm this. The relation of wind shifts and approaching lows was completely developed in Chap. 10 on Secondary Winds. An even earlier indication than either the wind or the barometer is the type of cloud observed. Thus, the appearance of cirrus and cirrostratus clouds in the western sky may presage the approach of a distant warm or occluded front. If these clouds move eastward and slowly thicken and lower, together with a fall in the barometer and a shift of the winds to an eastern quadrant, the approach of the warm or occluded front seems fairly certain.

Whether the low-pressure center, from which the front extends, will pass to the north or south of the observer is determined from the wind direction, as explained earlier. If the wind direction indicates a passage to the north, weather changes may be anticipated in accordance with the analysis of cyclone structure south of the center, as given in Chap. 14. It is of course very difficult if not impossible to judge whether or not the approaching front is occluded. If it should be, no warm sector conditions will pass.

Should the wind indicate the passage of the low to the south, again no warm sector will be observed. Rather there will be a continuous overcast with moderate precipitation, ending in heavier precipitation or showers, and with backing winds followed by clearing and invariably colder weather.

In general, in the middle latitudes of the Northern Hemisphere, a shift of the wind to the northwest, with or without typical cold-front showers, is the common associate of clearing weather. Fair-weather cumulus often prevails, serving as a further indication that the storm area has moved away to the east.

Some common weather proverbs may be mentioned in connection with forecasting from local observations:

1. When the dew is on the grass,
   Rain will not come to pass.
2. A morning fog that obscures the sun's ray
   Indicates the coming of a clear day.
3. Mackerel sky, twelve hours dry.
4. A veering wind means weather fair,
   A backing wind, foul weather's near.
5. Rainbow at night, sailor's delight,
   Rainbow in the morning, sailor take warning.

Proverbs 1 and 2, of course, refer to conditions that require clear nights, and hence some time lapse is necessary for any bad weather that may follow. Proverb 3 refers to cirrocumulus which is often associated with the outer fringe of the stratus cloud deck preceding the warm front. As a rule, precipitation will not fall for another 12 hours, until the front draws much closer. The fourth proverb may often, but not necessarily, be true. The reader can explain this one for himself. The fifth is slightly more involved. Rainbows are common features of showers or thundershowers and are always seen in the opposite part of the sky from the sun. A rainbow at night, with the sun setting in the west, must be in the eastern sky, indicating that the storm has already past. A rainbow in the morning must, in the same way, exist in the western sky, thereby heralding the approach of the storm.

Numerous other weather adages and examples of local forecasting could be cited. On the whole, however, such forecasting simply requires that the observer explain and interpret to himself the conditions he may see, drawing on his knowledge for this purpose.

CHAPTER 16

OPTICAL FEATURES OF THE ATMOSPHERE

The optical phenomena of the atmosphere are undoubtedly among the most weird and awe-inspiring spectacles in all nature. So strange are some of these features that observers have often ascribed them to tricks of their own fancy and imagination, rather than to plausible physical causes. Nowhere is there a more appropriate vantage point for the viewing of most of these atmospheric displays than on the open sea. Here, the unobstructed horizon allows for the observation of nearly the whole of the celestial dome at one time; and there is no artificial illumination of the skies to interfere with nocturnal optical displays.

In studying these features of the air, we shall consider them in accordance with the physical processes responsible for their existence. The optical effects resulting from these processes can be separated into (1) refraction features, (2) diffraction features, (3) diffusion and scattering features, (4) perspective features, and (5) electrically induced features.

Refraction

The features directly attributed to refraction are more numerous than those of the other groups. Refraction is the process in which rays of light are bent from a straight line in passing through a medium of varying density, or from one medium to another of different density. Many common examples of refraction exist: *e.g.*, a pencil or rod partly immersed in water appears to bend sharply at the water line and assume a distorted shape.

Light rays are refracted since they travel with different speeds in media of different density.

PRINCIPLES OF REFRACTION.—An elementary examination of the principles of refraction will aid materially in understanding refraction features in the atmosphere. In Fig. 16-1, we note that the ray AO is bent abruptly upon emerging from the denser medium (water) into the rarer medium (air), and follows the path OB. An observer with his eye at B appears to see the source of the light in the direction OA', rather than in the true direction, as a consequence of refraction.

The line NOP, perpendicular to the surface between the adjacent layers or media, is called the "normal." The ray AO striking this surface is called the "incident ray," and OB, the "refracted ray." Further, the angle between the incident ray and the normal AOP is known as the "angle of incidence," while NOB is known as the "angle of refraction."

In the figure the incident ray is in the dense medium. What then is the path of the ray when the source of light is in the rare medium? If the light source were at B, then BO would be the incident ray, and OA, the refracted ray, would be just the reverse of the first case. An observer at A would then see point B displaced in the direction made by extending line AO into the rare medium.

Without further explanation, three facts are evident from this discussion:

1. A ray of light perpendicular to the surface between two media never suffers refraction. Thus a ray parallel to line NOP, above, undergoes no bending or refraction.

2. When a ray of light emerges from a dense to a rare medium it is bent away from the normal. Thus, for the incident ray AO, the angle of refraction NOB exceeds the incident angle AOP.

3. When a ray of light enters a denser medium, the ray is refracted toward the normal. If BO is considered to be the incident ray, it is then bent in the direction AO, or toward the normal. Now, AOP is the angle of refraction.

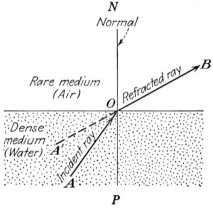

FIG. 16-1.—Refraction and nomenclature involved.

There is one other important fact, which can be developed from principle 2. As the angle of incidence of a ray, moving from the denser to the rarer medium, increases more and more, there finally comes a situation where the refracted ray is bent so far from the normal as not to enter the rare medium at all but travels parallel to the surface between the media. The angle of incidence at which this occurs is known as the "critical angle" and must naturally depend on the particular substance or medium involved. If the critical angle is exceeded by the incident ray, the refracted ray is bent entirely back into the dense medium, the phenomenon being known as "total reflection." The critical angle and total reflection are illustrated in Fig. 16-2. The critical angle can now be defined as the angle of incidence beyond which total reflection occurs.

DISPERSION.—Dispersion can be considered as a kind of differential refraction. We know that visible white light actually consists of light of many colors, which when blended produce white light. When white light is passed through a medium of varying thickness, such as a glass prism, the components of the light are refracted differently, in accordance with their respective wave lengths. The resulting color band is known as the "spectrum," consisting of red, orange, yellow, green, blue, and violet regions which grade into each other. These are the spectral colors commonly observed in rainbows. Dispersion is thus the process whereby white light is separated into its component colors. It is important to note that the wave length of blue light is about half that of red, and the blue-violet end of the spectrum is refracted more than the red,

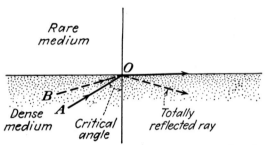

Fig. 16-2.—Critical angle and total reflection. Ray *BO*, exceeding the critical angle, is totally reflected.

which suffers the least bending, when white light is separated by dispersion. These last are important factors in causing certain of the prominent optical phenomena now to be studied.

Refraction Features

The behavior of light in the atmosphere shows the air to be extremely variable in density. For the most part this density difference is a direct result of differences of temperature and humidity within separate air layers. This nonhomogeneous character of the atmosphere is characterized both by a few well-defined and relatively thick layers and by numerous thin tapering layers which give the air a streaky property. Many common refraction features are a result of this condition.

ALTITUDE EFFECT.—Refraction does not always require two distinct layers of differing density. A simple variation of density within a single medium will also cause a bending of transmitted light rays. The atmosphere is an excellent example of such a medium. There is a steady increase in density of the air from its outer margins to the earth's surface. Consequently light from all celestial objects is refracted in passing through the atmosphere, except when at the zenith, for in this latter case the rays enter normal to the atmosphere. The effect of this refraction is to displace the apparent position of all celestial objects and give them a greater altitude above the horizon. The nearer the horizon, the greater is the refraction since the thickness of air traversed by the light increases. The refraction or altitude correction is familiar to all navigators who have taken sights on astronomical bodies. The effect of refraction is such as to cause the sun to appear above the horizon when it has just set below.

TWINKLING, SHIMMERING, AND SHADOW BANDS.—These are relatively simple and closely related effects resulting from streakiness in the atmosphere. The light from most astronomical bodies (except the more luminous ones) and from distant terrestrial sources undergoes a pronounced flickering known as "twinkling." Small density irregularities in the atmosphere cause numerous deflections to the relatively thin beam of light from these distant objects and result in this familiar effect.

Shimmering is an equally familiar sight. Objects that are observed across relatively warm surfaces appear to "dance" or "shimmer," suffering distortion. Some common examples of this are found in the behavior of light passing over hot radiators, chimney stacks, dark roadways, etc. In all such cases, the atmospheric density differences resulting from convection over the warm or hot medium cause irregular refraction which produces the shimmering.

Shadow bands are alternate, narrow, light and dark bands that flit rapidly over the ground immediately preceding and following the instant of totality of a solar eclipse. This effect is also directly ascribed to distortion of the restricted sunbeam by numerous thin zones of different atmospheric density, resulting for the most part from temperature inequalities. These features are rare only because total eclipses are rare and not because of the lack of the necessary atmospheric conditions.

OPTICAL OR REFRACTION HAZE.—Frequently, visibility becomes very restricted even though the air is perfectly free of both dust and water droplets. A definite white haze obstructs the vision, resembling very closely a thin fog or mist, despite the actual clarity of the air. "Tongues" and layers of air of different densities may be superimposed on each other or intermingled generally, producing a pronounced "optical heterogeneity" of the air. Irregular refraction is then so great that little light can travel any distance without suffering marked distortion, yielding the resulting poor visibility. Coast lines are frequently shrouded in this haze, being invisible from a short distance offshore as a result of marked temperature inequalities prevailing along shore boundaries.

HALOS.—For ages past, the huge rings or halos about the sun or moon have been taken to have portents and meanings of all sorts. Now we know them to be optical results of the refraction of sunlight by *ice crystals*, in high, thin, cirrus or cirrostratus clouds. Halos of two different radii have actually been observed: one, the halo of 22°, and the other, the halo of 46°. The angles of refraction within the ice spicules determine the type of halo that forms, although the halo of 22° radius is by far the more commonly observed. Mild dispersion usually occurs with this refraction, and the red light, being bent the least, appears on the inner portion of the curve, with the other spectral colors following outward. The green and blue are usually too weak to be seen.

For the production of halos, the ice crystals in the cloud must have a very heterogeneous arrangement. In this case the refracted light forms a general circle completely around the sun. However, if a particular uniform arrangement of ice crystals exists, the refraction occurs in one plane only, having the same altitude as the sun. Instead of a circle, only two bright spots on either side of the sun result. These images have nearly the same radius as the halo would have if the crystals

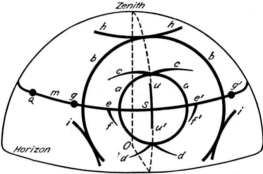

Fig. 16-3.—Perspective view of the sky showing: sun (*s*); ordinary halo of 22° (*a*); great halo of 46° (*b*); upper tangent arc of the halo of 22° (*c*); lower tangent arc of the halo of 22° (*d*); ordinary parahelia of 22° (*e*, *e'*); arcs of Lowitz (*f*, *f'*); parahelia of 46° (*g*, *g'*); circumzenithal arc (*h*); infralateral tangent arcs of the halo of 46° (*i*); the parahelic circle *m*); a paranthelion of 90° (*q*); plane of the horizon; and the observer (*o*).

were situated in all positions. They are known as "parhelia," or "sun dogs," there being a parhelion of both 22° and 46°. Very rarely, the parhelia of 22° become extended in a direction concave to the sun and are then named "arcs of Lowitz."

Although other associated phenomena are observed on rather infrequent occasions, we omit description of them. For reference purposes many of them are reproduced in Fig. 16-3, together with the features just mentioned.

RAINBOWS.—The formation of a rainbow involves simple refraction, total reflection, and dispersion of light. Rainbows are visible on occasions when the sun is shining and the air contains water spray or raindrops. This condition is frequent during or immediately following local showers. The bow is always observed in that portion of the sky opposite to the sun. The sun, the observer's eye, and the center of the rainbow arc are always on a straight line, thus, a rainbow formed at sunrise or sunset can appear as a complete semicircle on the horizon opposite to the sun.

In the formation of the rainbow, light entering the denser water drop is refracted toward the rear of it. Some light strikes the rear surface at such an angle as to be totally reflected and then passes out of the front

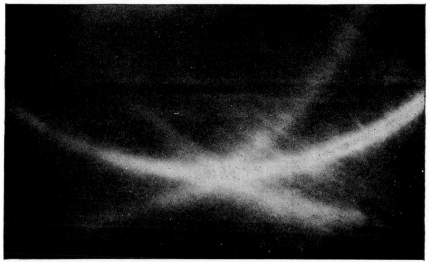

Fig. 16-4.—Halo features showing parahelic circle with oblique arcs through the anthelion. (*Courtesy of Wentworth, U. S. Weather Bureau.*)

portion. This process, repeated in identical manner for myriads of drops, produces the primary rainbow, which has a radius of nearly 42°. The color bands forming the rainbow differ from those of the halo, in that the red is on the outer, and the blue on the inner edge.

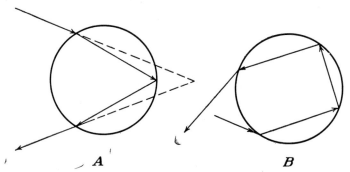

A   *B*

Fig. 16-5.—Refraction and total reflection of light within rain drops resulting in *A*, primary rainbow; and *B*, secondary rainbow.

If two internal reflections take place in the raindrop, a secondary bow of slightly larger radius occurs, with the color bands reversed. Tertiary bows are also observed.

LOOMING AND TOWERING.—Looming and towering are phenomena in which objects actually below the horizon are brought to appear above the horizon (looming), and visible objects are stretched or elongated upward, with an apparent increase in their height (towering). These effects occur frequently in high middle latitude or arctic waters, when a marked increase in the density of the air exists near the surface (the density at the surface may be normal, but a marked decrease in density with altitude would have the same effect). In this case, the altitude of

FIG. 16-6.—Rainbow with secondary bow to the right. (*Courtesy of Clarke, U. S. Weather Bureau.*)

terrestrial objects is increased in much the same fashion as that of astronomical bodies, described above.

Owing to this effect, lights actually well below the horizon are often visible to the mariner. With close approach, the refracted rays may no longer be intercepted and the light disappears. When the actual light is seen, the effect of towering may greatly increase its apparent height. Hulls, masts, and stacks of ships are similarly affected.

SUPERIOR MIRAGE.—The superior mirage requires much the same conditions as looming, with again, a rapid decrease in density of the air with increase in altitude. By virtue of the strong refraction resulting, the image of a ship, of any object below the horizon, may appear in the sky above the horizon and in an inverted position. Such conditions may develop when a pronounced inversion occurs some distance above a relatively cold surface. At times, the object itself may appear, together with its inverted counterpart directly above, almost as though a reflecting mirror surface were present. Occasionally, the density "stratification" of the air is such as to produce still a second mirage above the first, but this time in a normal upright position. Thus, ships have been seen near the horizon with an inverted image floating above it, and a second upright image above that. Owing to the appearance of the mirage above the actual object, the name "superior" is given to this type.

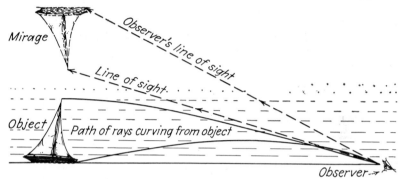

Fig. 16-7.—The formation of superior mirage from refraction in a layer of air having a rapidly increasing density near the surface.

INFERIOR MIRAGE.—The deceptive inferior mirage is rarely seen over the oceans but is common over highly heated land surfaces, particularly deserts. The mirage derives its name from the fact that it always appears below the actual object, inverted in position. The mirage

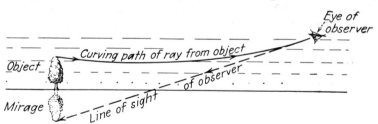

Fig. 16-8.—The production of an inferior mirage by refraction in a layer of air having a density decreasing rapidly near the surface.

is normally manifested by the inverted image of distant objects, which themselves are often beyond the range of vision; and by the inversion of the distant low blue sky giving the appearance of a lake, or water surface. The presence of the distant inverted image, shimmering in the sky mirage, creates the appearance of reflection from a water surface, so misleading to desert travelers.

This mirage is the result of a thin rarified layer of air (a few feet thick, at most), caused by the heating of the land surface. The observer's eye must be above this zone, in the denser overlying air. Light rays from the sky or distant objects, instead of being bent downward in passing through the rarified layer, as in the cases of looming or superior mirage, are refracted upward to the observer's eye. The observer's line of sight, being a straight line, projects this image back toward the earth, in the direction from which the refracted rays came, and creates the inferior mirage.

FATA MORGANA.—Some very remarkable, complicated, multiple mirages have been observed at times in the Straits of Messina, but more frequently in higher latitudes along the coasts of the Atlantic and the Pacific. These mirages combine the effects of inferior and superior mirages, looming, towering and the reverse, and general distortion, being produced by atmospheric zones of varying densities and thicknesses. The results of these complications transform the appearance of the coast-line features into strange and often grotesque sights. Shore cliffs and buildings may be extended as tremendous swelling towers and castles, or depressed and flattened into other strange shapes. Observers likened this phenomenon to the legendary castles of Morgan, le Fay. The term "Fata Morgana" has since been applied to any complicated mirage system.

In the same way, the legend of the Flying Dutchman is kept alive by the almost ghostly appearance and disappearance of entire ships. Mirages have had a profound part in the supernatural influence of nature on the unenlightened.

THE GREEN FLASH.—The green flash is another strange and beautiful example of refraction that requires an unobstructed horizon and relatively clear atmosphere, two requirements again achieved at sea. On rare occasions, the last bead of the setting sun (or rising sun) and the surrounding sky flash out in a deep, more or less brilliant green or blue green, which lasts for but a short time. We have noted above that the spectral colors of white light are refracted differently—violet the most and red the least. Thus, conditions may just occur, when only a small rim of the sun is visible on the horizon, so that the red, orange, and yellow portions of sunlight are not refracted sufficiently to reach the eye, while the green light is so refracted. This results in the appearance of the green flash.

Diffraction Features

When rays of light encounter obstacles of very small size, the rays are deflected from their normal path, usually in a straight line. This is the process of diffraction. The various wave lengths composing white light are diffracted somewhat differently, causing dispersion, or the separation of white light into its spectral colors. "Coronas" are the most common examples of atmospheric diffraction. They are rims of small radius and of subdued color, commonly observed surrounding and sometimes apparently touching the solar disk, caused by the diffraction of sunlight or moonlight through thin cloud veils. When discernible, the colors of shorter wave length, blue and green, appear on the inner portion of the corona, with red and orange forming the outer ring.

Diffusion and Scattering Features

Were it not for the diffusion or scattering of sunlight by the air, some of the greatest beauties of the atmosphere would be lost. Much compensation would exist however. Daylight, which is taken so much for granted requires the presence of an atmosphere. The effect of the air is to spread much of the entering sunlight fairly evenly over the sky, so that, except in the immediate vicinity of "Old Sol," the sky is more or less uniformly illuminated. This diffusion of sunlight actually gives greater illumination to the earth's surface as a whole, than if the rays were to shine in a direct beam.

Without the diffusion of sunlight the sky would appear black, with stars, planets, and moon always visible, in addition to the brilliant orb of the sun, whenever above the horizon. Such a condition seems paradoxical, yet it is only the brightness of the daytime sky (from diffusion), that prevents the observation of the other astronomic objects, for they are certainly there. In the absence of a diffusing atmosphere, the sun would shine forth brilliantly from the surrounding blackness of the sky. Intense contrasts of light would exist, with harsh shadows and glaring bright areas. Such a situation would of course be a great boon to the astronomer by greatly increasing his period of observation. Balloon observers ascending to heights above 14 miles, with most of the air below, have encountered such conditions.

The phenomenon of scattering explains, too, the existing blue of the sky, the brilliant colors of sunset, and the conditions of twilight. The blue of the sky has been a perplexing problem, long evading satisfactory explanation. It has finally been shown to be a feature resulting from scattering.

Scattering is the process whereby light, traveling in a straight path through the atmosphere, is disturbed by small particles of dust and air— small in comparison to the wave length of light. The effect of this disturbance is to give a random distribution to the light striking the particles and is much more pronounced for the shorter wave lengths— blue light. Thus, most of the scattered light is blue, causing the color of the clear sky to be blue. The more intense the scattering, the deeper is the blue color.

The striking crimson and scarlet hues often accompanying the rising and setting of the sun are similarly explained. We have noted earlier that the thickness of the atmosphere traversed by sunlight increases markedly with decrease of altitude. The effect of this additional amount of intervening dust and air particles may cause so pronounced a scattering as to permit the direct passage of only the longest or red wave lengths in the sunlight. The results of this require no further description.

Twilight is the name applied to that interval after sunset during which the sky is still illuminated. Were it not for the presence of the atmosphere, darkness would set in almost immediately after sunset. As it is, scattering and refraction "preserve" the sunlight for varying periods after the sun itself is no longer visible. The interval between sunset and the time when it is too dark for normal outdoor activities is defined as "civil twilight." Specifically, civil twilight is the period from sunset until the center of the sun has descended 6° below the horizon. "Astronomical twilight" is the period from sunset until the sun's center is 18° below the horizon. It is quite dark by that time. Clearly, the duration of the twilight period must vary with the path of the sun. When this path is very oblique to the horizon, as in summer, the period will be longer than when the path is more perpendicular. The "American Nautical Almanac" publishes tables giving the duration of twilight at different latitudes and different dates.

Perspective Features

Perspective effects are in part the results of physical conditions, and in part the results of optical illusions. We have already examined some of the perspective phenomena associated with clouds. They included the darkening of the clouds and the narrowing of the sky interval between, as the observer's view approaches the horizon. In these cases, a direct physical explanation accounted for the observed features.

The expansion in size of the sun or moon when near the horizon is a familiar feature, explained on the basis of perspective. The distance of the sky apparently increases with approach to the horizon. Thus, although the distance of the sky appears to change, the actual distance of the sun or the moon, and their actual angular diameter remain the same, regardless of celestial position. Consequently, in order to compensate for their seemingly greater distance when on the horizon, the size of the sun or the moon increases. The size increase is therefore illusory.

In the same way, any angular arc of the sky itself appears to be magnified with decrease in celestial altitude. This causes an apparent increase in diurnal motion of astronomical objects near the horizon, in order that they may traverse this apparently greater sky interval in the same time.

Another very common perspective feature that is explainable by optical illusion is the phenomenon known as the "crepuscular rays." Popularly, these rays are referred to by the phrase, "the sun draws water." The sun is so distant from the earth that its light rays approach

FIG. 16-9.—Crepuscular rays formed by a stratocumulus cloud masking the sun.

along parallel lines. In cloudy weather, when openings or rifts appear in the clouds, the path of the sunlight appears as a number of illuminated beams that seem to converge upward toward the opening. The beam itself is merely sunlight reflected by foreign matter in the air, along the path of the beam. The same effect is shown by the illuminated path of a bright searchlight at night, or by the projection beam in a motion-picture theater. These sunbeams, diverging from the gaps between clouds are called "crepuscular rays." The convergence at the cloud level is a common perspective illusion in which parallel lines seem to meet in the distance. A familiar analogy is the approach of railroad tracks toward each other, as the eye looks down the tracks.

Electrically Induced Features

There are few more strange or remarkable sights than the *aurora borealis*. When visible in the skies of the Northern Hemisphere, this

Fig. 16-10.—Aurora borealis as seen from Ogunquit, Maine, Aug. 12, 1919; painting by Howard Russel Butler. (*Courtesy of American Museum of Natural History.*)

phenomenon is often termed "aurora polaris," and in southern skies, "aurora australis." They are ghostly displays of light in the forms of streamers, rays, arcs, bands, curtains, draperies, sheets, or patches that seem to shimmer and flit across the sky. Auroras are most common in higher latitudes, centering around the magnetic poles. The shifting auroral patterns are most often a greenish white, though pronounced reds, yellows, and greens are very often observed.

Auroras are associated with vast magnetic storms on the sun, which appear as sun spots and are nearly always attended by magnetic disruptions on the earth that seriously impair the normal behavior of communication devices. As such, auroras are explained as resulting from solar discharges of electrified particles emitted by the magnetic storm areas, some of which approach the earth and tend to be attracted to the magnetic poles. The effect of this electrical bombardment of the upper rarified portions of the atmosphere is to cause excitation of the gases therein, with a consequent emission of radiation. We may compare this phenomenon to that of the familiar colored commercial-sign displays. Here, relatively high-voltage electric discharges are passed through tubes containing particular gases under low pressure. Light of characteristic color is then emitted, depending on the gas employed.

It will be recalled that one method of estimating the height of the atmosphere was the determination of the elevation of auroral displays.

CHAPTER 17

THE OCEANS

A pronounced reciprocal relationship exists between the atmosphere and the oceans. The movements of the air are responsible for most of the wave action and much of the current motion in the seas and, together with pressure variations, greatly affect the level of the oceans. The oceans in turn, covering nearly three-fourths of the earth's surface, have a most direct and important influence on the heating of the air, which, as we have noted earlier, is the cause of nearly all the other atmospheric variations. Then, the water content of the air is derived almost completely from the great expanses of ocean waters. So important are these effects of the oceans and the air on one another, that no treatment of the conditions of the atmosphere from a marine viewpoint would be complete without at least a brief examination of the physical properties of the sea.

The scientific study of the oceans is limited to a period of less than a century. Hence, the science of "oceanography," as this study is called, is one of the youngest of the natural sciences. With the publication of "The Physical Geography of the Sea," in 1855, by Lieut. Mathew Maury of the U.S. Navy, oceanography emerged as a definite field of study. To Maury goes the credit for developing one of the first world wind and current charts. This was accomplished through his intensive study of ships' logs and records.

The voyage of the British warship "Challenger," sponsored by the British Royal Society, was of further importance in advancing this new branch of knowledge. The "Challenger" cruised the oceans for $3\frac{1}{2}$ years engaged only in compiling oceanographic data, with the results filling 50 volumes. A number of other institutes and individuals have since carried on these original investigations and added greatly to the accumulation of our ocean knowledge. Nevertheless, to this day, owing to the vastness of the oceans and the basins they occupy, there is a tremendous amount of research still awaiting the oceanographer.

General Features of the Oceans

DIMENSIONS AND DISTRIBUTION.—The surface area of the earth is very close to 200,000,000 square miles. Of this, nearly 71 per cent is comprised of the waters of the oceans and their isolated parts (seas). Clearly the oceans are the dominant feature of the earth's surface. The continental masses divide these features of the earth into more or less distinct units. There is a great inconsistency in the definitions and nomenclature applied to the description of these water bodies. We follow here the terminology adopted by Sverdrup, Johnson, and Fleming.

The continental bodies with their north-south trend separate the water area into three primary oceans: the Atlantic, the Pacific, and the Indian. Two subdivisions are recognized in that the north polar extension of the Atlantic and the Pacific is termed the Arctic Ocean, and the southern extension, surrounding the continent of Antarctica, is designated commonly as the Antarctic Ocean. Many partly land-enclosed or more or less isolated sections of the primary oceans occur, being known commonly as "seas." The distribution of the land areas is such that the ratio of land in the Northern Hemisphere, to that in the Southern is greater than 2 to 1.

The average depth of the oceans is about 2.4 miles. This contrasts strongly with the average height of the land masses which is only 0.5 mile. Thus, the average ocean depth exceeds the average continental altitude by almost five times. The extreme conditions are not nearly so contrasting although again the marine basin has the advantage. Mount Everest, the highest peak, towers to a height of 29,100 feet. Modern sonic sounding methods have indicated the greatest known depths to lie in the Japanese trench, and in the Philippine trench farther south. In both of these deeps, the ocean descends to a depth of 34,000 to 35,000 feet. Table XXIII summarizes the areas, volumes, and mean depths of the oceans.

TABLE XXIII. DIMENSIONS OF THE OCEANS

Ocean	Area, millions of sq. mi.	Volume, millions of cu. mi.	Mean depth, ft.
Atlantic	32.15	64.72	13,112
Pacific	64.45	141.51	14,302
Indian	28.65	58.21	13,236
Total	125.25	264.44	13,750
Atlantic—including adjacent seas	41.53	70.94	11,129
Pacific—including adjacent seas	70.07	144.74	13,454
Indian—including adjacent seas	29.24	58.38	13,016
Total	140.84	274.06	12,533

THE OCEAN BASINS.—The ocean basins are the tremendous receptacles that contain the ocean waters. The continental limits form the sides of these basins. Although local differences are common, both on the floors and sides of the ocean basins, their chief features are essentially the same, and it is these features with which we are now primarily concerned.

In general there exists a gradual slope from the continental shore out to the 100-fathom depth limit. The width of this shelf extending seaward from the continent may vary considerably, depending on the topographic expression. Along rugged mountainous coasts, this zone, called the "continental shelf," may be very narrow. Along coasts exhibiting well-developed coastal plain areas, the shelf is simply the gently sloping seaward extension of the plain. The continental shelf is characterized by sediments carried out from the land and deposited on its floor. Since the greatest depth achieved by storm waves is 100 fathoms, this limit marks the end of the depositional extension of the coastal plain.

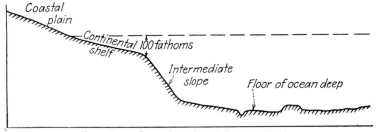

Fig. 17-1.—General profile of the ocean basins.

Beyond the 100-fathom line there is a more or less abrupt transition in slope, known as the "continental or intermediate slope." At times, this slope is so precipitous, that deeply towed fishing nets have become "snagged" onto it, as the fishing vessel crossed into the shallower waters over the continental shelf.

The continental slope continues until the true floor of the oceans, known as the "bathyal," or "abyssal region," is reached. The ocean floor, as pointed out above, is frequently marked with hollows and elevations which may be either steeply or gently sloping.

Temperature of the Oceans

The ocean temperatures are of direct importance in the effect of the sea upon the air. The most prominent feature of marine temperatures is the pronounced uniformity, or lack of variation. Since the overlying air depends closely on the surface temperatures beneath, it follows then that marine air conditions should be very uniform in temperature. That such is the case is a matter of common knowledge and observation. It is well known that marine climates are very moderate.

Let us account for this great constancy of the temperature of the sea. There are several factors involved, all of which are of importance. The oceans, like the continents, derive their heat from insolation. It is, then, in the disposal of this solar energy that the answer to the problem of thermal uniformity of the oceans lies. The principal factors involved in this energy disposal, which we shall consider briefly in order, are (1) reflection, (2) evaporation, (3) transparency, (4) specific heat, (5) movement of the oceans, (6) radiation.

1. REFLECTION.—The surface of the sea behaves much like a mirror, reflecting from 40 to 50 per cent of the incident insolation. Depending on local sea conditions and on the angle of incidence of the sun's rays, this value may be much higher. Thus, approximately half of the solar energy striking the sea surface is reflected, having absolutely no effect whatever on marine temperatures. Let us study what happens to the insolation that does penetrate the surface.

2. EVAPORATION.—We know that a huge quantity of moisture is evaporating continuously into the air. We have learned too that evaporation involves the absorption of latent heat of vaporization. Consequently much of the absorbed insolation is utilized in providing this necessary latent heat. The amount so absorbed in the process of evaporation is thereby lost for purposes of increasing the ocean temperature.

3. TRANSPARENCY.—The land is opaque. The oceans are transparent to a relatively great depth, which varies in amount with the marine locality. Thus, while the insolation striking the land causes a relatively large temperature increase in a small thickness of rock or soil, the energy striking the sea penetrates to greater depths and thus has a relatively small influence on the temperature of a greater thickness of water.

4. SPECIFIC HEAT.—The specific heat of a substance is the heat required to raise one gram of it, one degree centigrade. This is a constant for each substance. Pure water has one of the highest known specific heats, as it takes more heat to raise a given quantity of water over a particular temperature range than it does for most other matter. This factor is of extreme importance in causing the lag in marine temperatures, as compared to those of the land. The saline marine waters have only a slightly lower specific heat than pure water. Should the same amount of insolation be absorbed by equivalent quantities of land and water, the increase of water temperature would show a pronounced lag compared to that of the land. This same lag exists when water cools, for it must then rid itself of a relatively large amount of heat before the temperature can fall.

5. MOVEMENT OF THE OCEANS.—The oceans, as well as the air, engage in both horizontal and vertical motion. Convection is a prominent

feature of ocean behavior. As water cools at the surface, whether by conduction or by radiation, the cold water sinks before too much heat is lost. This is replaced by somewhat warmer water which in turn cools and descends. As a result, no particular volume of water is subjected to long-continued cooling.

6. RADIATION.—Water is a poor radiator of heat. Remember that good absorbers are good radiators of heat and poor absorbers are poor radiators. As we have noted, water warms slowly during periods of insolation. However, it cools equally slowly through radiation at night, again contributing to the observed temperature uniformity.

Because of the great depth of the oceans, any consideration of temperature conditions should distinguish between the surface conditions and the conditions at some depth. The sea temperatures vary with time, latitude, and depth.

ANNUAL AND DIURNAL SURFACE TEMPERATURE VARIATIONS.—The periodic temperature variation of the surface is twofold: annual and diurnal. The annual temperature variation of the oceans is by no means constant from place to place. Owing to the temperature lag considered above, the temperature range is never very large, rarely exceeding a maximum average range of 20°F. although the mean annual range is about 10°F. The greatest average surface temperature range is in the middle latitudes, occurring between 40° and 50° in the Northern Hemisphere, and between 30° and 40° in the Southern Hemisphere. The mean annual variation in the tropics is considerably less than that in the middle latitudes, and the range in the Northern Hemisphere exceeds that of the Southern Hemisphere. The predominance of land north of the equator thus shows its influence on marine temperature. The warm winds blowing offshore in the summer tend to increase slightly the temperature maximum for the oceans and are similarly responsible for lowering the minimum somewhat, when cold winds blow seaward from the much colder continents. Thus the maximum average range in the northern middle latitudes reaches 16°F., while the maximum southern middle latitude range reaches only 10°F. In the tropics in either hemisphere the range is from 1° to 5°.

The diurnal surface temperature variation is very small. This is to be expected after a consideration of the temperature lag considered earlier. This range averages only 0.35°F. It is greater for days with clear skies, than for those with an overcast. Clear days permit a greater influx of insolation during the day and a greater amount of radiation at night, than do overcast conditions. The range is also greater for calm days since wind causes wave action and produces mixing of the surface water with the water at a slight depth, thereby distributing the surface heat and lowering the temperature range.

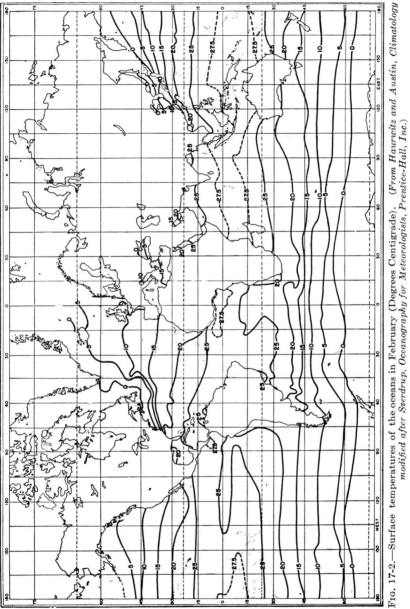

FIG. 17-2.—Surface temperatures of the oceans in February (Degrees Centigrade). (From Haurwitz and Austin, Climatology modified after Sverdrup, Oceanography for Meteorologists, Prentice-Hall, Inc.)

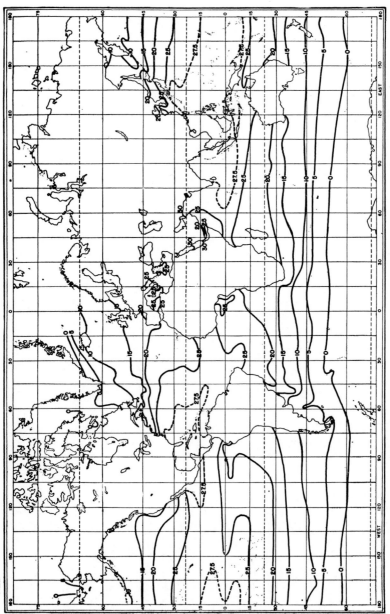

FIG. 17-3.—Surface temperatures of the oceans in August (Degrees Centigrade). (From Haurwitz and Austin, Climatology modified after Sverdrup, Oceanography for Meteorologists, Prentice-Hall, Inc.)

HORIZONTAL VARIATIONS.—A definite temperature gradient exists in both hemispheres from the equator to the poles. Marmer has estimated that the surface temperatures decrease poleward from the equator at the approximate rate of 0.5°F. for every degree of latitude. The temperature of the equatorial oceans averages about 80°F., while that of the polar seas approximates 30°F. It is significant to note that the peak marine surface temperatures occur north of the equator. This again is a reflection of the predominance of land north of the equator.

DEPTH VARIATIONS.—Since the sun is the ocean's source of heat, it follows that the temperature will vary inversely with depth. The temperature usually decreases very rapidly from the surface, downward. In lower latitudes this decrease is considerably more rapid than in the higher latitudes. Below 500 fathoms, the temperatures of the oceans regardless of latitude are nearly the same at given levels. In general, the temperature below 400 fathoms is at or below 40°F., but the further decrease below that level is a very gradual one. The waters in the vicinity of the ocean floor are just above freezing and show little variation from this. The cold polar ocean currents creeping equatorward along the ocean floor partly account for the cold subsurface waters of the tropics. Then, water, being a good insulator, prevents the conduction of much heat to any great depth. Thus the sea is cold. The average temperature of the oceans is barely 40°F.

MEASUREMENT OF SEA-WATER TEMPERATURES.—For purposes of distinction, the upper 3 feet of the ocean waters are to be considered as constituting the surface waters. The water below this level is designated as subsurface. Sufficient mixing occurs in the upper 3 feet to provide more or less uniform conditions there. Since the temperature of the surface waters is subject to many more disturbing influences than that of deeper water, small local variations exist in the upper level. Hence surface temperatures are not measured as precisely as subsurface temperatures.

There are two methods commonly employed for the determination of surface temperatures: the bucket and the intake method. In the first case, a sample of the surface water is hauled aboard in a bucket and the temperature measured by means of an accurate standard thermometer. The sample should be taken from the bow rather than the stern end of the vessel in order to avoid the wake as much as possible. There are many practical difficulties involved in obtaining water samples on the deck of a ship by this technique. In addition, many sources of error are introduced by the use of a small isolated sample of water. When temperature readings of such a sample are taken, the thermometer should remain immersed in the water. Water samples should obviously be taken as far from discharge outlets as possible.

The condenser-intake method provides a means of obtaining more accurate surface temperature observations. The only serious condition is that the thermometer must be properly located where free movement of the incoming water exists and where it can be read conveniently, without involving any parallax error. An excellent place of exposure is on the intake pipe between the pump and the ship's side. This avoids exposing the thermometer to possible warm-water pockets or currents which may exist farther on in the circulation system.

The method actually utilized depends to a great extent on both the type of vessel and the observer. We emphasize again that the observer must always seek to minimize sources of error.

The subsurface temperatures may also be obtained by one of two methods: the sampling bottle and the registering thermometer. The first technique consists of lowering a special thermally insulated sampling bottle to the desired depth. After being returned to the deck, an accurate, standard thermometer with a large scale spread is inserted, and the temperature noted.

A more accurate but, at the same time, more expensive method involves lowering a special type of registering thermometer, known as a "reversing thermometer." This is actually a rather complicated maximum-type thermometer which is inverted or reversed in position at the depth required for the temperature observation. Subsurface temperatures are usually recorded to 0.1°F., and often closer. For scientific work of this kind, the centigrade scale is normally used, with accuracies of closer than 0.05°C. being required.

Surface and subsurface temperature records may be made by connecting thermographs to the intake pipe.

Salinity and Composition

To the average person the terms "sea" and "salty" are almost inseparable. Numerous legends and stories have arisen to account for the saline property of the oceans. It is a well-known observation that, whenever sea water evaporates, a relatively thick salty crust remains. In round figures, there are 35 pounds of salt in every 1,000 pounds of sea water. By definition, the salinity value of any sample of ocean water is expressed as pounds of salt per 1,000 pounds of water (including salt).

Through chemical and spectroscopic analyses, 49 elements have so far been identified in sea water. Doubtless more will be isolated in time. Aside from the basic hydrogen and oxygen, which compose water in the ratio of 2 to 1 by volume, everything else is in solution in the sea water. This testifies very appropriately to the statement that water is the "universal" solvent. It is beyond the scope of this brief treatment to consider the conditions of all these elements in the sea. We shall examine only the major saline constituents.

The average *surface* salinity of the oceans is 35.66. Table XXIV below shows the percentage composition of the more common salts that comprise this total.

TABLE XXIV. COMPOSITION OF SEA WATER (IN SOLUTION)

Substance	Per Cent
Sodium chloride	77.8
Magnesium chloride	10.9
Magnesium sulphate	4.7
Calcium sulphate	3.6
Potassium sulphate	2.5
Calcium carbonate } Magnesium bromide }	0.5
Others	

The surface salinity of the oceans is not constant. Clearly, areas where excessive evaporation occurs, together with high temperatures which aid in evaporation, will have a higher salt concentration than areas where evaporation is less and where precipitation is more abundant. Obviously, evaporation concentrates a solution while the addition of fresh water by precipitation dilutes it. Marine waters near large rivers show a much lower salt content owing to the introduction of large amounts of fresh water. Restricted water bodies into which numerous rivers discharge usually show salinities far below normal. The Baltic Sea thus has a salinity of less than 10.

There is a marked surface variation of salinity with latitude. It reaches its highest value in the vicinity of the horse latitudes in both hemispheres. This is accounted for by the large amount of evaporation afforded by the warming, dry, descending air of these zones. The salinity here approximates 36. The salinity then decreases toward the equator. It reaches a minimum within the doldrums, as a result of the overabundant rainfall, together with the calm air, which tends to retard evaporation. The waters here have an average salinity of about 35.

Poleward from the horse latitudes the salinity declines steadily, falling to a value below 30 in the polar seas. Several factors account for this decline:

1. The continuous melting of large ice masses in arctic and polar regions provides a steady supply of fresh water which dilutes the salt concentration.

2. Evaporation is greatly reduced by the generally prevalent low temperatures of the higher latitudes.

3. The rivers of the higher latitudes, being relatively cold, carry a lesser load of material in solution than those in warmer regions and thereby add a smaller quantity of salt to the ocean.

It is significant to note that curves representing the variation of surface salinity with latitude and the variation of evaporation with latitude are nearly identical.

Since the factors of temperature variation, evaporation, and precipitation are chiefly surface influences, it follows that the salinity in ocean layers beneath the surface should be much more constant. Such is indeed the case. Again a variation exists with latitude, corresponding to the surface variations, but on a much smaller scale.

The salinity of the oceans decreases slightly with depth down to 1 mile, below which it is relatively constant or may increase slightly, giving the total volume of the seas an average value of 34.75.

We should mention briefly the probable origin of the salt content of the oceans. From time immemorial the rivers have been washing into the sea. All of them carry a greater or lesser quantity of mineral material in solution. The ceaseless cycle of evaporation from the seas, precipitation over the land, and the consequent drainage of streams back into the oceans, maintains a more or less uniform ocean volume. But during this cycle the salt carried to the sea by the rivers is left behind and becomes more and more concentrated. Accordingly, the ocean salinity is growing steadily, if imperceptibly higher. At present it is interesting to note that the total mass of salt in the oceans has been calculated to be near 50,000,000,000,000,000 tons. One of the methods of computing the age of the earth in its present condition is to determine the annual discharge of salt into the oceans by its numerous rivers. Dividing this into the total quantity of salt present, one value is obtained. This of course assumes that the present rate of discharge is typical of that throughout the geologic ages. This method indicates the earth to be approximately five hundred million years old.

Ice of the Oceans

The effect of ice in the sea on safe navigation cannot be overstressed. Scores of disasters have marked the end of ill-fated vessels that traversed the zones of floating ice. The classic example of ice catastrophe was the sinking of the "unsinkable" "Titanic" on a clear, calm night in April, 1912, after collision with an iceberg. More than 1,400 persons were lost in this disaster.

SOURCES OF ICE.—The perennial cold temperatures of the polar latitudes in both hemispheres are such as to provide for widespread freezing of sea and fresh water in those regions. Nearly all the actual freezing is accomplished during the long, dark, polar winters. The ice found in the sea as a result of this freezing is of two sources: (1) frozen sea water and (2) frozen fresh water originating as glaciers on neighboring land masses. We shall consider the ice formed from sea water first.

Salt water freezes at lower temperatures than does fresh water. The depression of the freezing point depends on the salt concentration of the water. The average depression of the freezing point of the oceans is 3.5°F., with freezing setting in at 28.5°. However, as saline ocean water freezes, the material in solution does not enter into the freezing

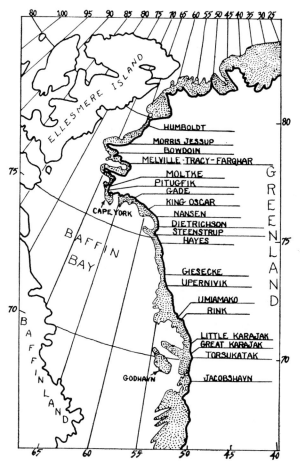

Fig. 17-4.—The principal iceberg glaciers that discharge into Baffin Bay are the origin of nearly all the icebergs drifting into lower latitudes in the western North Atlantic. (*From U. S. Hydrographic Office.*)

process until a much lower temperature (about 17.5°) is reached. Thus marine ice has a lower salinity than the waters forming it. The salinity of ice formed from sea water also decreases with age, as the salt slowly sinks through the ice.

Field Ice.—In the freezing process, water reaches its greatest density when it has cooled to 39°. Below that temperature its density decreases.

At the freezing point, the ice formed has a density of nine-tenths that of
the water, as a result of the expansion due to freezing. Consequently,
the freezing waters and the ice formed tend to remain at the surface.
This fact, together with the poor conduction property of ice, restricts the
pronounced cooling to the surface layers of the sea. Hence the thickness

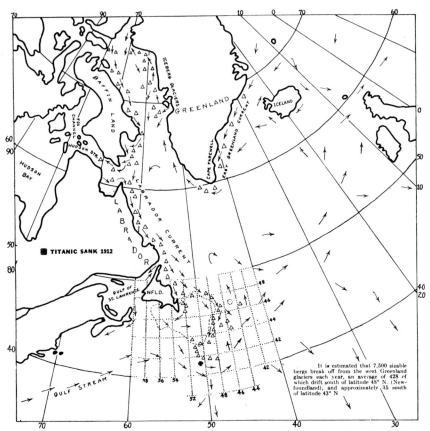

Fig. 17-5.—Drift of icebergs from their source into the North Atlantic. (*From U. S.
Hydrographic Office.*)

of the marine ice sheet, known as "field ice," rarely ever exceeds 10 feet
and averages from 5 to 10 feet. Snow accumulations may increase the
thickness of the ice sheet after formation. The formation of marine
field ice in the higher arctic and polar regions precludes navigation there
in the winter. With the coming of warm weather the ice sheet breaks
and separates into innumerable small sections, called "ice floes." These
floes then drift toward lower latitudes under the influence of the polar
easterlies and the cold ocean currents.

Icebergs.—As troublesome as the floes may be, it is the ice of the second source that constitutes the chief menace to navigation, in the form of icebergs. As a result of continued snowfall with little melting, tremendous thicknesses of ice form on the land masses in high latitudes. These accumulations are hundreds of feet thick and are known as "gla-

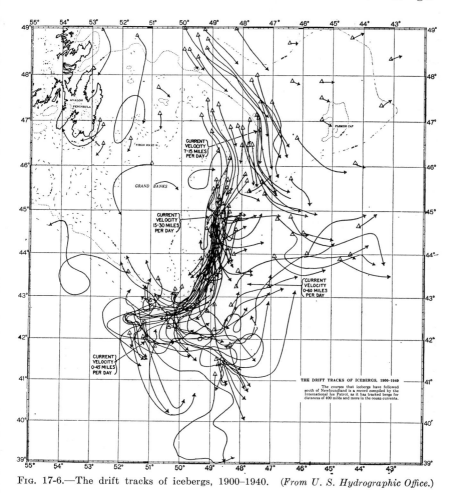

Fig. 17-6.—The drift tracks of icebergs, 1900–1940. (*From U. S. Hydrographic Office.*)

ciers." Under the influence of gravity they migrate seaward. Upon reaching the coast, huge sections of ice break into the sea from the parent mass, being then known as "icebergs." This process, called "calving," is common after the winter season, when warm weather sets in.

Since ice has nine-tenths the density of water, it follows that nine-tenths of the mass must be below the surface, with one-tenth above.

It is erroneous to state that the depth of an iceberg is nine times that of its height above water. This will be true only when it is of uniform cross section. Should the base be more massive than the upper section, this ratio will be much less. Icebergs have been observed extending to 250 feet above the water line. Their length varies from a few tens or hundreds of feet up to a quarter of a mile.

After being severed from the parent glacier, icebergs drift equator-ward. They are but little affected by wind motion. Owing to their greater extent below the sea surface, their behavior is influenced solely

FIG. 17-7.—Large iceberg broken by dynamite explosion (plate fogged).

by existing currents. The shallower ice floes are affected by both winds and currents, so that the motion of icebergs and floes in the same area may at times be at great variance.

In both hemispheres, ice is rarely encountered in latitudes lower than 40°. The larger floes and icebergs have disappeared through melting and breaking. As they become warmed, cracks develop throughout their masses. An abrupt breakage then occurs along this crack, attended by a sudden explosive report that carries for many miles.

Icebergs are rarely encountered in North Pacific waters, owing to a lack of developing grounds. Most of the North Atlantic icebergs originate from the great continental glacier covering Greenland and drift southward with the Labrador Current.

Ice in the North Atlantic receives much more attention than elsewhere since many common shipping lanes lie in the ice area. Actually, ice-bergs are far more numerous and common in Antarctic or South Pacific and Atlantic waters. Their danger to shipping, however, is less in these less frequented areas.

During the ice season from January to June or July, in the North Atlantic, the U.S. Coast Guard maintains a constant ice patrol. The latest ice conditions are then issued via radio by the Hydrographic Office. Further information is obtainable in the daily memoranda, weekly bulletins, and the monthly pilot charts of this office. Pilot charts contain much valuable information on average ice conditions for a given month.

Waves

The surface of the sea is in nearly constant undulating motion. Almost all of this movement of wave and swell which is apparent to the eye is a direct reflection of the behavior of the wind above. In this section we consider only the nature of waves produced by the wind.

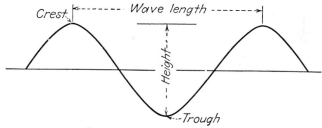

Fig. 17-8.—Wave nomenclature.

Before considering the characteristics of ocean waves, let us review the terminology used. The crest is the peak or highest point of the wave; the trough is the lowest point. The vertical distance between crest and trough is the height. The distance between any two similar phases of successive waves is the wave length, *i.e.*, the distance between two successive crests, troughs, or such. The period of a wave is the time interval between the passage of one crest past a given point and the passage of the succeeding one. It is clear that, the greater the length of the wave, the longer will this period be.

It should be remembered that there is no actual forward displacement of water as the waves progress through the sea. There is rather a propagation of *wave motion* through the water, which acts as a medium for wave action. As a wave is transmitted through the water medium, the water undergoes an oscillatory motion, moving upward and forward in the crest, and downward and backward in the trough. As the wave crest below is propagated along the line *ABC* (Fig. 17-9) a particle of water within the crest moves in the curved path from 1 to 2. As the crest passes point *C*, the water between 1 and 2 now becomes a trough, with the water particle now moving from 2 to 1. An object floating on the water surface, such as a cork, clearly demonstrates this oscillating motion.

Since waves are the direct result of wind action, the velocity and size of the wave are proportional to the velocity of the wind. From a long series of personal observations and the reduction of observations made by others, Cornish concludes that waves and swell move with a velocity of eight-tenths the velocity of wind, or

$$C = 0.8V$$

where C is the wave velocity and V is the wind velocity.

As noted earlier in Chap. 8 on Winds, the height of a wave is a function of the wind velocity. In the open ocean the height of a wave

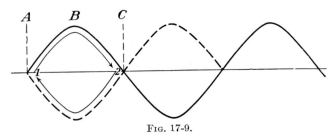

FIG. 17-9.

in feet is about one-half the velocity of the wind, expressed in miles per hour.

$$H = 0.5V$$

Cornish believes the wave height is nearer 0.7 the velocity of the wind. The confusion again is from lack of complete oceanographic data. On the whole, the maximum wave height observed on the seas rarely exceeds 40 to 50 feet. Frequently, the extreme violence of the wind shears off the crests of the waves and gives them a lower appearance than they have as a result of this flattening. In such cases the sea surface appears covered with the foam and spray whipped out by the wind.

The actual dimensions exhibited by a system of waves depends on

1. The depth of water
2. The strength of the wind
3. The duration of the wind
4. The fetch of the wind
5. The preexisting state of the sea

The "fetch" is defined as the distance that the wind travels over the water surface. The maximum wave height developed by gale winds requires a fetch of 600 to 900 miles. A formula has been developed from a consideration of a large number of observations, which gives the maximum wave heights that may be expected from gale winds with a given fetch. Accordingly, the height in feet equals 1.5 times the square root of the fetch (in miles), or

$$H = 1.5 \sqrt{F}$$

A definite relationship exists between the length, period, and velocity of ocean waves, which we summarize briefly below. As space does not permit an examination of the simple derivations of these formulas, the reader is referred to general texts on the subject.

We have noted in our definitions that the length and period of waves are directly related. But the frequency and the period are inversely

Fig. 17-10.—"Weather Rail Under." (*Courtesy of The Ship's Bulletin, S.O.N.J.*)

related. For example, if the frequency of a given train of waves is 10 waves per second, then the period is 0.1 second. From these relationships the velocity equals the length divided by the period, or

$$C = \frac{L}{P}$$

Two other formulas enable the determination of the velocity when either the length or the period alone is known. These are

$$C = 2.25 \sqrt{L}$$
$$C = 5.1 \times P$$

Hence the velocity is equal to $2\frac{1}{4}$ times the square root of the length, or a little over five times the period. The velocity of the wind originally producing the wave can then be computed, since the wave velocity was determined above to be eight-tenths of the wind velocity.

Since the length of a wave is more difficult to determine than the period, it can be found from the formula below, where the length equals 5.5 times the square of the period:

$$L = 5.5 \times P^2$$

In all these formulas, the period is expressed in seconds, the velocity in miles per hour, and the length in feet.

When the height of a wave exceeds one-seventh the length, the wave becomes too steep and breaks. This accounts for the numerous white-

Fig. 17-11.—"Smashing Through." A tanker plunges through heavy seas. (*Courtesy of The Ship's Bulletin, S. O. N. J.*)

caps on the sea surface, where the height of the waves frequently develops faster than the length.

The period of a wave is probably the simplest feature to determine. This is accomplished by noting the time between the rise, fall, and rise of a patch of foam or other floating object at some distance from the ship. Once the period is determined, after several such observations, the other features may be calculated from the formulas above.

The presence of foreign matter in the sea has a pronounced effect on the reduction of wave action. The energy expended in overcoming the friction introduced by such matter weakens wave motion very noticeably. But of much greater importance to the mariner is the effect of foreign matter on the surface, rather than within the sea. In particular, heavy animal or vegetable oils are well known for their value in calming stormy waters. Even a relatively thin oil film greatly

Fig. 17-12.—Huge waves batter a U. S. carrier causing a roll of 27½ degrees from the horizontal. (*Official U. S. Navy Photograph.*)

Fig. 17-13.—Rough sea during a North Atlantic gale. (*Courtesy of The Ship's Bulletin, S.O.N.J.*)

reduces the danger in rough seas. The calming effect lies in the fact that oil has a lower surface tension than water and a higher viscosity (thickness or sirupiness). The lower surface tension of the oil film causes a steepening of the wave and results in its breaking before it reaches a great height. The effect of the greater viscosity of the oil film is to prevent the development of the waves beyond a relatively small height. Many a vessel and small boat has been saved by the prompt use of oil to calm the surrounding waters.

Tides

The tides are extremely important in their effect on navigation in coastal waters. For that reason a great wealth of literature dealing with the practical aspects of tides exists. Elaborate tide tables have been developed for the principal seaports and adjacent coastal zones. We shall therefore treat the tides here in brief, simply as a physical feature of the oceans.

The tides are the result of the gravitational forces of the moon and sun on the earth. They are complicated by the relative motions of these three bodies with reference to each other. The motions particularly responsible for the complications of the tides are the rotation of the earth and the revolution of the moon about the earth. Further difficulties are introduced by the fact that the planes of motion of the sun and moon lie at an angle to the equator.

Despite the intricacies of the problem, the tide-producing forces can be worked out separately for the sun and the moon and the results then superimposed, the net result being the observed tide-producing force. If the earth were covered with a uniform layer of water, the explanation of observed tidal phenomena would be simplified. However, the water areas of the earth are anything but uniform. They vary in size, shape, depth, volume, area, etc. As a consequence, the application of the tide-producing forces to the various observed conditions has not yet completely explained all the observed tidal phenomena.

The influence of the sun and moon in causing tides is identical with the exception of the magnitude of the results. Although the sun is all-important in controlling the behavior of the earth as a heavenly body and the behavior of the atmosphere, it paradoxically yields to the moon in the production of tides. The tidal force varies directly with the mass of the attracting body, but inversely as the *cube* of the distance of the body. Although the sun is far more massive than the moon, its distance from the earth is so much greater that the tide-producing force of the moon is $2\frac{1}{4}$ times greater than that of the sun.

LUNAR TIDES.—As a result of the horizontal component of the moon's gravitational attraction on the waters of the earth, two protuberances form in the seas on exactly opposite sides of the earth, one being directed toward the moon and the other away.

Since the main tide depends on the moon which rises, on the average, 52 minutes later each day, the tidal wave that follows the moon's apparent motion (caused by the earth's rotation) will recur 24 hours and 52 minutes later at a given point. But about 12 hours and 25 minutes later, the high tide opposite the moon will pass, yielding two high-tide levels with two intervening low-water periods. This feature of two high and two low tides a day (lunar) is known as the "semidiurnal tide."

The tidal bulges are never directly beneath the moon; the complications mentioned above are responsible. There may be a time interval of many hours (in some cases, much longer), between the passage of the moon and the dependent high tide, across a given meridian. This

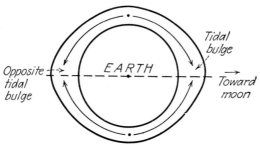

Fig. 17-14.—Formation of two tidal waves on opposite sides of the earth. The arrows show the directions in which the tide-producing force acts.

interval between meridian passage of the moon and tide is known as the "tidal lag." The tidal lag is characteristic of a given locality and thus permits of the prediction of the tides well in advance.

If a graph is constructed, in which time is one coordinate and the height of the tide is the other, the tidal curve results, which shows the variation of tide level with time. Each place has its characteristic tide curve. Even a rapid examination of tidal curves shows that there is a change in tide level from day to day at a given locality, and also a pronounced change from place to place. It is noted that some ports experience two equally high tides a day, while others experience a pair of very unequal tides in a day; still others experience but one high and one low tide a day. This latter feature is known as a "diurnal tide." Further, the tidal range at the same place undergoes great variation from day to day.

Most of these variable features result from the moon's change in declination. Only twice a month is the moon directly over the equator, producing the maximum tidal bulges in the plane of the equator on these occasions. At these times the lunar tide-producing forces are distributed uniformly over the halves of the globe facing toward and away from the moon, respectively. Were the earth uniformly covered with water, all points would have two equally high tides in a day, although the range from high to low water would diminish with latitude. The complications introduced by the great variance of the water bodies of the earth prevent this uniformity from being completely realized even when the moon is over the equator.

The moon's motion places it either above or below the equator and causes the tidal protuberances to have the relationship shown in Fig. 17-15. Points on the equator exhibit equally high and low tides. Places above or below the equator, such as P, exhibit unequal tidal ranges during the day. Point P experiences a high tide. But 12 hours later, at

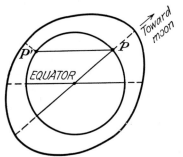

P', only a very low high tide is experienced. Points farther north may experience only one high tide a day. Clearly, the same tidal situation will be experienced only when the moon is again in that same declination.

Again, owing to the size, shape, and volume of the different water bodies, further difficulties are introduced by each sea, which complicate the variations due to the moon's declination. Thus, New York City and neighboring coastal waters have two equally high tides a

Fig. 17-15.—The diurnal inequality of the tides owing to the moon's declination.

day; the West Coast ports exhibit two high tides which differ greatly in magnitude while Gulf ports show only the diurnal tide of one high- and one low-water period per day.

SOLAR TIDES.—In response to solar tide forces, the seas behave in a similar fashion, but with less response. Solar tides manifest themselves by strengthening or reducing lunar tide effects. Thus, twice a month at full or new moon, when the sun and moon are in a straight line, the solar and lunar tide-producing forces are added. Hence, twice a month we have the highest of the high tides, and the lowest of the low tides, the phenomenon being known as the "spring tide."

When the moon is at first or last quarter, or at "quadrature," the maximum solar and lunar tide-producing forces are at right angles. The effect is naturally to lessen the high lunar tide and increase the low-water level, which is in the direction of the solar high tide. Thus we obtain the lowest of the high tides and the highest of the low tides at first and last quarters. This is known as the "neap tide."

APOGEE AND PERIGEE TIDES.—One other cause of variation must be mentioned. The moon's path about the earth is an ellipse, with the earth lying somewhat nearer one end of it than the other, the difference being 26,000 miles. The closest position of the moon is called "perigee" and the farthest position "apogee." Remember that the tide-producing force varies inversely as the cube of the distance. Since the average lunar distance is only 240,000 miles, the 26,000-mile difference is important. Clearly, high perigee tides will be much higher than high apogee tides. Perigee and apogee tides must occur once a month, respectively. If the perigee tide occurs during spring tide conditions, the greatest tidal extremes are then realized.

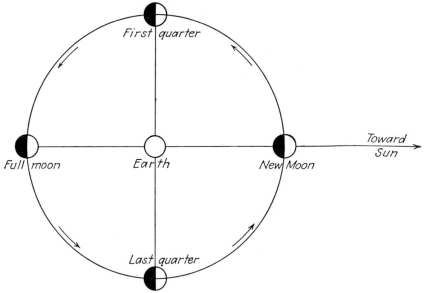

Fig. 17-16.—Relative monthly positions of sun, moon, and earth.

The tidal wave moves westward through the seas. The depth of the oceans is such that the tides in the open sea are nearly imperceptible, having a range estimated between 2 and 3 feet at the most. As the tide reaches continental or island shores, the shape and slope of the sea floor and the shape of the coast line determine the heights to which the tidewaters will rise. In the Bay of Fundy, east of Maine, a range of more than 50 feet is known.

Some of the complexities of the problem of the tides have been indicated in this section. A complete treatment of this difficult problem involves the application of technical mechanics beyond our present scope.

Ocean Currents

Ocean currents are among the most significant of the marine factors as regards their effect on atmospheric conditions. The transportation of large quantities of warm and cold waters by the movement of the surface layers of the sea determines to a great extent the climatic conditions experienced by many coastal areas.

According to common terminology, a "current" is a progressive movement of a part of the sea. In the case of waves and tides no continuous displacement of the water occurs in a given direction; the motion is cyclical or oscillatory. The direction of motion of a current is known as its "set"; the velocity is known as the "drift." Mariners often term

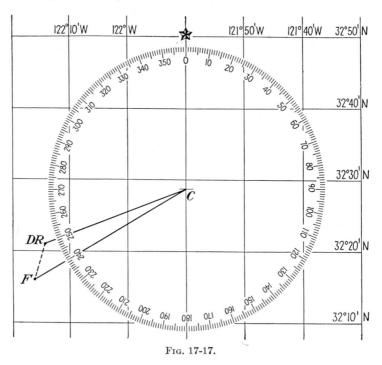

Fig. 17-17.

a slowly moving current a "drift" and reserve the name "current" for movements of sea water having relatively higher velocities.

OBSERVATION OF OCEAN CURRENTS.—Owing to the great length and breadth of the seas and the lack of suitable fixed stations, reliable observations on the set and drift of currents are and have been difficult to obtain. Several methods have been employed to this end:

1. Marine charts and logs, after the completion of a "run," are often of great value in estimating the features of prevailing currents. The difference between "dead-reckoning" and astronomical "fix" positions are for the most part a result of current influence. Thus (Fig. 17-17) after a given time, a vessel leaving the coast, at C, might arrive at dead-reckoning position, DR. However, the fix obtained through celestial

observation places the vessel at *F*. Aside from calculation errors, the difference between *F* and *DR* is due mainly to the surface current. If the ship has traveled for 10 hours and the difference in positions is 20 nautical miles, the current drift is 2 knots in the direction shown (the set).

2. Drift bottles provide another source of data of current behavior. These are sealed bottles weighted so as to float just beneath the water surface, thereby avoiding the effects of the winds. A return postal card is enclosed, giving the date and location at the time it is released. The finder is requested to add the new date and location when removing the bottle from the sea and forward the card.

3. Lighthouses, lightships, and vessels temporarily "hove to" also supply direct observational indications of the drift and set of the current in their particular vicinity.

CAUSES OF OCEAN CURRENTS.—
Much still remains for the complete
explanation of ocean current behavior. However, several factors have
been identified that are directly
involved in initiating and maintain-
ing current flow.

FIG. 17-18.—Generalized diagram of con vection in the oceans.

1. *Temperature Differences (Polar-Equatorial).*—We noted earlier that the primary circulation of the atmosphere owes its existence to the temperature gradient between equatorial and polar regions. A grand convectional circulation system has developed as a consequence. A similar effect occurs in the oceans. As a result of equatorial overheating, the waters of the tropics suffer expansion, however slight, tending to raise the surface level above the colder, denser, polar water surface level. To relieve the gradient thus formed, warm equatorial waters move poleward, at the surface. To compensate for this loss of equatorial surface waters, causing a decrease in pressure, the waters of the depths begin moving equatorward. To compensate for this loss of water in the depths, surface waters in polar regions must subside. Consequently, a primary ocean circulation is set up, with warm waters moving poleward at the surface, and cold water moving equatorward in the depths.

2. *Differences in Salinity.*—We have considered previously the causes of salinity differences. When they exist, a difference in density of the ocean water is established. The more saline water is the denser and has a greater pressure than neighboring less saline water; this causes a subsurface flow from the denser to the less dense water. This too is responsible for causing a relative surface-level difference. Again compensation occurs with the higher level surface waters flowing in the direction of the denser or more saline waters.

3. *Atmospheric Pressure Differences.*—Obviously, atmospheric pressure variations must cause variations of surface level of the oceans, in the same way that fluctuations of the mercury surface in a barometer occurs. Areas of permanent low pressure will have a higher ocean surface level than water areas subject to permanent high-pressure conditions. This again causes a flow of water in response to this surface gradient.

4. *Winds.*—A close correlation exists between the direction of most of the prevailing winds and the ocean currents. Owing to this relationship, the wind has for many years been accepted as the chief cause of ocean currents. It is now known to be but one of many factors. The effect of wind in producing currents depends on the length of time the wind has blown, the strength of the wind, and the depth of water involved. The surface waters naturally exhibit the most pronounced effect, while a rapid decrease occurs with depth. In general, it is estimated that a wind-produced current flows with a velocity of 1½ per cent of the velocity of the wind.

CURRENT MODIFICATIONS.—There are two essential factors influencing current behavior other than the causative factors: (1) rotational deflection and (2) continental deflection. Currents, like winds react to the Coriolis force of rotation, suffering a deflection to the right in the Northern and to the left in the Southern Hemisphere. From mathematical calculations and from currents and wind observations, it has been shown that currents in the Northern Hemisphere set from 40° to 45° to the right of the wind direction, and a corresponding distance to the left in the Southern.

The contour of the continents is also of paramount importance in causing current changes. Currents must naturally conform to the trend of the coasts on which they impinge.

The world ocean currents clearly show the influence of these two factors (Figs. 17-19). It is noticed immediately on a world ocean-current chart, that each ocean is characterized by tremendous surface whirls which are clockwise in the northern latitudes and counterclockwise in the southern.

Clearly, the currents flowing poleward from the equator must be relatively warm, whereas currents moving equatorward are relatively cold. The current chart distinguishes between these warm and cold currents.

Note that currents, unlike winds, are named according to the direction *toward* which they flow.

EQUATORIAL CURRENTS.—In view of the prominence of the equatorial currents, particularly as regards extent and volume of water transported, it is natural to give them the foremost position in our current considera-

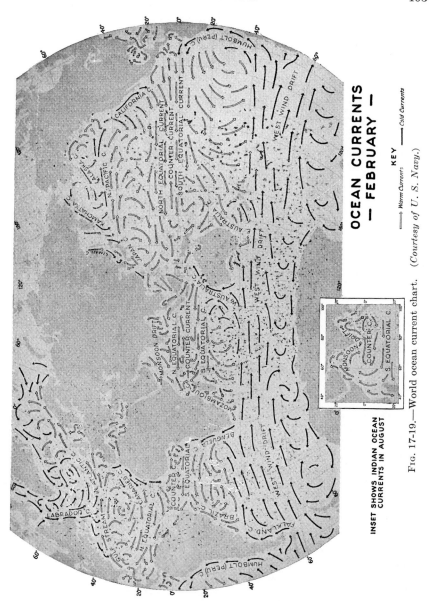

OCEAN CURRENTS
— FEBRUARY —

KEY

→ Warm Currents   → Cold Currents

INSET SHOWS INDIAN OCEAN
CURRENTS IN AUGUST

Fig. 17-19.—World ocean current chart.   (*Courtesy of U. S. Navy.*)

tion. For the most part, the equatorial currents set nearly due west, having drifts that vary from 0.6 knot, near their origin, near the western sides of the continents, to as high as 2.5 knots, off the South American coast. The origin of these currents is generally ascribed to the convergence of the trade winds, which have a pronounced westward component. The correlation in motion between the trades and the equatorial currents is too strong to overlook, although as explained earlier, there is still much to be done in this field of study.

Two basic divisions of the equatorial current are recognized: the North Equatorial Current and the South Equatorial Current. Separating these, for most of their extent, is the equatorial countercurrent, which sets to the east. The mean position of the countercurrent lies a few degrees north of the equator, approximating the mean position of the doldrums, where the effect of the trades is no longer experienced.

The South Equatorial Current in the Atlantic is split by the eastward promontory of South America, part flowing southwest along the Brazilian and Argentina coasts and part continuing northwestward ultimately reaching the Caribbean Sea and the Gulf of Mexico.

The equatorial currents in the Pacific continue westward for great distances before suffering interruptions. The northern branch, after striking the coast of Taiwan, is deflected northward. The southern branch divides near the Fiji Islands, with one part continuing westward and north of west, toward New Guinea, while the other part curves southward along the east coast of Australia.

In the Indian Ocean the South Equatorial Current is similar to that of the North Pacific and North Atlantic Ocean. It bends southward upon approaching Madagascar and Africa. The North Equatorial Current, being subject to monsoon wind behavior, varies with the seasons in accordance with the monsoon wind variations.

CURRENTS OF THE NORTH ATLANTIC.—After coursing through the Caribbean and Gulf, and between the islands of the West Indies, the waters of the South Equatorial Current join with the water of the North Equatorial Current in the Straights of Florida and give rise to the Gulf Stream. So unique is this current, that special attention will be given to it.

The Gulf Stream is considered to originate in the Straights of Florida. The magnitude, velocity, and constancy of this current are so pronounced, compared to the other currents of the seas, as to make it truly remarkable. Its effect on weather and climatic conditions of the North Atlantic, as well as on shipping, cannot be emphasized too strongly. The Gulf Stream differs notably from the surrounding ocean waters in its higher temperature, deep blue-indigo color, seaweed content, and direction and velocity of motion.

The greatest velocity of about 3.5 knots is reached in the straits off the Cape of Florida. Elsewhere in this general area, the velocity falls to 2.5 knots. A further decrease to about 1 knot occurs by the time Cape Hatteras is reached. The stream flows northward to 31° whence it curves with the coast line, to the northeast, continuing in that general direction until off Newfoundland. The more or less abrupt change from warm to cold water along the western and northwestern boundaries of the Gulf Stream is called the "cold wall."

East of Newfoundland the now slowly moving Gulf Stream is usually named the "North Atlantic Drift." This separates into two branches: one continues on northeastward, warming the shores of Iceland, Norway, and northern Great Britain; the second curves to the east and turns southward on approaching the European shore. This equatorward current is frequently termed the "Canaries Current," or the "Northeast Trade Drift." The Canaries Current enters the North Equatorial Current, completing a giant circulation which consists of North Equatorial Current, Gulf Stream, Northeast Drift, and the Canaries Current. Part of the latter flows along the northwest African coast and unites with the countercurrent off the Guinea coast to form the relatively strong Guinea Current, which sets to the east.

The cold Labrador Current originates in the Davis Strait between Greenland and North America. It sets approximately southward, meeting the Gulf Stream between latitudes 40° and 43°. Upon this meeting, some of the cold current is turned westward and then southward, flowing along the coast, in a parallel but opposite direction to the Gulf Stream. Much of the Labrador Current sinks beneath the warmer Gulf Current and continues southward at lower levels.

The cold wall formed by the meeting of these two contrasting currents is very pronounced. We have already considered the resulting fogs that frequently form from this meeting. The Labrador Current is responsible for most of the dangerous ice being carried southward in the North Atlantic.

THE SARGASSO SEA.—Within the central area of the strong North Atlantic whirl, there exists a body of calm water known as the "Sargasso Sea," the name being derived from the great quantity of sargassum, a type of seaweed, contained in these waters. This area corresponds approximately with the position of the Azores high, the North Atlantic portion of the calm horse latitude belt. The waters of the Sargasso Sea are warm and. if anything, a deeper and clearer blue than the waters of the Gulf Stream. Huge mats of seaweed abound here. It was at one time believed that this material drifted in from the surrounding warm waters, in much the same manner as sediment settles out in the relatively calm center of a stirred liquid. However, study of this marine vegetation showed it to be original to the Sargasso waters, being a deep-sea type of weed which flourishes near the water surface, without anchorage to the floor, as is the case with the common shallow water seaweed. Despite stories to the contrary, the seaweed here, extensive as it may be, offers little impediment to a ship's speed. Since such tales arose in the sailing-ship era, it is very likely that the absence of prevailing winds in this area, rather than the presence of seaweed, accounted for the loss in speed.

CURRENTS OF THE SOUTH ATLANTIC.—The southern branch of the South Equatorial Current, flowing southward along Brazil, is known as the Brazil Current, which returns to the east again at about 40° and continues toward Africa, under the name of "Southeast Trade Drift." The relatively cold current returning northward to the Equatorial Current, along the coast of Africa, is called the "Benguella Current."

CURRENTS OF THE NORTH PACIFIC.—Upon curving northeastward, the North Equatorial Current, becomes the warm *Kuroshio*, or Japan Current, which is very similar in many respects, to the Gulf Stream. The varying monsoons off Asia have a pronounced influence on the velocity and hence the volume of water transported by the Kuroshio. The Japan Current turns eastward at 40° and is then known as the "North Pacific Current." Part of this returns southward to the Equatorial Current, just east of the 180th meridian. The other branch, which continues toward North America, splits up, upon its arrival there. That portion turning southward is relatively cold and is known as the "California Current," while the northward branch is called the "Alaska Current."

The cold currents passing southward from the Bering Straits are responsible for the fog so prevalent over the Aleutians and neighboring waters.

CURRENTS OF THE SOUTH PACIFIC.—The South Equatorial Current, which turns southward at Australia, known as the "East Australia Current," is clearly a warm flow. This then joins the prevailing West Wind Drift, returning to South America, where a deflection to the north occurs. The relatively cold current flowing northward along Chile and Peru is known by the names "Humboldt," "Chilean," and "Peruvian," currents.

In general there is a pronounced current drift between 40° and 50°S., in the zone of the roaring forties, which seems again to be directly dependent on the strong prevailing westerlies in those latitudes and is known as the "West Wind Drift."

Further modifications and movements of the surface waters are shown in the generalized current chart of the world (Fig. 17-19).

EFFECT OF OCEAN CURRENTS ON AIR MASSES.—Clearly ocean currents must have a marked effect on air-mass conditions, since air masses derive their original and most of their modified properties from the surface beneath. The oceans thus have a direct effect in shaping world weather.

It will be remembered that the cold continents in winter become the centers of strong high-pressure areas, particularly in the region of the horse latitudes. Consequently, a vigorous motion of the prevailing westerlies occurs from the continents to the neighboring oceans to the east or leeward. As outbreaks of cold polar air occur over the continents, this air is carried out over the warm currents, the Gulf Stream and the

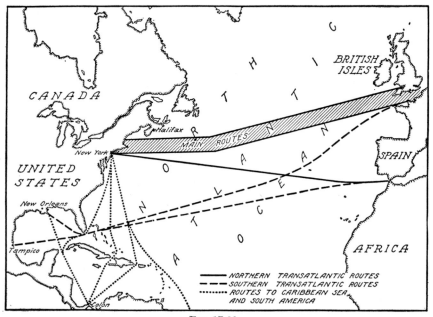

Fig. 17-20.

Japan Current, in the case of North America and Asia, respectively. Very marked and vigorous frontal activity develops as this cold continental air moves out across the warm water to the east of the continent. The resulting cyclonic activity has already been examined.

In addition to the effect on frontal activity, conditions within the air masses are greatly modified as a result of passage across a contrasting ocean surface. When a cold air mass traverses a warm surface, warming of the lower layer of the air mass occurs. This produces convection with attendant cumulus and often cumulonimbus clouds, frequently yielding showers.

When a mass of air is warmer than the underlying ocean surface, widespread advection fogs, often accompanied with low stratus clouds, tend to form.   As explained previously, the extensive fogs of Newfoundland, the Aleutians, and the California coast have this origin.

Average Weather Conditions of the Oceans

Having examined the important physical properties of the oceans, we should consider also the average weather features encountered along the more common shipping lanes.   The average oceanic weather summaries reproduced below (pages 408–420) were compiled by the U.S. Weather

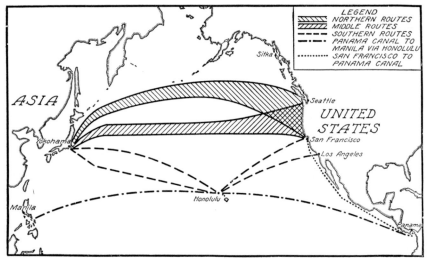

Fɪɢ. 17-21.

Bureau and give monthly weather summaries for the North Atlantic and North Pacific oceans.   Figures 17-20 and 17-21 indicate the principal ocean routes along which these average conditions are experienced.

MONTHLY AVERAGE WEATHER CONDITIONS OF THE NORTH ATLANTIC OCEAN
AND WEST INDIAN WATERS

January.—Along the northern steamer routes to Europe frequent storms, accompanied by high winds and much rain or snow, are common in January.   Many of these disturbances enter the ocean from North America, intensifying as they travel over the open sea; others arise over the ocean.   Cyclones are often of wide extent, and a single disturbance may cover more than half the width of the North Atlantic between the British Isles and Newfoundland, fluctuating in extent and intensity from day to day.   The prevailing winds along most parts of the main steamer lanes are from a westerly direction, often attaining gale and sometimes hurricane force.   Strong northerly to northwesterly winds are common in January along the coast of the United States from

New England to the Carolinas, usually decreasing in strength southward from Cape Hatteras.

Over most of the ocean between latitudes 5° and 25°N., the northeast trade winds blow with considerable regularity, except in the Gulf of Mexico where the winds are more variable with usually a few occasions when they reach gale force, and these mostly from a northerly quarter.

Fog in January occurs more frequently from Newfoundland waters to Cape Cod than in other parts of the North Atlantic, but is to be expected even there on only 3 to 5 days in the month. Fog occurs occasionally south of Cape Hatteras and in the Gulf of Mexico. On the whole, January is the month of least fog frequency over the main trans-Atlantic routes.

Travel over southern waters is, as a rule, pleasant in January. On the northern routes, despite the frequent storms, a voyage eastbound to Europe may at times be made with little accompaniment of bad weather because the steamer may cross at about the same rate of travel as a spell of good weather moving eastward between stormy depressions.

February.—The average weather conditions of February over the North Atlantic and adjacent waters are very similar to those of January. If anything, the weather of February averages even stormier than that of January, although particular years may show the reverse of this condition.

Westerly winds and severe gales commonly prevail over northern transatlantic ship lanes in February, and northers occasionally blow across the Gulf of Mexico and Florida Straits. The weather of the tropics is, for the most part, agreeable and free from severe storminess.

March.—Since March is a transition month between winter and spring, weather conditions characteristic of both periods are met on the North Atlantic. Wintry weather, however, continues to predominate, although there is a lessening of the average number of days with gale winds along the transatlantic steamship routes, as storms show a tendency to decrease in frequency and violence toward the end of the month. The prospects are, therefore, in the average, somewhat more favorable for transatlantic travel. While March averages less stormy than the two preceding months in many parts of the ocean, nevertheless an individual March may prove to be the stormiest month of the season if winter conditions run late, intensifying the contrast with approaching spring.

Southeast of Newfoundland, in the general neighborhood of the Grand Banks, fog is more frequent than in any other of the colder months, and may be expected along this section of the steamship routes on an average of about 2 days in 5. Coastal fogs, Hatteras to Nova Scotia, are about half as frequent in March as those over the Grand Banks.

Travel in the Gulf of Mexico, Caribbean Sea, and the tropical North Atlantic is usually very pleasant in March.

April.—With April more settled weather conditions appear over the middle and northern waters of the North Atlantic. Storms of the middle-latitude type continue to occur, but they are less severe than during the preceding months of the year, and the intervals of favorable weather are of longer duration. Winds of gale force still occur quite frequently, however, over a considerable mid-ocean area north of the 40th parallel of latitude.

The belt of the northeast trades of the tropical parts of the ocean begins to shift to northward and in April lies mostly between 5° and 25°N. latitude. The trades begin to establish a steadier regime over the West Indian region, being less broken up by winds from other directions under the influence of winter disturbances.

Fog shows a definite increase from Newfoundland and the Grand Banks to Cape Cod, and may be expected to occur on 12 days during April over the Grand Banks, and on 2 to 6 days southwest of Cape Cod.

May.—The weather over the northern half of the North Atlantic is much more moderate in May than in April and, therefore, May is spoken of as being a generally pleasant month for travel. Storms continue to occur with considerable frequency but with much lessened severity and duration, so that a voyage to Europe is more likely than otherwise to be free from serious discomfort. Over much of the southern part of the ocean the northeast trades prevail with increasing steadiness and intensity. Gales are rare south of the 35th parallel of latitude. May is regarded as perhaps the pleasantest month for ocean travel in the West Indian and Caribbean area.

Fog continues to increase in frequency from the Grand Banks southwestward to the Virginia Capes, and may be expected on half of the days of the month between Newfoundland and Nova Scotia.

June.—The weather throughout the North Atlantic is for the most part quiet and pleasant in June. A small amount of storminess occurs annually somewhere along the northern steamer routes, but rough weather is comparatively rare, as a rule, and gales, usually of moderate strength only, show average occurrence on only 1 day in about 15 or 20 over the stormiest part of the ocean.

In the southern North Atlantic, June marks the beginning of the West Indian hurricane season. These tropical storms, however, are very rare this month and, when they do occur, are not usually of marked severity and are almost entirely confined to the western Caribbean Sea and the Gulf of Mexico. Travel in June over any part of the ocean is likely to be attended by little weather discomfort or hazard due to storminess. Ocean fog, however, is found at its maximum frequency along the transatlantic routes during June and July. Over the Grand Banks, where fog is perennially of heaviest occurrence, the average expectancy amounts to 20 or more days of the month, usually diminishing quite rapidly east of the 45th meridian, and also south of the 40th parallel, although there is in June usually some fog as far south as the Virginia Capes and considerable in the vicinity of Long Island.

July.—This is a favorable month for transatlantic travel. Few storms occur along the middle and northern routes, and gales as a consequence are infrequent and rarely of great force. A few storms of considerable severity that occur in these latitudes are continuations of tropical cyclones which, forming in the neighborhood of the West Indies, sometimes move northward and then eastward across the steamer lanes to Europe. The West Indian hurricane season is not yet far advanced in July. These storms are not of annual occurrence this month, the average number being about 2 in 5 years. The July hurricane, when established, usually moves westward into the Gulf of Mexico or northward up the east coast of the United States, only a few moving on into the open North Atlantic.

Fog continues as in June at maximum frequency over the Grand Banks area, and is still quite common from New Foundland southwestward to the Virginia Capes. The frequency usually increases in July over the middle and eastern parts of the main transatlantic routes.

August.—Weather conditions in higher latitudes of the North Atlantic Ocean continue favorable for travel. Such storms as occur there are few in number and, unless they are of tropical origin, weak in force, and cause only scattered winds of gale intensity. The prevailing winds continue from a westerly direction along the middle-latitude steamship routes to Europe. Trade winds are at their maximum northern extension over tropical waters. In tropical waters the West Indian hurricane gains in average frequency and force. About three times as many of these storms occur in August as in July, the average being a little more than one annually in the month. Many of the August hurricanes originate far to the eastward of the West Indies. The storms at first usually move to westward, with some continuing their course across the Caribbean Sea and the Gulf of Mexico, but the greater number recurve to northward at some portion of the path, later moving eastward into the open Atlantic. Storms that pursue these courses are the only ones of August that cause high winds of consequence on the middle and northern sailing routes.

Fog diminishes in frequency and general extent during this month. The regions where fog forms on the greatest number of days lie eastward of Newfoundland and New England, and in these limited areas, fog may be expected to occur on from 7 to 12 days in August.

September.—With the approach of autumn, quieter weather conditions that generally characterize the summer over higher latitudes are gradually replaced by the first advances of colder weather and increased atmospheric activity. Cyclonic gales increase somewhat in frequency along the routes to Europe. The weather remains mostly fair for northern transatlantic tourist travel, however, as the chances of missing are more favorable than for encountering storms. In southern latitudes the West Indian hurricane reaches its peak of occurrence, with an average of three occurring in September annually. This average is not dependable for any given month, however, for in some years September has shown none, while in others there have been as many as five in this month. The entire West Indian region is subject to these storms. Many enter the Gulf of Mexico, while a greater number recurve from the Caribbean on a northerly track to eastward of the American coast. Many of the latter continue to advance with considerable energy into northern waters, and thus add in considerable degree to the hazard of storms along the northern steamship routes during the month.

Fog decreases in average frequency during September. The foggiest regions are of quite limited extent to eastward of New England and Newfoundland. There is usually some increase in fog north of the Azores.

October.—During October autumnal storms increase in energy along the central and northern transatlantic routes, many of them arriving as moderate disturbances from the continent. The probability of experiencing rough weather on a voyage to Europe is, on the average, nearly two times as great as in September. Occasional high-latitude storms of the month are of great intensity, with an accompaniment of winds of hurricane or near-hurricane velocity. Pleasant, bracing weather, however, is frequently experienced along the northern routes and gale winds do not occur, on the average, on more than 1 day in 6 over even the windiest part of the main route between New York and the British Isles.

An average of between two and three hurricanes occur annually in October in tropical waters. This is some decrease from the frequency in September, and the probability that one will form diminishes rapidly in the latter half of the month. After the middle of October there is little likelihood that tropical disturbances will move westward into the Gulf of Mexico. A considerable number of these storms pass northward over the western part of the ocean, then northeastward along the steamship routes; and in October the North Atlantic storms are about equally divided between those of tropical and those of more northern origin.

Fogginess shows a further decrease along the northern routes. The Grand Banks and vicinity continue to be the region of maximum occurrence, and fog occurs there on about 1 day in 3 in October.

November.—November is usually a stormy month over northern waters of the North Atlantic. While winter conditions there have by no means become fully established, the month may occasionally develop into one of the severest of the cold-weather season. Storms of the winter type increase along the American coast, where, on the average, gales occur on about 1 day in 10. The heaviest weather of the month on the ocean is experienced, as a rule, to the northward of the 45th parallel. Storminess is less frequent to the southward, but extends in some degree to the tropics.

West Indian hurricanes show a great decrease, but they still form occasionally in tropical waters in November. Averages show only about one in 2 years, however, in this month. The weather over southern waters is little beset by storms; the area of northeast trade winds is receding but these winds still continue to dominate much of the ocean south of the 25th parallel of latitude. Fog continues to decrease somewhat in area and frequency over western and northern waters.

December.—December is usually one of the stormiest months of the cold season over all parts of the ocean except in the tropics. Widespread storms are frequent along the northern and middle steamship routes, accompanied by much rain, sleet, or snow, and high seas. The traveler on the route to Europe is, therefore, quite likely to encounter rough, disagreeable weather during at least part of a voyage. This is not invariably true, of course, since many ships make the passage in December, without experiencing severe weather; this is more commonly the case when ships are eastbound. Conditions are favorable for travel in the West Indies and Caribbean region. Tropical storms of the hurricane type are so rare this month as not to be feared. Occasional continental-type storms occur in the Gulf of Mexico; although they may cause rough weather, they are rarely severe.

Average fog conditions do not change much from October and November, although there is often some extension of fog southward beyond Cape Hatteras.

MONTHLY AVERAGE WEATHER CONDITIONS OF THE NORTH PACIFIC OCEAN

January.—Along the northern routes from California, Oregon, and Washington ports to Japan much stormy weather, with rain, sleet, or snow, occurs. Gales, especially along the middle and western parts of the routes, are frequently strong, and sometimes rise in velocity to that of a hurricane. Strong gales at times blow along the upper United States coast, but the probabilities of heavy weather increase to the westward. Along the middle routes, that is, between 30° and 42°N. latitude, storminess decreases from north to south. Occasional storms, mostly of moderate intensity, occur between California and the Hawaiian Islands. South of 30° latitude over the eastern half of the ocean, but south of 25° latitude on the western half, and thence to near the equator, the prevailing winds are the northeast trades. Gales occur infrequently over this region.   In southeastern Asiatic waters the northeast monsoon, often accompanied by thick, rainy weather, is the prevailing wind. Tropical cyclones occur in January in this region on an average of about one in 2 years.   On a voyage between West Coast ports and the Panama Canal strong northerly winds are sometimes encountered in crossing the Gulf of Tehuantepec.

Fog is rarely experienced on the Pacific in January, except in coastal waters, both American and Asiatic.   On the average, the chance of meeting coastal fogs, practically all of which occur north of the tropics, is about 1 in 10.

Air temperatures on the North Pacific show a wide range between near-freezing in the extreme north and the mild conditions peculiar to the tropics.   In the north, temperatures are bracing during fair weather, but are raw and penetrating during the more common periods of cloudy and rough to stormy weather.

January as a whole, is a favorable month for tourist travel in tropical waters, but some stormy weather is to be expected along the northern routes.

February.—The weather conditions of February are quite similar, as an average, to those of December and January.   The northern routes continue to be stormy, although in individual years the degree of storminess may vary considerably from that of either of the two preceding months.   High winds, on the average, are slightly less frequent in February than in the two preceding months, but it may be the stormiest or the least stormy month of the winter season in a given year.

In the Asiatic tropics typhoons are of least frequency in February, only eight being of record in the Weather Bureau during the 35-year period 1901–1935.   These storms, therefore, offer only a small hazard to the traveler bound for the Philippine Islands.

March.—Although March is the month of change from winter to spring conditions, the northern routes of the North Pacific are quite likely to be stormy, especially along the western half from the vicinity of the Aleutian Islands to Japan, frequently with heavy snow accompanying the high winds.   On the average, for a long term of years, there is a lessening in the occurrence of gales over that of the preceding 3 months.   Therefore, although March is sometimes the stormiest month of the season, it is usually more favorable for travel along the routes between western ports of the United States and Japan than the preceding cold months.

The chilling air temperatures, together with the high humidities which are prevalent along the northern steamship routes during much of the month, add to the discomfort of travel, particularly during cloudy and stormy weather.   On fair days, however, the brisk, cool air is invigorating, with temperatures ranging mostly between 35° and 55°. Along middle latitude routes to Japan temperatures are higher and more comfortable, and the probability of encountering storms here is much less than farther north; therefore, the traveler may well hope for a generally pleasant voyage across these waters. If the transpacific itinerary between West Coast ports and Japan includes a stop at the Hawaiian Islands, the ship usually enters the northeast trade winds and mild temperatures when about half way to Honolulu. After leaving the islands favorable weather conditions are likely to continue during the greater part of the remainder of the voyage.

Along the lower routes to the Philippine Islands the northeast trades are the prevailing winds, the the weather is generally ideal from the standpoint of temperature. In Far Eastern waters there is an occasional typhoon, but the occurrence there in March is on an average of only one in about 3 years.

April.—April is a rather fickle month as regaras weather along the upper transpacific routes, and occasionally severe storms occur. On the average, however, the weather conditions show a decided improvement over those of any previous month since September, as regards storminess, and since October, as regards temperature. There is a small increase in the probability of encountering fog, especially along the western half of the routes. Cold weather is yet to be expected, with average temperatures ranging between 35° and 50°.

Along the middle routes storminess is much less frequent and severe. Gales are most likely to be experienced in these latitudes west of mid-ocean, and especially within a few days' journey to and from Japan. Here storms entering the ocean from Asia are likely to occur during about 3 days of the month, and an occasional cyclone, moving northward from the tropics, may be encountered. Temperatures in these latitudes average between 50° to 55° on the north, and 65° to 68° on the south, being slightly lower in coastal waters than elsewhere on the ocean in like latitudes. Some fog is likely to be met, more especially in coastal waters.

Pleasant conditions prevail as a rule south of the 30th parallel to the equator. Storm winds are rare in this belt in April. In Far Eastern waters—east and north of the Philippine Islands—a typhoon occurs on the average of once in about 3 years. Between about latitudes 5° and 25° to 30° the prevailing winds are the refreshing northeast trades. Temperatures average about 65° to 68° near the 30th parallel, increasing southward to 75° to 80° or slightly higher in equatorial waters.

May.—May is usually a pleasant month for travel on the North Pacific. Along the northern routes, however, some storminess may be expected, although with decreasing likelihood as the month advances.

It should be realized by the traveler crossing the Northern Pacific in May that these waters are more or less subject to gales through most of the year, and that some rough weather is possible, despite the fact that the majority of vessels making Northern Pacific crossings in May do not encounter winds of gale force. Along the middle routes gales are usually infrequent, but decreasing in probability from north to south between the 40th and 30th parallels. Occasional storms, some of tropical origin, move northward east of Japan. Fog is one discomfort likely to be experienced over northern waters this month; it occurs, on an average, on some 6 to 8 days in May in the region of greatest frequency, along that part of the northern routes between the Aleutian Islands and northern Japan.

In tropical waters of the Far East, cyclonic storms, or typhoons, while showing an increase in occurrence over that of April, are yet infrequent, with only 25 occurring in 35 years of record. The probability of a vessel encountering one of these storms is, therefore, small. A voyage across southern North Pacific waters this month is likely to be very pleasant, with northeast trades the prevailing winds.

In higher latitudes (40° to 50°N.) temperatures, ranging on the average between 45° and 60°, assure to the traveler some degree of comfort on deck, with bracing winds during fair weather.

June.—June is generally the pleasantest month of the year for transpacific travel. The northern routes are comparatively free of stormy weather and gales, and such rough conditions as do occur are likely to be of much less extent and intensity than are general in the colder months. Fog is the principal source of travel discomfort in higher latitudes this month, as it occurs rather frequently along the western coast of the United States and over a considerable strip of ocean between the western Aleutians and Japan. North of the 40th parallel the air temperatures show little change from May and continue to average between about 45° and 60°.

Storms rarely occur in June along the middle routes, except over the western part of the ocean where occasional cyclones move from the tropics, skirting eastern Japan and traveling thence in a generally northeasterly direction into high latitudes on the ocean.

Along the southern transpacific routes the equable trade winds largely prevail. Storms in this belt are almost entirely confined to the western portion where the typhoon, gaining in frequency with late spring and early summer, occurs on an average of one in June. These tropical cyclones are likely to occur at any point to the westward of the 145th meridian of east longitude across the Philippine Islands or northwestward to China. Owing to their infrequent occurrence in June, however, they are seldom experienced by travelers on any one voyage during this month. It is well to mention the fact that a second region for the development of tropical storms is found off the west coast of Mexico. In June, however, these cyclones are infrequent. This region is of interest to travelers going on routes between the United States, or Honolulu, and the Panama Canal.

July.—July is also a favorable month for North Pacific travel, with increasingly comfortable outside temperatures prevailing (52° to 65°), and with storminess at its minimum for the year over the northern routes. July, however, is the foggiest month of the year in northern waters, especially so on the western half of the ocean in high latitudes. There is much less fog in middle latitudes, and south of latitude 30° it is practically nonexistent.

Except for fog in northern waters, the typhoons in the Far East, and the cyclones that occasionally occur west of Mexico, the general weather conditions likely to be experiences on the North Pacific are at their best in July.

There is an average of three tropical cyclones (typhoons) per year in July (104 in 35 years of record) over the southwestern part of the ocean. These originate mostly at a considerable distance east of the Philippines. Some move westward and cross the islands into the China Sea, and some move northwestward or northward toward China or Japan, usually accompanied by strong gales or winds of hurricane violence. These dangerous storms are under close observation by the Far Eastern weather services, so that shipping, as a rule, is informed of their presence and direction of movement. Thus vessels, in great measure, are enabled to avoid them.

The occurrence of moderate to dangerous cyclonic storms on the waters west of Mexico averages about two in every 3 years this month. In this region there are likely to be frequent calms and thunderstorms with oppressive weather in July.

August.—Favorable weather for travel continues along higher latitudes of the North Pacific. Cyclones forming over these waters are of little energy, and gale winds are few and rarely of high force, unless due to an occasional storm entering the region east and northeast of Japan from the tropics. There is little change from the weather of July, except for a slight rise in average temperature, August over the northern routes being the warmest month of the year. There is some decrease in the occurrence of fog, the decrease being very marked in the latter half of the month.

Except in coastal regions, the northeast trades are the prevailing winds between latitudes 10° and 35°N. South of latitude 10° southeast trades and calms are prevalent.

Tropical cyclones, or typhoons, of the Far East are more numerous as a rule in August, with an average of about four, than in any other month. They are likely to occur over any part of the ocean north of 10° latitude and west of 150°E. longitude. Their paths are most frequently toward the northwest so that, although a few cross the northern Philippines, the great majority move toward China or southern Japan. In tropical waters west of Mexico about one cyclone occurs on the average this month. The usual life of these storms is about 3 days, according to available records, and one-half of them attain hurricane intensity.

September.—With the coming of early autumn weather, while temperatures (still averaging between about 52° and 65°) do not change materially over northern waters of the Pacific as compared with those of August, the early storms of winter type begin to make their appearance, the probability of their occurrence increasing as the month advances. While September continues as a generally favorable month for travel along the higher latitude routes between the United States and Japan, some rough weather may be expected, with the probability increasing slightly as the ship goes westward. The western part of the route is subject at times not only to the autumn types of northern storms, but to those that originate in the tropics of the Far East and proceed thence into higher latitudes. In middle latitudes practically the only storminess to be expected in September is that resulting from the passage of tropical storms northward across waters south and east of Japan.

In southern latitudes, the only weather hazard to tourist travel is the typhoon of the Far East and the tropical cyclone which occurs at varying distances from the west coast of Mexico. The region over which the typhoon occurs in September extends from about 8°N. latitude northward into the extra-tropics, and between Asia and about longitude 150°E. This type of cyclone is less likely to form in September than in August, but yet three or four as an average occur annually in the month, although in some years there is an entire lack of these dangerous storms in September. The cyclones of the Mexican coast region are most frequent in September, with an average of nearly two this month. These storms are most likely to be encountered by ships plying between United States West Coast ports, or Honolulu, and the Panama Canal.

Fog is still to be expected along the northern routes, as well as along the American coast from Vancouver southward to Cape San Lucas at the tip of the Peninsula of California, with foggiest localities between Vancouver and San Francisco, and along the middle and western parts of northern routes. Here it may occur on several days in September.

October.—The storms of autumn increase in frequency, extent, and energy during October along the northern transpacific steamship routes, and the average number of days with gales increases over the entire ocean north of the 30th parallel of latitude. The expectancy of stormy weather is uncertain for a particular October, as the weather, while sometimes moderately quiet and pleasant, is occasionally of full winter severity with possible local winds of hurricant violence. Ships crossing these waters, however, frequently encounter no gale winds either along the San Francisco-Yokohama or the Seattle-Yokohama routes.

As an average, about three tropical cyclones occur in October in tropical waters of the Far East, and about one on the waters west of Mexico. This is some decrease in both regions from the frequency in September. After the middle of October the probability of occurrence of tropical cyclones diminishes rapidly. Typhoons occur over the same region as those of September. The majority form in low latitudes and, moving first to the northwestward, recurve into a northeasterly direction, and pass the east coast of Japan on their way into higher latitudes. A less number move westward across the Philippines into the China Sea, and still fewer continue from the tropics to the coast of China. Most of the tropical cyclones of the southeastern Pacific this month pass up the western coast of Mexico and across the entrance to the Gulf of California, then dissipate.

Fog decreases materially on the average over all parts of the ocean subject to it, both along the northern routes and the coasts, but is likely to be met on a few days in October along the routes mentioned.

Temperatures have fallen since September. Between latitudes 50°N. and 40°N. the average temperature runs from about 40° to about 60°, and farther southward, from about 60° to 75° to 80° or higher over equatorial waters.

November.—November is usually a stormy month on North Pacific waters north of the 35th parallel of latitude. Winter conditions have not, on the average, fully set in here, but the month in some years has been the stormiest of the season, while in other years ocean liners have had quiet passages between our West Coast ports and the Orient. To the traveler who enjoys fine, bracing weather, and has no fear of periods of rough weather, the outlook for a northern transpacific voyage in November is not unpleasant. South of latitude 35° the probability of encountering storms lessens rapidly until in the tropics; few, if any, gales may be expected except on waters of the Far East, where typhoons still occur. The tropical cyclones are only about one-half as numerous as in October, so that the chance of encountering one on a voyage to the Philippines is remote. The typhoons that do occur this month are more likely to travel in low latitudes than to run into higher latitudes toward Japan.

In tropical American waters cyclones are rare this month off the Mexican west coast. High winds are infrequent along the Panama-

California route, but high offshore winds are occasionally experienced on the California coast and in the Gulf of Tehuantepec off the south coast of Mexico.

Fog is not often met this month on the open ocean. It is more likely to form off the West Coast of the United States in November than elsewhere along the Pacific lines of tourist travel.

In northern waters of the Pacific the temperature is several degrees lower than in October, and may at times be near or a few degrees below freezing in the vicinity of the Aleutian Islands and thence westward toward northern Japan. The temperatures between the Aleutians and the 40th parallel of latitude average between about 35° and 55°, being lower on the western than on the eastern side of the ocean.

December.—December is more often than otherwise a stormy month on northern waters of the North Pacific, and is frequently stormy thence southward well into middle latitudes. Occasionally, also, gales occur almost as far south as the tropics from storms of enormous extent the centers of which may be far distant to the northward. Many northern storms of the month enter the ocean from Asia, while others develop over the ocean itself. Somewhat more wintry weather may be expected, on the average, over the western than over the eastern half of the ocean. Rain, sleet, or snow are likely to accompany these stormy conditions.

In the tropics there are few storms, even including the typhoons of the Far East, which in this month occur on the average of only one per year in December, and therefore are to be considered only as a remote possibility to the traveler en route to the Philippine Islands. The northeast trades, which blow to the southward of 25° to 28° latitude, are fairly strong this month. Off the coast of China the northeast monsoon blows frequently in December, often accompanied by thick, rainy weather and strong winds to fresh gales. Occasionally a storm of moderate severity occurs between the California coast and the Hawaiian Islands. Off the south coast of Mexico, in the Gulf of Tehuantepec, violent northerly winds sometimes blow. However, December is a favorable month for travel in tropical parts of the ocean, and may not be unfavorable for a ship bound between northern ports.

Fog is infrequent along the northern routes in December although the weather may be thick at times as a result of stormy conditions. Some fog is likely to be met along the American coast.

Along the most northerly transpacific routes temperatures are low, with occasional freezing weather near the Aleutian Islands. Temperatures most likely to be experienced along the routes between Seattle or San Francisco and Yokohama range between about 40° and 55°. Southward from the 40th parallel temperatures increase gradually to the comfortable warmth of the tropics.

BIBLIOGRAPHY

Popular Works

Bottley, C. M.: "The Air and Its Mysteries," D. Appleton-Century Company, Inc., New York, 1940.

Brooks, C. E.: "Why the Weather," Harcourt, Brace and Company, New York, 1935.

Brooks, C. E.: "The Weather," Ernest Benn, Ltd., London, 1927.

Humphreys, W. J.: "Ways of the Weather," J. Cattell Press, Lancaster, Pa., 1942.

Shaw, Sir N.: "Drama of the Weather," Cambridge University Press, London, 1939.

Stewart, C.: "Storm," Random House, Inc., New York, 1941.

Wenstrom, W. H.: "Weather and the Ocean of Air," Houghton Mifflin Company, Boston, 1942.

General Works

Albright, J. G.: "Physical Meteorology," Prentice-Hall, Inc., New York, 1937.

Blair, T. A.: "Weather Elements," Prentice Hall, Inc., New York, 1940.

Brands, C. J.: "A Course in Meteorology," McGraw-Hill Book Company, Inc., New York, 1944.

Geddes, A. E.: "Meteorology," Blackie & Son, Ltd., Glasgow, 1939.

Milham, W. I.: "Meteorology," The Macmillan Company, New York, 1912.

Petterssen, S.: "Introduction to Meteorology," McGraw-Hill Book Company, Inc., New York, 1941.

Advanced General and Technical Works

Brunt, D.: "Physical and Dynamical Meteorology," Cambridge University Press, London, 1939.

Byers, H. R.: "General Meteorology," McGraw-Hill Book Company, Inc., New York, 1944.

Hewson E. G., and R. W. Longley: "Meteorology—Theoretical and Applied," John Wiley & Sons, Inc., New York, 1944.

Humphreys, W. J.: "Physics of the Air," McGraw-Hill Book Company, Inc., New York, 1940.

Taylor, C. F.: "Aeronautical Meteorology," Pitman Publishing Corporation, New York, 1941.

Weather Forecasting

Abercromby (revised by Goldie): "Weather," Sherwood Press, Cleveland, Ohio, 1936.

Byers, H. R.: "General Meteorology," McGraw-Hill Book Company, Inc., New York, 1944.

Namias, J.: "Introduction to the Study of Air Mass and Isentropic Analysis," American Meteorological Society, 1940.

Petterssen, S.: "Weather Analysis and Forecasting," McGraw-Hill Book Company, Inc., New York, 1940.

Shaw, Sir N.: "Forecasting Weather," Constable & Company, Ltd., London, 1940.

Starr, V.: "Basic Principles of Weather Forecasting," Harper & Brothers, New York, 1942.

Climatology

Blair, T. A.: "Climatology," Prentice-Hall, Inc., New York, 1942.
Brooks, C. E.: "Climate," Ernest Benn, Ltd., London, 1932.
Haurwitz, B., and J. M. Austin: "Climatology," McGraw-Hill Book Company, Inc., New York, 1944.
Kendrew, W. G.: "Climate," Oxford, Clarendon Press, New York, 1938.
Landsberg, H.: "Physical Climatology," State College, Pa., 1941.
Miller, A. A.: "Climatology," Methuen & Co., Ltd., London, 1931.

Miscellaneous Works

"Admiralty Weather," British Hydrographic Department, London, 1938.
Grant, H. D.: "Cloud Atlas," Coward-McCann, Inc., New York, 1944.
Maguire, C. J.: "Aerology," McGraw-Hill Book Company, Inc., New York, 1931.
Tannehill, I.: "Hurricanes," Princeton University Press, Princeton, N. J., 1938.
Tannehill, I.: "Weather around the World," Princeton University Press, Princeton, N. J., 1943.
U. S. Navy: "Aerology for Pilots," McGraw-Hill Book Company, Inc., New York, 1943.
Ward, R.: "Climates of the United States," Ginn and Company, Boston, 1925.

U.S. Government Publications

Civil Aeronautics Authority, Bulletin 25: "Meteorology for Pilots."
Department of Agriculture: "Atlas of Climatic Charts of the Oceans," 1938.
Hydrographic Office: "Radio Weather Aids to Navigation."
U.S. Navy: "Aerographer's Manual."
U. S. War Department Publication TM-1-235: "The Weather Observer."
U.S. Weather Bureau:
    Circular F: "Barometers and Measurement of Atmospheric Pressure."
    Circular M: "Instructions to Marine Meteorological Observers."
    Circular R: "Preparation and Use of Weather Maps at Sea."
    Circular S: "International Codes for Clouds and States of the Sky."
    Bulletin 42: "Weather Forecasting," Bliss.
    Miscellaneous Publication 236: "Weather Forecasting from Synoptic Charts," Weightman.
    "Psychometric Tables—Vapor Pressure Relative Humidity, and Temperature of the Dew Point," 1941.

Oceanography

Bigelow, H. B.: "Oceanography," Houghton Mifflin Company, Boston, 1931.
Cornish, V.: "Ocean Waves," Cambridge University Press, London, 1934.
Marmer, H. A.: "The Sea," D. Appleton-Century Company, Inc., New York, 1930.
Sverdrup, H. V.: "Oceanography for Meteorologists," Prentice-Hall, Inc., New York, 1943.
Sverdrup, H. V., M. W. Johnson, and R. H. Fleming: "The Oceans," Prentice-Hall, Inc., New York, 1942.

APPENDIX A

EXPLANATION OF TELETYPE SYMBOL WEATHER REPORTS

Effective January 1, 1943 with Revisions as of October, 1945

(Based on instructions contained in Weather Bureau Circular N, 1941)

(To illustrate the method used in transmission and deciphering of symbol weather reports, the following example of such a report is given. Each element of the report is connected by a line with a description of symbols and conditions which might be used in that particular phase of the report. Elements of observations are always transmitted in the same order; therefore all symbol weather reports may be deciphered by reference to this chart.)

WA   S   1624E

Station	Type of report	Time of report
Lists of station names and their representative call letters are posted on the Weather Bureau Airport Station bulletin boards for the information of all concerned.	"S," meaning "special report," appears when crucial changes have occurred in the weather conditions since the last report.	Time groups are in figures based on the 24-hr. clock, with following letters showing the standard of time used, e.g., "1440E" means 2:40 P.M., Eastern Standard Time; "0030C" means 12:30 A.M. Central Standard Time; "2359M" means 11:50 P.M., Mountain Standard Time; "2015P" means 8:15 P.M., Pacific Standard Time, etc.
	The absence of the observation type letter group "S" indicates an observation where no crucial changes have occurred since the last transmitted observation.	
	"LCL," meaning "local extra observation," appears only on reports sent over local circuits. Such reports are made every 15 minutes during periods of low ceiling and/or visibility.	"SPL" reports which are sent alone and all "LCL" reports bear the time of observation immediately following, after 1 space, the observation-type letter group "SPL" or "LCL."
	The number following "S" indicates the number of special reports since midnight, i.e., S1, S2, etc.	"SPL" reports appearing in sequences do not show the time-of-report group and the time of observation is considered as the time of all other reports in the sequences as indicated in the sequence heading.

423

E 30 ⊕ 15 ① 2V TRW— BD—

Ceiling	Sky	Visibility	Weather	Obstructions to vision
The absence of a "ceiling" group indicates an "unlimited" ceiling (above 9,750 ft.). Figures representing the number of *hundreds* of feet which apply are used to indicate the height of the ceiling between 51 and 9,750 ft., inclusive, above the station, *e.g.*, "35" indicates 3,500 ft., "3" indicates 300 ft., etc. The figure naught (0) is used when the ceiling is zero (below 51 ft.). Method of determining ceiling height is indicated by letters preceding the figure; *i.e.*, A-Airplane B-Balloon observations E-Estimated M-Measured "P" indicates ceiling obscured by precipitation. A plus sign (+) is used preceding the ceiling figures to indicate the ceiling balloon was blown from sight at the height represented by the figures and before reaching the clouds. The leter "W," immediately following the figure (s) for ceiling, indicates that the height of the ceiling is changeable.	"X" indicates that precipitation or obstructions to vision are present and reduce the ceiling to zero and/or the visibility to less than one-fourth mile and make the sky unobservable. The sky condition is indicated by the following symbols unless the condition given above is present ○ Clear ① Scattered clouds ⬤ Broken clouds ⊕ Overcast ①/High scattered ⬤/High broken ⊕ High overcast ⊕⬤ Overcast, lower broken ⊕① Overcast, lower scattered ⬤⬤ Broken, lower broken ⬤① Broken, lower scattered ①⬤ Scattered, lower broken ①① Scattered, lower scattered ⊕/⬤ High overcast, lower broken ⊕/① High overcast, lower scattered ⬤/⬤ High broken, lower broken ⬤/① High broken, lower scattered ①/⬤ High scattered, lower broken ①/① High scattered, lower scattered The plus (+) or minus (−) sign *preceding* the cloudiness symbol indicates "dark" and "thin," respectively. Height of lower scattered clouds is indicated by the entry of a figure, representing the hundreds of feet applying, immediately preceding the scattered clouds symbol.	The value of the visibility below 15 miles is indicated by figures representing the nearest mile. Beyond 15 miles the visibility is given to the nearest 5 miles. The letter "V," immediately following the figure for visibility, indicates a fluctuating visibility.	The "weather" element of the report is indicated, when appropriate, by the following symbols: R—Light rain R Moderate rain R+Heavy rain S—Light snow S Moderate snow S+Heavy snow ZR—Light freezing rain ZR Moderate freezing rain ZR+Heavy freezing rain L—Light drizzle L Moderate drizzle L+Heavy drizzle ZL—Light freezing drizzle ZL Moderate freezing drizzle ZL+Heavy freezing drizzle E—Light sleet E Moderate sleet E+Heavy sleet A—Light hail A Moderate hail A+Heavy hail AP—Light small hail AP Moderate small hail AP+Heavy small hail SP—Light snow pellets SP Moderate snow pellets SP+Heavy snow pellets SQ—Light snow squall SQ Moderate snow squall SQ+Heavy snow squall RQ—Light rain squall RQ Moderate rain squall RQ+Heavy rain squall T Thunderstorm T+Heavy thunderstorm SW—Light snow showers SW Moderate snow showers SW+Heavy snow showers RW—Light rain showers RW Moderate rain showers RW+Heavy rain showers Tornado (always written out in full).	The "obstructions to vision" element of the report is indicated, when appropriate, by the following symbols: F− −Damp haze F− Light fog F Moderate fog F+ Heavy fog GF− Light ground fog GF Moderate ground fog GF+ Heavy ground fog IF− Light ice fog IF Moderate ice fog IF+ Heavy ice fog H Hazy K− Light smoke K Moderate smoke K+ Heavy smoke D− Light dust D Moderate dust D+ Heavy dust BS− Light blowing snow BS Moderate blowing snow BS+ Heavy blowing snow GS− Light drifting snow GS Moderate drifting snow GS+ Heavy drifting snow BD− Light blowing dust BD Moderate blowing dust BD+ Heavy blowing dust BN− Light blowing sand BN Moderate blowing sand BN+ Heavy blowing sand

$$+ \oplus \text{NW}$$

152/	68/	60	→\22 + ↑1618E/	996/	OCNL LTNG IN CLDS

Barometric pressure	Temperature	Dew point	Wind	Altimeter setting	Remarks
The barometric pressure is indicated by a group of 3 figures; tens, units, and tenths of millibars involved. Thus a pressure of 1,015.2 millibars would be written as "152"; 999.9 as "999"; 1,025.7 as "257"; etc. Sent only by stations equipped with mercurial barometers.	Temperature is indicated by figures giving its value to the nearest degree Fahrenheit. Values below 0°F. are indicated by the entry of a minus sign (−) immediately preceding the figures for temperature. Zero is entered as 0.	Dew point is indicated by figures giving its value to the nearest degree Fahrenheit. Values below 0°F. are indicated by the entry of a minus sign (−) immediately preceding the figures for dew point.	The wind *direction* is indicated by arrows, as follows: ↓ North ↓ ⟋ North-northeast ⟋ Northeast ← ⟋ East-northeast ←East ← ⟍ East-southeast ⟍ Southeast ↑ ⟍ South-southeast ↑ South ↑ ⟋ South-southwest ⟋ Southwest → ⟋ West-southwest →West → ⟍ West-northwest ⟍ Northwest ↓ ⟍ North-northwest The *velocity* is indicated by figures representing its value in miles per hour, "calm" being indicated by the letter C. If estimated, this is indicated by the entry of the letter E immediately following the velocity figures. The *character* of the wind is indicated, when appropriate, by entry, immediately following the velocity, of a minus sign (−) for "fresh gusts" and a plus sign (+) for "strong gusts." No indication of character means the wind is steady. *Wind shifts* which have occurred at the reporting station are indicated, immediately following the other wind data, by an arrow showing the direction (to 8 points only) from which the wind was blowing prior to the shift, followed by the local time, on the 24 hour clock, at which the shift occurred, with following letter showing the standard of time used. The intensity of the shift is indicated by the minus sign (−) for "light," the absence of a sign for "moderate," and the plus sign (+) for "heavy," the signs being entered immediately following the standard-of-time letter.	Indicated by a group of 3 figures representing the inch and hundredths of an inch of pressure involved. Thus, 30.00 would be written as "000"; 29.98 as "998"; etc. Sent only by designated stations equipped with mercurial barometers.	Remarks are transmitted in authorized English abbreviations and teletype symbols. Lists of the abbreviations available for inspection at all the Weather Bureau Airport Stations. The teletype symbols used are shown on this chart.

Special data

Special data comprising pressure change and characteristic, 5,000-ft. pressure at selected stations, cloud, thunderstorm, and snow depth data, Great Lakes water temperature, etc., data from selected stations, etc., are entered in code at certain times by the stations designated to do this, as separate groups, immediately following the report proper. These data are intended primarily for the preparation of maps for forecasting.

Missing data

Elements normally sent, but for some reason missing from the transmission, will be indicated by the letter "M" entered in the report in place of the missing data.

Example The report given above would be deciphered as follows: Washington—special report at 4:24 P. M., Eastern Standard Time; ceiling estimated at 3,000 feet; overcast, lower scattered clouds at 1,500 feet; visibility 2 miles, variable; thunderstorm; light rain shower; light blowing dust; barometric pressure, 1,015.2 millibars; temperature 68 F.; dew point 60 F.; wind west-northwest 22 miles per hour, strong gusts; moderate wind shift from the south at 4:18 P. M., Eastern Standard Time; altimeter setting, 29.96 inches; dark to northwest, occasional lighting in clouds.

APPENDIX B

AVERAGE MONTHLY WEATHER SUMMARIES FOR PRINCIPAL PORTS AND ISLANDS OF THE WORLD

Line 1.—Mean *daily* maximum temperatures for each month. When preceded by an asterisk (*), the mean *monthly* maximum temperatures are given instead.

Line 2.—Mean *daily* minimum temperatures for each month. When preceded by an asterisk (*), the mean *monthly* minimum temperatures are given instead.

Line 3.—Relative humidity for 0800 or 0900 for each month. When preceded by an asterisk (*), the *mean daily* humidity is given instead.

Line 4.—The number of days with rain in each month (0.01 in. or more).

Line 5.—Average number of days with wind of gale force in each month. When preceded by an asterisk (*), the number of days with strong winds or over are given.

Line 6.—Average number of days with fog for each month.

NOTE: The mean temperature for a period is usually obtained by taking the average for the highest and the lowest temperatures for that period.

	Jan.	Feb.	Mar.	April	May	June	July	Aug.	Sept.	Oct.	Nov.	Dec.
				Aberdeen—57°10′N. 2°06′W.								
1	42	40	43	50	55	60	63	63	59	53	47	43
2	33	33	34	37	42	47	50	50	47	42	37	34
3	82	81	81	79	79	77	79	80	81	84	93	83
4	18	17	20	17	17	15	17	18	17	20	19	19
5	0.4	0.3	0.1	0.1	0	0	0	0	0	0.1	0.1	0.6
6	0.5	0.3	1	0.9	3	3	1.5	2	2	2	1	0.7
				Acapulco—16°50′N. 99°56′W.								
*1	85	87	87	87	89	89	89	89	88	88	88	87
*2	70	70	70	71	74	76	75	75	75	74	72	70
*3	79	78	77	77	75	79	79	79	82	80	80	80
4	0.5−	0.5−	0.5−	1	4	15	11	14	18	12	4	1
*5	0	0	0	0	0.3	0.5	0	0.2	0	0.2	0.2	0.7
6	0	0	0	0	0	0	0	0	0.1	0	0	0
				Accra—5°33′N. 0°12′W.								
1	87	88	89	88	87	84	82	81	82	85	87	88
2	73	74	75	75	74	73	72	70	72	73	73	73
3	79	79	78	78	79	83	83	83	83	80	78	79
4	1	1	3	5	8	9	4	2	4	5	2	1
5	0.7	1	1	2	3	1	0	0	0	0.7	0.7	0.3
6	0	0	0	0	0	0	0	0.3	0.3	0	0	0
				Adelaide—34°56′S. 138°35′E.								
1	86	86	81	73	66	60	59	62	68	73	79	83
2	62	62	59	55	50	47	45	46	48	51	45	59
3	38	40	47	56	68	77	76	69	61	51	43	39
4	4	4	6	9	13	16	16	16	14	11	8	6
5	2	1	0.7	1	0.6	1	2	2	0.3	2	2	2
6	0	0	0	0.1	1	3	4	1	2	0	0	0

	Jan.	Feb.	Mar.	April	May	June	July	Aug.	Sept.	Oct.	Nov.	Dec.
*1	66	67	70	75	80	83	86	87	86	83	77	69
*2	51	51	54	58	64	69	73	74	72	68	62	54
*3	68	66	67	69	72	74	76	74	70	70	67	65
1	11	7	4	1	1	0.1	0	0	0	1	6	10
5	1	1.5	0.6	0.3	0.1	0	0	0	0	0	0.5	1
6†	4	2	2	2	1	0.4	0	0.2	0.8	1	5	6

Alexandria—31°12′N. 29°53′E.

Algiers—36°48′N. 3°02′E.

	Jan.	Feb.	Mar.	April	May	June	July	Aug.	Sept.	Oct.	Nov.	Dec.
1	59	60	63	66	71	76	81	82	79	73	66	61
2	47	48	60	53	58	63	67	69	66	59	55	50
3	65	65	55	65	65	65	68	70	69	67	67	68
4	15	13	1	11	9	5	2	2	7	10	13	15
5	3	4	3	4	2	2	1	1	1	2	2	3
6	—	—	—	—	—	—	—	—	—	—	—	—

Amsterdam—52°23′N. 4°55′E.

	Jan.	Feb.	Mar.	April	May	June	July	Aug.	Sept.	Oct.	Nov.	Dec.
1	41	42	47	54	62	68	70	70	65	57	47	42
2	31	31	35	39	45	51	54	54	49	43	37	33
3	89	87	84	78	75	75	77	80	83	87	89	91
4	10	8	11	8	9	9	11	11	10	13	11	13
5	3	2	2	1	0	0	0	1	1	2	2	2
6	—	—	—	—	—	—	—	—	—	—	—	—

Antigua—17°05′N. 61°50′W.

	Jan.	Feb.	Mar.	April	May	June	July	Aug.	Sept.	Oct.	Nov.	Dec.
*1	82	83	83	85	86	86	87	87	88	87	85	84
*2	70	70	70	71	73	74	74	75	74	73	72	71
3	73	70	67	69	71	72	73	73	75	74	75	74
4	20	15	14	13	15	16	19	18	18	19	19	20
*5	0	0	0	0.3	0.3	0	0.3	0	0	0.3	0	0.7
6	0	0	0	0	0	0	0	0	0	0	0	0

Ascension Island—7°55′S. 14°24′W.

	Jan.	Feb.	Mar.	April	May	June	July	Aug.	Sept.	Oct.	Nov.	Dec.
1	85	87	88	87	86	84	83	82	82	82	83	83
2	74	75	76	76	75	74	72	72	71	71	72	73
3	72	69	68	68	67	70	66	68	72	71	71	72
4	3	3	5	7	5	5	5	7	8	9	6	4
5	0	0	0	0	0	0	0	0	0	0	0.1	0.1
6	0	0	0	0	0	0	0	0	0	0	0	0

Athens—37°58′N. 23°43′E.

	Jan.	Feb.	Mar.	April	May	June	July	Aug.	Sept.	Oct.	Nov.	Dec.
*1	54	55	60	67	76	84	90	89	83	74	63	57
*2	42	43	46	52	59	67	72	72	66	60	52	46
3	73	71	69	64	60	56	48	48	56	66	72	74
4	13	11	10	9	8	5	3	3	4	8	12	13
5	2	2	1	1	0.7	4	0.7	1	0.7	0.5	1	2
6	4	5	5	3	3	1	0.7	0.6	2	4	4	6

† Number of days with mist or haze.

	Jan.	Feb.	Mar.	April	May	June	July	Aug.	Sept.	Oct.	Nov.	Dec.

Auckland—36°50′S. 174°50′E.

	Jan.	Feb.	Mar.	April	May	June	July	Aug.	Sept.	Oct.	Nov.	Dec.
*1	73	74	72	68	62	59	57	58	61	63	67	70
*2	59	60	58	55	51	48	46	47	49	51	54	57
3	72	72	74	76	78	79	79	77	76	75	74	73
4	10	10	11	13	19	20	21	19	17	17	15	10
5	3	2	2	2	4	6	3	4	4	4	4	3
6	0.1	0.2	0.2	0.2	0.7	0.8	1.1	0.4	0.4	0.1	0.1	0.1

Bahia—13°00′S. 38°30′W.

1	87	87	87	86	83	80	80	80	82	83	85	85
2	73	74	73	73	72	70	69	69	70	71	72	73
3	83	83	83	84	84	84	83	83	83	83	83	84
4	16	18	18	22	24	24	25	21	17	15	15	16
5					Records not given							
6	1	1	2	3	2	2	2	4	4	2	2	2

Baltimore, Md.—39°18′N. 76°37′W.

*1	42	43	51	62	73	82	82	83	77	66	54	44
*2	28	28	35	45	55	64	69	67	61	49	39	30
*3	67	65	62	59	50	62	63	66	67	65	66	67
4	11	10	12	11	11	11	11	11	8	8	9	11
5	1	1	1	1	1−	1−	1	1−	1−	1−	1	1
6	3	2	2	1	1−	1−	1−	1−	1	1	2	3

Bangkok—13°45′N. 100°28′E.

*1	92	93	95	97	95	93	92	92	91	91	89	89
*2	67	70	73	76	76	76	76	76	75	75	71	67
3	68	60	63	62	65	69	68	66	73	74	68	67
4	1	3	4	6	17	18	19	19	21	17	7	3
5	—	—	—	—	—	—	—	—	—	—	—	—
6	—	—	—	—	—	—	—	—	—	—	—	—

Barbados—13°06′N. 59°37′W.

*1	84	86	87	88	89	88	88	88	89	88	87	85
*2	70	70	71	73	74	75	74	74	74	73	73	71
3	69	68	66	65	65	69	72	72	72	73	73	72
4	19	12	11	11	12	18	19	19	16	17	17	17
5	0	0	0	0	0	0	0	0	0	0	0	0
6	0	0	0	0	0	0	0	0	0	0	0	0

Barcelona—41°23′N. 2°08′E.

1	55	57	60	64	70	78	82	83	78	71	62	57
2	40	42	44	48	54	60	65	62	62	54	48	65
3	70	69	69	69	68	67	66	68	70	70	71	70
4	5	5	6	8	7	6	3	4	6	8	6	5
5	1	2	2	2	0.8	1	1	0.4	0.2	0.9	2	1.5
6	5	3	2	1	0.9	0.7	0.8	0.8	1	2	3	4

	Jan.	Feb.	Mar.	April	May	June	July	Aug.	Sept.	Oct.	Nov.	Dec.

Bengasi—32°07′N. 20°02′E.

	Jan.	Feb.	Mar.	April	May	June	July	Aug.	Sept.	Oct.	Nov.	Dec.
*1	60	63	68	73	78	81	83	84	84	81	72	64
*2	51	53	56	60	65	69	73	74	72	68	60	55
3	78	74	74	66	71	73	84	80	74	73	76	77
4	11	8	6	2	1	0	0	0	2	4	7	13
5	—	—	—	—	—	—	—	—	—	—	—	—
6	0.7	1	0.7	0.6	0.7	1	2	1.5	0.3	0.5	1	0.9

Bergen—60°24′N. 5°19′E.

	Jan.	Feb.	Mar.	April	May	June	July	Aug.	Sept.	Oct.	Nov.	Dec.
1	39	39	42	48	55	60	64	62	57	50	43	40
2	31	31	32	37	43	48	52	52	47	41	36	33
3	81	79	77	73	75	76	81	82	82	80	80	81
4	21	19	17	16	16	16	16	20	19	20	20	22
5	2	1.5	1.0	0.4	0.2	0.2	0.1	0.2	0.7	1.0	1.0	2.0
6	3	2	3	3	3	3	5	3	4	3	3	3

Beyrouth—33°54′N. 35°28′E.

	Jan.	Feb.	Mar.	April	May	June	July	Aug.	Sept.	Oct.	Nov.	Dec.
*1	62	63	66	72	78	83	87	89	86	81	73	66
*2	51	51	54	58	64	69	73	74	73	69	61	65
3	70	71	71	72	71	69	67	66	66	65	66	59
4	15	14	11	6	3	1	1	1	1	4	9	13
5	1.5	1	0.6	0.4	0.2	0.1	0.1	0	0.2	0.1	0.6	1
6	—	—	—	—	—	—	—	—	—	—	—	—

Bizerte—37°17′N. 9°50′W.

	Jan.	Feb.	Mar.	April	May	June	July	Aug.	Sept.	Oct.	Nov.	Dec.
1	58	59	63	67	73	79	85	85	83	77	68	61
2	46	47	50	53	59	65	71	72	69	63	75	49
3	75	74	72	70	68	65	66	63	67	70	73	75
4	15	12	11	9	6	3	2	2	5	9	12	15
5	3	5	7	5	2	2	2	4	2	5	6	8
6	—	—	—	—	—	—	—	—	—	—	—	—

Block Island, R.I.—41°10′N. 71°33′W.

	Jan.	Feb.	Mar.	April	May	June	July	Aug.	Sept.	Oct.	Nov.	Dec.
*1	37	36	41	49	59	68	74	74	68	60	50	42
*2	25	25	30	39	47	56	63	63	58	50	39	30
*3	76	76	79	80	83	85	85	84	81	76	76	75
4	13	11	12	11	11	10	10	9	8	9	10	11
5	14	9	10	8	3	1	1	1	1	7	10	12
6	3	3	4	4	6	8	7	5	4	2	2	2

Bombay—18°54′N. 72°49′E.

	Jan.	Feb.	Mar.	April	May	June	July	Aug.	Sept.	Oct.	Nov.	Dec.
*1	83	83	86	89	91	88	85	84	85	88	87	85
*2	68	69	73	77	81	80	78	77	77	77	74	70
*3	73	71	75	77	77	82	87	87	86	81	73	72
4	0.2	0.2	0.1	0.1	0.8	14	21	19	13	0.3	0.7	0.1
5	—	—	—	—	—	—	—	—	—	—	—	—
6	—	—	—	—	—	—	—	—	—	—	—	—

	Jan.	Feb.	Mar.	April	May	June	July	Aug.	Sept.	Oct.	Nov.	Dec.

Bordeaux—44°50′N. 0°36′W.

	Jan.	Feb.	Mar.	April	May	June	July	Aug.	Sept.	Oct.	Nov.	Dec.
*1	50	45	58	62	68	75	79	80	77	67	55	49
*2	35	37	38	42	47	53	56	55	51	46	55	49
*3	87	79	73	70	69	67	67	66	70	80	85	88
4	17	16	11	15	14	10	11	9	8	14	18	17
5	11	8	5	5	5	4	6	5	8	10	8	9
6	6.9	6.3	5.9	6.6	6.7	5.8	5.5	49	4.9	5.6	7.1	7.1

Boston, Mass.—42°21′N. 71°4′W.

	Jan.	Feb.	Mar.	April	May	June	July	Aug.	Sept.	Oct.	Nov.	Dec.
*1	36	37	43	54	66	75	80	78	71	62	49	40
*2	20	21	28	38	49	58	63	62	55	46	35	24
*3	71	68	64	68	70	72	72	76	76	74	72	72
4	12	10	12	11	11	10	10	10	9	9	10	11
5	1	1	1	1	0	0	0	0	0	0	1	1
6	1	1	1	1	1	1	1	1	2	2	1	1

Brisbane—27°28′S. 153°02′E.

	Jan.	Feb.	Mar.	April	May	June	July	Aug.	Sept.	Oct.	Nov.	Dec.
1	85	84	82	79	73	69	68	71	76	80	83	85
2	69	68	66	62	55	51	48	50	55	60	64	67
3	67	71	72	74	74	74	75	70	65	61	60	63
4	14	14	15	12	10	9	8	7	9	9	10	12
5	0.7	0.9	0.2	0	0.3	0.4	0.6	0.1	0.3	0.7	1.0	0.2
6	0.4	0.6	1.0	3	4	4	4	2	2	1	0.4	0.3

Buenos Aires—34°35′S. 58°29′W.

	Jan.	Feb.	Mar.	April	May	June	July	Aug.	Sept.	Oct.	Nov.	Dec.
1	85	83	79	72	64	57	57	60	64	69	76	82
2	63	63	60	53	47	41	42	43	46	50	56	61
3	69	72	76	80	83	84	84	79	78	76	73	69
4	7	6	7	7	6	6	6	6	7	8	8	8
5	1	0.5	0.6	0.8	1.0	0.8	0.6	0.9	1.0	1.5	1.0	0.4
6	1	2	6	8	9	5	7	4	4	3	2	2

Cadiz—36°3′N. 6°17′W.

	Jan.	Feb.	Mar.	April	May	June	July	Aug.	Sept.	Oct.	Nov.	Dec.
*1	60	62	64	67	72	77	81	83	80	73	67	61
*2	48	50	52	55	59	64	68	69	67	60	55	49
3	75	73	72	71	68	65	66	64	69	71	74	76
4	9	9	10	8	5	2	0.4	0.2	3	7	7	9
5	0.5	0.5	1	0.4	0.6	0.4	0.5	0.6	0.2	0.5	0.5	0.5
6	1	0.8	1	0.3	0.3	0.5	1	0.3	0.5	1	1	2

Calcutta—22°32′N. 88°24′E.

	Jan.	Feb.	Mar.	April	May	June	July	Aug.	Sept.	Oct.	Nov.	Dec.
*1	77	81	91	95	95	91	89	88	88	87	82	77
*2	56	60	69	76	78	79	79	79	78	75	65	56
3	85	82	80	79	79	85	88	89	87	85	82	81
4	1	2	2	3	7	13	18	18	13	6	1	0.4
5	—	—	—	—	—	—	—	—	—	—	—	—
6	—	—	—	—	—	—	—	—	—	—	—	—

	Jan.	Feb.	Mar.	April	May	June	July	Aug.	Sept.	Oct.	Nov.	Dec.
Cape Town—33°56′S. 18°29′E.												
1	80	80	78	73	67	63	63	63	66	70	73	77
2	60	61	59	55	51	48	47	48	50	53	56	59
3	65	66	69	73	76	79	80	79	76	71	67	64
4	4	4	5	7	11	13	13	12	11	9	7	5
5	4	3	2	1	0.6	2	1	1	0.8	3	0.4	3
6	2	1	4	3	2	1	1	2	1	2	0.6	0.4
Caracas, Venezuela—10°30′N. 66°55′W.												
*1	75	77	78	80	80	78	77	78	79	79	77	75
*2	56	56	57	60	62	62	61	61	61	61	60	58
*3	78	76	76	76	77	80	80	80	80	81	82	81
4	6	2	3	4	9	14	15	15	13	12	13	10
5	—	—	—	—	—	—	—	—	—	—	—	—
6	—	—	—	—	—	—	—	—	—	—	—	—
Carnarvon—24°54′S. 113°39′E.												
1	88	89	88	84	78	73	70	73	75	78	81	85
2	71	72	71	65	58	53	51	53	57	61	65	68
3	59	61	58	58	59	63	62	61	57	57	58	60
4	1	2	1	2	4	7	6	5	3	1	1	0
5	7	1.1	0.7	0.3	0	0	0.3	0.2	0.7	0.2	0.3	0.6
6	0	0	0	0.4	0.3	0	0.4	0.2	0	0.1	0	0
Cebu, Philippines—10°18′N. 123°54′E.												
*1	88	88	90	91	93	92	91	91	91	91	90	89
*2	71	71	72	74	74	73	73	73	73	73	72	72
*3	77	75	73	73	75	77	77	76	77	78	78	78
4	13	11	9	7	11	16	17	16	16	18	15	16
5	—	—	—	—	—	—	—	—	—	—	—	—
6	—	—	—	—	—	—	—	—	—	—	—	—
Charleston, S.C.—32°41′N. 79°53′W.												
*1	57	60	65	71	80	86	88	87	83	75	66	59
*2	43	45	50	57	66	72	75	75	70	61	51	44
*3	74	73	72	70	71	73	75	77	77	73	71	74
4	10	10	9	7	9	11	13	12	10	7	7	9
5	1−	1−	1	1	1−	1−	1−	1−	1−	1−	1−	1−
6	4	3	2	1−	1−	1−	1−	1−	1	1	2	3
Chatham Islands—43°52′S. 176°42′E.												
*1	64	63	62	59	55	51	50	51	53	56	58	61
*2	52	52	51	48	45	43	40	41	43	45	47	40
3	78	79	78	80	82	83	82	81	81	80	78	78
4	12	12	15	15	20	21	23	20	18	15	16	13
5	3	2	2	2	2	2	3	3	3	4	3	2
6	1.7	1.2	1.3	0.3	0.8	0.3	0.3	0.4	1.5	2.4	2.0	2.2

	Jan.	Feb.	Mar.	April	May	June	July	Aug.	Sept.	Oct.	Nov.	Dec.
*1	47	47	49	53	58	63	67	68	64	59	52	48
*2	41	40	41	45	49	54	58	59	56	51	45	42
*3	81	79	78	76	77	78	76	77	79	80	81	83
4	16	14	15	13	11	10	8	11	11	17	16	19
5	—	—	—	—	—	—	—	—	—	—	—	—
6	—	—	—	—	—	—	—	—	—	—	—	—

Cherbourg—49°39′N. 1°38′W.

Constantinople—41°02′N., 28°58′E.

*1	46	45	52	60	71	78	82	82	75	68	68	51
*2	38	36	40	46	55	62	67	68	62	57	49	43
3	79	77	71	66	64	60	60	61	65	71	76	73
4	10	8	9	7	7	60	3	4	6	7	11	12
5	0.9	0.5	0.4	0.2	0.2	0.2	0.4	0.3	0.4	0.1	0.3	0.6
6	4	4	5	1	1	1	1	1	3	6	5	4

Copenhagen—55°41′N. 12°39′E.

1	35	35	39	47	57	65	68	66	60	51	43	32
2	29	29	31	37	45	53	56	56	51	44	37	46
3	88	87	86	77	72	73	75	78	81	84	86	88
4	15	14	15	12	13	12	15	16	14	17	16	17
5	0.1	0.2	0.4	0.1	0.1	0	0	0	0.1	0.3	0.3	0.4
6	9	7	5	3	2	0.9	0.5	0.9	2	4	5	6

Corfu—39°37′N. 19°57′E.

1	56	57	61	67	75	82	87	87	82	74	65	59
2	44	45	47	62	58	64	69	69	65	60	53	48
3	76	76	74	74	73	71	67	67	70	76	76	77
4	13	12	9	9	6	5	2	2	5	11	11	13
5	0.3	0.1	0.1	0	0.1	0	0	0.1	0	0.1	0	0.1
6	0.9	0.8	1	1.5	9	0.1	3	1	1	4	3	2

Cristobal—9°21′N. 79°54′W.

*1	84	84	85	86	86	86	85	86	86	86	84	85
*2	76	76	77	77	76	76	76	76	75	75	75	76
*3	79	77	77	79	84	85	86	85	85	85	85	83
4	14	11	10	14	20	23	24	24	22	23	25	20
5	—	—	—	—	—	—	—	—	—	—	—	—
6	0	0	0	0.1	0	0.1	0	0.1	0	1	1	1

Curaçao—12°06′N. 68°56′W.

*1	83	84	84	86	86	87	87	88	89	88	86	84
*2	75	74	74	76	76	76	77	77	77	77	79	78
3	77	78	76	76	76	76	77	77	77	77	79	78
4	14	8	7	4	4	7	9	8	6	9	15	16
5	—	—	—	—	—	—	—	—	—	—	—	—
6	—	—	—	—	—	—	—	—	—	—	—	—

	Jan.	Feb.	Mar.	April	May	June	July	Aug.	Sept.	Oct.	Nov.	Dec.

Dakar—14°40′N. 17°26′W.

	Jan.	Feb.	Mar.	April	May	June	July	Aug.	Sept.	Oct.	Nov.	Dec.
*1	81	82	82	82	83	88	88	87	89	91	88	82
*2	64	64	65	66	68	73	76	76	76	77	73	67
3	65	74	81	79	79	78	79	82	82	82	74	67
4	—	—	—	—	—	—	—	—	—	—	—	—
5	—	—	—	—	—	—	—	—	—	—	—	—
6	—	—	—	—	—	—	—	—	—	—	—	—

Danzig—54°24′N. 18°40′E.

	Jan.	Feb.	Mar.	April	May	June	July	Aug.	Sept.	Oct.	Nov.	Dec.
1	33	35	40	49	59	66	71	69	63	53	32	36
2	25	26	30	36	44	52	56	55	50	42	34	28
3	86	85	82	76	74	73	73	75	78	82	85	87
4	14	12	14	13	13	12	14	15	13	13	14	15
5	3	3	3	0.7	0.8	0.4	1.0	0.6	1.0	2	2	3
6	3	2	3	2	2	1	0.2	0.6	2	3	4	4

Dover—51°07′N. 1°19′E.

	Jan.	Feb.	Mar.	April	May	June	July	Aug.	Sept.	Oct.	Nov.	Dec.
1	44	45	47	52	59	63	67	67	64	57	51	47
2	35	35	37	41	47	52	56	56	53	47	41	37
3	88	85	80	78	74	74	75	76	76	78	73	85
4	16	14	16	13	10	12	12	13	13	17	16	18
5	0.7	0.6	0	0	0	0.1	0	0	0.1	0.3	1	1
6	4	3	2	0.8	0.2	0.8	0.5	0	0.3	0.8	2	2

Dublin—53°22′N. 6°21′W.

	Jan.	Feb.	Mar.	April	May	June	July	Aug.	Sept.	Oct.	Nov.	Dec.
1	46	47	49	53	58	64	66	65	62	55	50	47
2	35	34	35	37	42	47	51	50	46	41	38	35
3	87	86	85	82	81	81	82	83	85	86	87	87
4	21	18	19	17	16	15	18	19	16	19	19	21
5	4	2	1	1	0.3	0.4	0.1	0.3	1	1	3	3
6	1.5	3	1.5	2	0	0.6	0.4	1	0.2	2	1	4

Durban—29°51 S. 31°0 E.

	Jan.	Feb.	Mar.	April	May	June	July	Aug.	Sept.	Oct.	Nov.	Dec.
*1	85	85	84	81	78	76	75	76	76	78	81	83
*2	68	68	66	63	58	54	54	56	59	61	64	63
3	73	73	73	71	69	63	65	63	69	70	73	73
4	14	15	15	13	11	11	8	6	5	5	6	10
5	—	—	—	—	—	—	—	—	—	—	—	—
6	—	—	—	—	—	—	—	—	—	—	—	—

Eastport—44°54′N. 66°59′W.

	Jan.	Feb.	Mar.	April	May	June	July	Aug.	Sept.	Oct.	Nov.	Dec.
*1	28	28	26	45	55	63	69	62	63	54	43	32
*2	13	14	23	32	40	47	52	53	49	42	31	19
3	77	76	76	76	78	81	84	84	82	80	79	77
4	15	13	14	12	11	12	11	10	10	11	12	14
5	3.5	3.0	2.8	1.9	0.8	0.3	0.2	0.2	0.4	1.3	2.3	3.0
6	2	2	3	3	6	8	12	12	6	4	2	2

	Jan.	Feb.	Mar.	April	May	June	July	Aug.	Sept.	Oct.	Nov.	Dec.
				Emden—53°22'N. 7°12'E.								
1	37	39	45	53	61	66	69	68	69	55	46	40
2	29	30	34	38	45	50	55	54	50	43	37	33
3	91	89	85	79	75	76	78	80	83	88	90	92
4	15	14	15	12	13	12	14	16	14	17	16	16
5	3	2	2	1	0.9	0.5	0.6	1	1	2	2	3
6	8	6	4	2	1	1	1	1	3	5	7	7
				Falmouth—50°09'N. 5°05'W.								
1	47	47	49	53	58	63	66	65	62	56	51	49
2	40	39	40	43	47	52	55	55	53	48	44	42
*3	84	82	81	80	80	81	82	83	84	85	84	84
4	20	17	18	15	14	13	15	16	15	21	20	23
5	7	6	4	3	0.8	0.3	0.9	0.9	2	5	5	8
6	1	0.6	1	0.3	0.6	0.3	0.3	1	0.6	0.6	0.7	0.1
				Galveston, Tex.—29°18'N. 94°47'W.								
*1	63	65	71	76	81	86	87	88	86	80	71	65
*2	48	52	59	66	71	76	77	77	75	67	58	51
*3	79	78	77	78	78	77	76	76	76	75	76	77
4	8	7	7	6	6	6	5	5	9	7	7	8
5	1	1	2	3	2	1−	1−	1−	1	0	1	1
6	3	2	2	1	0	0	0	0	0	1	2	3
				Georgetown—6°50'N. 58°12'W.								
1	84	84	84	85	85	85	85	86	87	87	86	84
2	74	74	75	76	75	75	75	75	76	76	76	75
3	80	78	76	77	81	73	82	81	79	78	79	82
4	20	16	17	16	22	25	23	17	8	8	13	22
5	0.1	0.1	0	0	0.1	0	0.1	0.1	0.1	0	0	0
6	0.1	0.1	0.3	0.1	0	0	0.1	0	0.1	0.1	0.1	0.1
				Gibraltar—36°06'N. 5°21'W.								
1	61	62	63	67	72	78	82	83	79	72	66	62
2	49	50	51	54	58	63	67	69	66	60	54	50
3	77	77	77	75	73	71	72	72	75	77	79	78
4	10	10	11	9	6	2	0.5	1	4	8	11	11
5	1	1	1	0.3	0.3	0.1	0.1	0	0.1	0.2	0.9	1
6	0.3	0.1	0.3	0.1	0.1	0	0.3	0.3	0.1	0.2	0.1	0.1
				Glasgow—55°53'N. 4°18'W.								
1	42	43	45	51	57	63	65	63	59	52	46	43
2	35	35	36	39	43	48	51	51	48	42	38	35
3	85	83	80	76	75	75	78	80	82	84	85	86
4	20	17	18	15	16	15	18	18	17	19	18	21
5	1	1	0.9	0.3	0.1	0.1	0.1	0.1	0.3	0.4	0.7	1
6	3	2	1	0.4	0	0	0	0.1	1	3	4	4

	Jan.	Feb.	Mar.	April	May	June	July	Aug.	Sept.	Oct.	Nov.	Dec.
				Grand Banks—47°05′N. 55°46′W.								
*1	32	29	33	40	50	61	67	69	63	53	45	37
*2	21	18	22	29	35	46	53	56	50	41	33	27
3	84	83	87	85	86	88	90	89	88	85	83	86
4	26	20	23	17	13	13	11	13	14	18	25	26
5	4	3	0.5	2	0.5	0	0	0	0.2	0.2	2	1
6	2	1	5	6	6	11	10	8	5	6	6	5
				Greenwich—51°29′N. 0°00′.								
1	45	46	50	56	65	69	73	72	67	59	49	45
2	35	35	36	39	45	49	53	53	49	44	37	36
3	85	82	75	71	68	67	67	71	75	80	84	86
4	15	14	15	12	13	11	13	13	11	15	15	16
5	0.7	0.3	0.1	0.2	0.1	0	0	0	0	0.2	0.7	1.0
6	13	10	7	2	0.4	0.1	1	0	2	6	10	12
				Halifax—44°39′N. 63°66′W.								
*1	32	31	38	48	59	68	74	74	67	57	46	38
*2	19	15	23	31	40	48	55	56	50	41	32	20
3	89	88	83	77	76	78	84	85	86	85	86	88
4	16	14	15	14	14	14	13	13	12	13	14	15
5	5	4	5	4	2	1	1	1	1	2	4	4
6	3	3	3	4	6	6	7	6	4	4	3	3
				Hamburg—53°33′N. 9°59′E.								
1	36	38	43	52	61	67	69	68	63	54	44	39
2	28	30	33	39	46	53	56	56	51	44	36	32
3	90	88	82	73	70	72	76	78	81	85	89	91
4	18	17	19	16	16	15	19	19	15	19	18	19
5	5	3	4	2	1.3	0.8	1.3	2	2	3	3	4
6	14	11	9	6	2	1.1	2	4	8	12	14	14
				Hamilton, Bermuda—32°17 N. 64°46 W.								
1	68	68	68	71	76	81	85	86	84	79	74	70
2	58	57	57	59	64	69	73	74	72	69	63	60
3	78	78	77	77	80	80	77	77	76	77	75	78
4	16	15	15	11	11	11	12	14	13	14	15	15
5	0.5	0.6	0.4	0.2	0	0	0.1	0.1	0.5	0.3	0.4	0.3
6	0	0	0	0.1	0	0	0	0	0	0	0	0
				Havana, Cuba—23°08′N. 82°21′W.								
1	79	79	81	84	86	88	89	89	88	85	81	80
2	65	65	67	69	72	74	74	75	74	73	69	67
*3	75	73	71	71	74	77	75	76	78	78	75	75
4	8	6	5	5	10	13	12	14	15	15	10	8
5	3	2	3	3	1	2	1	2	2	2	3	1
6	1	2	2	1	1	0.5	0.3	0.4	0.4	0.6	0.5	1

	Jan.	Feb.	Mar.	April	May	June	July	Aug.	Sept.	Oct.	Nov.	Dec.

Helsingfors—60°10′N. 24°57′E.

	Jan.	Feb.	Mar.	April	May	June	July	Aug.	Sept.	Oct.	Nov.	Dec.
1	27	26	30	41	54	64	67	65	56	46	36	65
2	17	14	19	30	40	50	55	53	45	38	29	21
3	88	87	83	78	71	69	74	79	83	86	88	89
4	18	15	14	12	13	12	14	17	17	18	18	18
5	3	5	3	2	2	1	0.7	2	3	7	8	3
6	9	10	13	8	4	3	1	2	11	14	10	11

Hobart, Tasmania—42°53′S. 147°20′E.

	Jan.	Feb.	Mar.	April	May	June	July	Aug.	Sept.	Oct.	Nov.	Dec.
1	71	71	68	63	57	53	52	55	59	54	66	69
2	53	53	51	48	44	41	39	41	43	63	48	51
*3	56	60	61	67	71	76	75	70	64	61	57	55
4	10	8	10	12	13	14	14	14	14	15	14	11
5	9	5	6	8	6	7	6	6	9	10	11	8
6	0	0.3	0.2	1	4	6	5	2	0.2	0	0.2	0.2

Hong Kong—22°18′N. 114°10′E.

	Jan.	Feb.	Mar.	April	May	June	July	Aug.	Sept.	Oct.	Nov.	Dec.
*1	64	63	67	75	82	85	87	87	85	81	74	68
*2	56	55	60	67	74	78	78	78	77	73	65	59
*3	75	79	83	85	84	83	83	83	78	72	68	69
4	6	8	11	12	16	20	19	17	14	8	5	5
5	0	0	0.2	0	0	0.2	0.3	0.5	0.3	0.2	0.2	0
6	4.2	5.0	8.7	7.6	2.4	1	1.1	2.5	2.1	0.6	0.9	2.3

Honolulu—21°19′N. 157°52′W.

	Jan.	Feb.	Mar.	April	May	June	July	Aug.	Sept.	Oct.	Nov.	Dec.
*1	76	76	76	78	80	81	82	83	83	82	79	77
*2	65	66	66	68	70	71	72	73	73	72	70	68
*3	72	72	70	68	68	68	68	68	68	69	70	72
4	14	11	13	13	12	13	13	13	13	14	14	16
5	0.7	0.3	0.2	0.1	0	0	0	0	0	0	0	0.2
6	0	0	0	0	0	0	0	0	0	0	0	0

Inverness—57°28′N. 4°13′W.

	Jan.	Feb.	Mar.	April	May	June	July	Aug.	Sept.	Oct.	Nov.	Dec.
1	43	44	46	51	56	61	64	63	60	53	47	43
2	34	34	35	38	42	48	50	51	47	42	37	34
3	85	85	82	77	76	77	79	79	81	84	86	86
4	14	11	14	11	12	11	14	15	12	13	13	15
5	3	2	1	1	0.2	0.1	0	0.3	0.6	1	3.0	2
6	3	2	2	2	2	3	1	2	4	5	4	6

Jacksonville, Fla.—30°20′N. 81°39′W.

	Jan.	Feb.	Mar.	April	May	June	July	Aug.	Sept.	Oct.	Nov.	Dec.
*1	65	67	72	77	83	88	90	89	85	78	70	65
*2	47	49	54	60	66	72	74	74	72	64	54	48
*3	75	73	70	67	68	73	75	76	78	75	74	76
4	9	8	8	7	9	13	15	15	13	10	7	8
5	1	2	3	1	1	2	3	1	1	1	1	1
6	3	2	1	0	0	0	0	0	0	1	2	3

	Jan.	Feb.	Mar.	April	May	June	July	Aug.	Sept.	Oct.	Nov.	Dec.
Jamaica, Kingston—17°58′N. 76°48′W.

Jamaica, Kingston—17°58′N. 76°48′W.

	Jan.	Feb.	Mar.	April	May	June	July	Aug.	Sept.	Oct.	Nov.	Dec.
1	86	86	86	87	87	89	90	90	89	88	87	87
2	67	67	68	70	72	74	73	73	73	73	71	69
*3	78	78	77	78	79	78	76	79	82	84	82	80
4	5	4	4	5	7	6	5	9	10	12	7	5
5	1	0	0	0	1	0	0	3	0	0	0	0
6	—	—	—	—	—	—	—	—	—	—	—	—

Kiel—54°20′N. 10°09′W.

	Jan.	Feb.	Mar.	April	May	June	July	Aug.	Sept.	Oct.	Nov.	Dec.
1	36	37	42	49	59	66	69	67	62	54	43	38
2	29	30	33	37	45	52	55	54	50	44	35	32
3	92	90	87	81	77	79	81	85	87	90	91	92
4	10	9	10	8	8	13	10	9	9	12	11	8
5	4	4	4	2	2	1	1	2	0.8	2	2	4
6	7	5	4	2	1	0.7	0.6	1	2	4	7	8

Le Havre—49°29′N. 0°06′E.

	Jan.	Feb.	Mar.	April	May	June	July	Aug.	Sept.	Oct.	Nov.	Dec.
*1	45	47	52	58	65	70	74	73	70	61	52	47
*2	36	37	38	42	47	53	57	57	52	47	41	38
*3	87	85	81	78	78	79	79	79	82	84	86	88
4	16	16	16	15	13	12	11	14	14	15	15	17
5	—	—	—	—	—	—	—	—	—	—	—	—
6	—	—	—	—	—	—	—	—	—	—	—	—

Leningrad—59°56′N. 30°16′E.

	Jan.	Feb.	Mar.	April	May	June	July	Aug.	Sept.	Oct.	Nov.	Dec.
1	23	24	33	45	58	66	71	66	57	45	34	26
2	12	12	18	31	42	51	57	53	45	37	27	18
3	87	85	89	71	64	63	68	74	68	81	86	87
4	17	15	13	11	12	12	13	15	14	15	17	18
5	0.2	0.2	0.2	0	0	0	0	0.2	0.1	0.2	0.1	0.3
6	3	4	4	4	1.5	0.9	0.9	3	6	6	4	5

Lima—12°04′S. 77°01′W.

	Jan.	Feb.	Mar.	April	May	June	July	Aug.	Sept.	Oct.	Nov.	Dec.
*1	81	83	84	80	75	69	67	67	68	70	74	78
*2	64	66	65	62	59	57	56	56	56	58	60	62
*3	77	78	78	77	83	85	85	84	84	81	80	79
4	2	2	3	5	11	17	22	24	21	13	6	5
5	0.6	0.1	0.2	0.1	0.2	0	0	0.1	0.1	0.1	0.6	0.9
6	6	6	8	9	7	4	6	5	4	4	4	4

Lisbon—38°43′N. 90°09′W.

	Jan.	Feb.	Mar.	April	May	June	July	Aug.	Sept.	Oct.	Nov.	Dec.
*1	56	58	61	64	69	75	79	80	76	69	62	57
*2	46	47	49	52	56	60	63	64	62	57	52	47
3	79	75	72	70	68	65	62	61	66	72	77	79
4	13	12	13	11	9	5	2	2	7	11	13	13
5	0.4	0.5	0.4	0.2	0.0	0.2	0.0	0.1	0.2	0.2	0.4	0.5
6	5	3	2	0.7	0.3	0.3	0.3	0.5	1	2	4	5

	Jan.	Feb.	Mar.	April	May	June	July	Aug.	Sept.	Oct.	Nov.	Dec.
				Liverpool—53°24'N. 3°04'W.								
1	43	44	47	52	58	64	66	65	61	54	49	45
2	35	36	37	40	45	51	54	54	51	45	40	37
3	86	85	83	79	77	76	79	80	80	82	85	87
4	17	16	17	14	15	13	15	17	15	18	18	19
5	1	1	0.6	0.2	0.1	0.2	0	0.2	0.3	0.4	1	1
6	3	7	5	2	2	0	0.8	0.8	3	2	3	5
				London—51°30'N. 0°05'W.								
1	43	45	49	55	62	68	71	70	65	56	49	45
2	35	35	36	40	45	51	54	54	49	44	39	36
*3	85	82	79	75	73	73	73	76	80	85	86	86
4	15	15	14	13	12	12	13	13	12	16	16	16
5	—	—	—	—	—	—	—	—	—	—	—	—
6	—	—	—	—	—	—	—	—	—	—	—	—
				Malta—35°54'N. 14°31'E.								
1	59	60	62	66	71	79	84	85	81	76	68	62
2	51	51	52	56	61	67	72	73	71	66	59	54
3	77	77	75	75	73	70	66	68	71	73	75	78
4	13	10	8	5	3	1	0.2	0.7	3	7	11	14
5	0.1	0	0.1	0	0.1	0	0	0	0	0	0.2	0
6	0.6	0.2	0.4	0.1	0.2	0.2	0.2	0.2	0.1	0.6	0.6	0.6
				Manila, Philippines—14°35'N. 120°59'E.								
*1	86	88	91	93	93	90	88	88	87	88	87	86
*2	63	69	71	73	75	75	75	75	74	74	72	70
*3	78	74	71	70	76	81	85	85	86	84	83	81
4	5	3	3	4	11	16	22	22	21	17	13	9
5	0	0	0	0	1	1	1	7	7	4	1	1
6	—	—	—	—	—	—	—	—	—	—	—	—
				Marseille—43°18'N. 5°23'E.								
1	52	55	59	65	72	78	83	82	77	67	59	53
2	37	38	41	45	51	57	61	60	56	50	43	38
3	68	64	62	60	59	57	54	57	63	69	70	70
4	7	6	8	8	7	3	2	3	6	6	9	7
5	4	4	6	4	3	2	2	2	2	3	3	3
6	2	1	1	1	0	0	0	0	0	1	1	2
				Martinique—14°36'N. 61°05'W.								
*1	83	84	85	86	86	86	86	87	88	87	86	84
*2	69	69	69	71	73	74	74	74	74	73	72	70
3	86	84	84	84	84	85	86	87	87	88	88	87
4	19	15	15	13	18	21	22	22	20	19	20	19
5	—	—	—	—	—	—	—	—	—	—	—	—
6	—	—	—	—	—	—	—	—	—	—	—	—

	Jan.	Feb.	Mar.	April	May	June	July	Aug.	Sept.	Oct.	Nov.	Dec.

Melbourne—37°49'S. 144°58'E.

	Jan.	Feb.	Mar.	April	May	June	July	Aug.	Sept.	Oct.	Nov.	Dec.
1	78	78	74	68	61	57	55	59	63	67	71	75
2	57	57	55	51	47	44	42	43	46	48	51	54
*3	60	61	65	70	76	77	78	72	68	66	63	60
4	8	7	9	11	13	14	14	14	14	13	11	9
5	4	2	2	2	2	3	4	4	4	4	5	4
6	0.1	0.4	0.6	2	3	4	5	2	0.9	0.4	0.1	0.2

Memel—55°43'N. 21°07'E.

	Jan.	Feb.	Mar.	April	May	June	July	Aug.	Sept.	Oct.	Nov.	Dec.
1	31	32	37	48	60	67	70	67	61	51	41	34
2	23	23	27	35	44	51	56	55	49	41	33	26
3	90	89	86	79	75	76	78	80	82	85	87	90
4	15	13	14	11	12	10	13	15	14	16	17	18
5	4	3	2	0.7	0.7	0.4	1	3	3	4	5	5
6	5	5	5	3	3	2	1	1	3	3	5	5

Messina—38°12 N. 15°33'E.

	Jan.	Feb.	Mar.	April	May	June	July	Aug.	Sept.	Oct.	Nov.	Dec.
1	56	56	59	63	68	75	81	82	78	75	65	59
2	47	49	50	55	63	71	76	76	70	65	57	53
3	69	68	66	63	62	62	60	60	63	68	70	70
4	14	13	12	11	7	5	2	4	7	12	14	16
5	—	—	—	—	—	—	—	—	—	—	—	—
6	—	—	—	—	—	—	—	—	—	—	—	—

Miami, Fla.—25°47'N. 80°11'W.

	Jan.	Feb.	Mar.	April	May	June	July	Aug.	Sept.	Oct.	Nov.	Dec.
*1	74	75	77	80	83	85	87	87	86	82	78	75
*2	62	61	64	68	71	74	76	76	75	73	67	62
*3	74	72	70	69	72	74	73	73	76	75	71	74
4	9	6	7	7	12	13	15	15	18	16	10	7
5	1—	1—	1—	1—	1—	1—	1—	1—	1—	1—	1—	1—
6	1—	1—	1—	1—	0	0	0	0	0	1—	1—	1

Montevideo—34°55'S. 56°13'W.

	Jan.	Feb.	Mar.	April	May	June	July	Aug.	Sept.	Oct.	Nov.	Dec.
1	82	82	79	73	65	60	58	59	64	68	75	80
2	61	61	59	54	47	45	43	43	47	50	54	58
3	65	67	68	70	72	74	75	72	71	69	65	64
4	7	6	6	8	8	7	7	8	8	7	8	7
5					Records Not Given							
6	0	0	2	2	6	9	9	6	5	3	1	1

Montreal—45°30'N. 73°35'W.

	Jan.	Feb.	Mar.	April	May	June	July	Aug.	Sept.	Oct.	Nov.	Dec.
1	26	25	33	42	56	66	73	62	65	54	42	31
2	9	4	19	29	39	49	57	57	50	42	31	18
3	87	86	84	82	76	77	80	81	82	82	84	86
4	12	11	13	12	12	12	11	11	10	12	16	14
5	2	1	2	0	0	0	0	0	0	1	1	1
6	0	1	1	1	0	0	0	0	0	1	1	0

	Jan.	Feb.	Mar.	April	May	June	July	Aug.	Sept.	Oct.	Nov.	Dec.

Nagasaki—32°44′N. 129°52′E.

	Jan.	Feb.	Mar.	April	May	June	July	Aug.	Sept.	Oct.	Nov.	Dec.
1	49	50	57	66	73	78	85	87	82	73	63	53
2	36	36	41	50	57	65	72	74	68	58	48	40
3	70	69	70	73	75	83	82	78	76	71	71	70
4	16	13	15	14	13	17	14	12	14	11	11	15
*5	10	10	12	11	9	9	8	7	5	7	8	5
6	0.2	0.3	0.7	1.0	1.0	2.0	0.4	0.1	0.1	0.2	0.1	0.3

Naha—26°13′N. 127°41′E.

	Jan.	Feb.	Mar.	April	May	June	July	Aug.	Sept.	Oct.	Nov.	Dec.
1	67	70	70	76	80	86	89	89	87	82	76	70
2	55	55	59	64	68	75	77	77	75	70	64	58
3	74	75	77	81	83	85	81	82	81	78	75	73
4	19	18	17	15	18	16	15	18	18	16	15	16
*5	14	13	11	5	4	1.5	3	4	7	9	12	13
6	0.1	0.1	0.1	0.1	0.2	—	0.1	—	0	0	—	—

Nantes—47°15′N. 1°34′W.

	Jan.	Feb.	Mar.	April	May	June	July	Aug.	Sept.	Oct.	Nov.	Dec.
*1	47	50	53	58	64	70	75	74	71	62	52	46
*2	37	38	39	42	47	52	56	56	52	47	41	37
*3	86	83	76	75	74	72	71	75	76	83	88	87
4	19	16	12	15	15	13	13	13	11	18	21	20
5	7	4	2	1	1	0	1	1	3	3	5	8
6	6.6	6.7	6.3	6.5	6.6	6.8	5.8	6.0	5.7	6.3	7.3	7.3

Nantucket, Mass.—41°17′N. 70°06′W.

	Jan.	Feb.	Mar.	April	May	June	July	Aug.	Sept.	Oct.	Nov.	Dec.
*1	39	37	42	50	59	68	74	74	69	60	51	42
*2	26	25	31	38	47	55	62	62	58	49	40	31
*3	78	78	78	77	80	82	83	82	80	76	77	77
4	13	12	13	12	11	10	9	9	9	10	12	13
5	8	4	6	6	3	1	1	1	2	4	6	6
6	3	4	5	5	5	9	10	7	5	2	2	3

Naples—40°52′N. 14°15′E.

	Jan.	Feb.	Mar.	April	May	June	July	Aug.	Sept.	Oct.	Nov.	Dec.
1	51	53	58	63	69	74	83	82	77	69	61	54
2	43	44	47	52	57	67	69	69	65	59	52	46
3	71	71	69	69	67	66	63	64	68	73	73	72
4	12	11	12	11	9	6	3	4	7	11	13	13
5	—	—	—	—	—	—	—	—	—	—	—	—
6	—	—	—	—	—	—	—	—	—	—	—	—

Nassau, Bahamas—25°05′N. 77°21′W.

	Jan.	Feb.	Mar.	April	May	June	July	Aug.	Sept.	Oct.	Nov.	Dec.
1	76	77	78	80	83	86	88	88	87	85	80	78
2	67	67	68	69	72	75	76	76	76	75	71	69
3	76	74	71	71	73	73	72	72	73	74	74	75
4	9	7	6	6	11	13	16	16	17	14	9	8
5	0.5	0.5	0.3	0.3	0.2	0	0	0.2	0.3	0.3	0.5	0.5
6	0.2	0	0	0	0.1	0	0	0	0	0	0	0.2

	Jan.	Feb.	Mar.	April	May	June	July	Aug.	Sept.	Oct.	Nov.	Dec.

Norfolk, Va.—36°50′N. 76°18′W.

	Jan.	Feb.	Mar.	April	May	June	July	Aug.	Sept.	Oct.	Nov.	Dec.
*1	49	50	57	66	75	83	87	85	76	70	59	51
*2	34	34	40	48	58	66	70	70	65	55	44	36
*3	79	69	67	65	67	69	72	73	73	70	69	71
4	11	11	11	10	11	11	12	12	8	8	8	10
5	2	1	2	1	1	1	1	1−	1−	1	1−	1
6	2	2	1	1−	1	1	1−	1−	1	2	2	2

New London, Conn.—41°22′N. 72°06′W.

	Jan.	Feb.	Mar.	April	May	June	July	Aug.	Sept.	Oct.	Nov.	Dec.
*1	37	36	45	55	67	75	80	78	73	63	51	40
*2	22	22	29	38	48	57	63	62	56	45	35	26
*3	75	74	72	70	73	77	78	79	78	76	73	74
4	14	13	14	12	12	10	12	10	11	11	12	12
5	1	1	0	0	0	0	0	0	0	0	1	1
6	2	2	2	2	3	2	1	1	1	1	1	1

New Orleans, La.—29°57′N. 90°04′W.

	Jan.	Feb.	Mar.	April	May	June	July	Aug.	Sept.	Oct.	Nov.	Dec.
*1	62	65	71	77	83	88	89	89	86	78	70	63
*2	47	49	55	61	68	74	75	75	73	64	54	48
*3	76	74	73	71	70	71	73	74	71	73	74	75
4	10	9	9	7	9	13	15	14	10	7	7	10
5	1−	1−	1−	1−	0	1−	1−	1−	1−	0	1−	1−
6	4	2	2	1	1−	1−	1−	1−	1−	0	1−	1−

New York, N.Y.—40°48′N. 73°58′W.

	Jan.	Feb.	Mar.	April	May	June	July	Aug.	Sept.	Oct.	Nov.	Dec.
*1	37	38	45	57	68	77	82	80	74	64	51	41
*2	25	24	30	42	53	61	66	66	60	49	37	29
*3	67	65	63	62	63	66	67	70	70	67	68	67
4	12	10	12	11	11	10	10	10	9	9	9	11
5	12	10	13	11	6	5	4	3	4	7	10	11
6	3	2	2	1	2	1	1	1	1	2	2	3

Odessa—46°29′N. 30°46′E.

	Jan.	Feb.	Mar.	April	May	June	July	Aug.	Sept.	Oct.	Nov.	Dec.
*1	36	37	45	56	70	77	81	80	72	62	50	42
*2	15	19	26	39	51	59	64	63	53	42	31	20
3	88	84	82	73	68	66	62	61	67	77	83	87
4	9	8	9	7	8	9	7	5	5	6	8	10
5	3.2	3.1	2.1	1.5	0.5	0.3	0.3	0.5	0.3	1.8	2	2.6
6	6	6	7	3	2	0	1	1	2	5	5	7

Oran—35°42′N. 0°39′W.

	Jan.	Feb.	Mar.	April	May	June	July	Aug.	Sept.	Oct.	Nov.	Dec.
1	61	63	66	69	73	79	83	84	80	74	69	63
2	45	46	49	53	58	73	68	69	66	59	53	47
3	77	76	75	74	73	72	74	75	77	77	77	77
4	9	7	7	7	5	3	1	1	4	6	8	8
5	1.5	2	2	1	0.3	0.5	0.2	0	0.2	0.3	0.8	1
6	—	—	—	—	—	—	—	—	—	—	—	—

	Jan.	Feb.	Mar.	April	May	June	July	Aug	Sept.	Oct.	Nov.	Dec.
				Osaka—34°39′N. 135°26′E.								
1	48	48	54	6ɔ	73	79	87	90	82	72	62	52
2	33	32	37	47	55	64	73	74	67	55	44	36
3	72	71	71	72	72	77	77	75	77	76	76	72
4	9	10	13	13	13	15	12	11	14	11	10	9
*5	10	8	8	6	6	5	5	4	3	2	2	2
6	1.0	0.8	0.9	0.5	0.3	0.5	0.2	0.2	0.5	1.0	2.0	2.0
				Oslo—59°55′N. 10°43′E.								
1	—	—	—	—	—	—	—	—	—	—	—	—
*2	19	22	26	33	42	51	55	53	46	33	28	23
3	78	74	71	66	62	62	68	74	79	80	81	78
4	7	6	7	6	7	7	10	11	7	10	8	8
5	0.1	0.1	0.2	0.1	0.1	0.1	0.1	0.1	0.1	0.1	0.1	0.2
6	10	8	2	2	0	0	0	0	3	5	8	10
				Palermo—38°07′N. 13°21′E.								
1	58	56	60	63	69	75	79	82	77	71	63	58
2	47	47	49	54	61	67	72	74	68	63	55	49
3	76	72	69	68	66	65	62	62	66	70	72	75
4	15	13	13	10	6	4	2	2	6	11	13	16
5	—	—	—	—	—	—	—	—	—	—	—	—
6	—	—	—	—	—	—	—	—	—	—	—	—
				Papeete, Tahiti—17°32′S. 149°34′W.								
*1	88	88	87	87	87	84	84	84	86	87	87	87
*2	74	75	75	74	72	70	68	68	71	71	71	72
3	87	75	81	80	80	81	78	78	75	73	78	79
4	16	16	17	10	10	8	5	6	6	9	13	14
5	—	—	—	—	—	—	—	—	—	—	—	—
6	—	—	—	—	—	—	—	—	—	—	—	—
				Perth—31°57′S. 115°50′E.								
1	85	85	81	76	69	64	63	64	66	69	75	81
2	63	63	61	57	53	50	48	48	50	53	57	61
3	49	49	51	56	65	71	71	67	63	59	53	50
4	3	3	4	7	14	17	17	18	14	12	6	4
5	1.1	1.1	0.8	1.0	1.6	1.8	2.4	2.7	2.7	2.1	1.5	0.6
6	0.1	0.3	0.5	0.6	0.5	1.1	0.2	0.8	0.2	0.1	0.1	0.1
				Philadelphia, Pa.—39°58′N. 75°17′W.								
*1	40	41	49	61	72	80	85	82	76	65	52	43
*2	26	27	34	43	54	63	68	67	61	50	39	30
*3	70	69	67	64	64	66	66	68	69	66	68	69
4	12	11	12	11	11	10	11	11	9	9	9	10
5	2	2	3	3	2	1−	1	1−	1	2	2	2
6	1	1	1	1−	1−	1−	1−	1−	1	1	1	1

	Jan.	Feb.	Mar.	April	May	June	July	Aug.	Sept.	Oct.	Nov.	Dec.

Plymouth—50°22′N. 4°08′W.

	Jan.	Feb.	Mar.	April	May	June	July	Aug.	Sept.	Oct.	Nov.	Dec.
1	47	47	50	55	60	65	67	67	64	57	52	49
2	38	38	38	42	47	52	55	55	52	46	42	40
3	87	87	84	80	80	80	81	82	83	86	87	88
4	19	15	16	14	13	12	14	15	14	18	18	22
5	3	1.5	0.6	0.6	0.1	0.1	0.1	0.3	0.4	2	2	3
6	4	3	3	0.5	0.7	0.3	0.5	0.5	0.5	0.8	3	5

Ponta Delgada, Azores—37°45′N. 25°41′W.

	Jan.	Feb.	Mar.	April	May	June	July	Aug.	Sept.	Oct.	Nov.	Dec.
*1	69	68	73	74	78	81	86	89	85	81	76	71
*2	42	38	40	42	47	49	53	55	52	49	47	43
3	—	—	—	—	—	—	—	—	—	—	—	—
4	19	15	17	13	13	9	9	9	13	14	16	18
5	1.3	1.0	0.8	0.4	0.3	0.1	0	0	0.2	0.4	0.4	1.1
6	—	—	—	—	—	—	—	—	—	—	—	—

Port-au-Prince—18°34′N. 72°22′W.

	Jan.	Feb.	Mar.	April	May	June	July	Aug.	Sept.	Oct.	Nov.	Dec.
1	87	88	89	89	90	92	94	93	91	90	88	87
2	68	68	69	71	72	73	74	73	73	72	71	69
*3	63	63	63	68	72	67	64	68	72	74	72	67
4	5	7	10	14	16	9	9	13	16	14	9	5
5	—	—	—	—	—	—	—	—	—	—	—	—
6	—	—	—	—	—	—	—	—	—	—	—	—

Port Darwin—12°28′S. 130°51′E.

	Jan.	Feb.	Mar.	April	May	June	July	Aug.	Sept.	Oct.	Nov.	Dec.
1	90	90	91	93	91	88	87	89	92	94	94	92
2	77	77	77	76	73	69	67	70	74	77	78	78
3	75	77	72	62	55	54	51	53	57	59	62	69
4	19	19	16	8	2	0	0	0	2	6	11	16
*5	5	0	8	2	6	2	0	0	13	0	10	6
6	0	0	0	0	0.2	0.6	1.0	1.6	0.7	0.1	0	0

Portland, Me.—43°39′N. 70°15′W.

	Jan.	Feb.	Mar.	April	May	June	July	Aug.	Sept.	Oct.	Nov.	Dec.
*1	30	32	39	50	61	71	76	74	67	57	45	34
*2	15	16	24	36	45	54	60	59	52	43	31	21
*3	72	72	70	68	72	73	76	78	79	78	74	72
4	12	11	12	11	12	11	11	11	10	10	11	11
5	1	0	1	0	0	0	0	0	0	1	1	1
6	1	1	2	2	2	3	4	5	4	3	1	1

Port Moresby—9°29′S. 147°09′E.

	Jan.	Feb.	Mar.	April	May	June	July	Aug.	Sept.	Oct.	Nov.	Dec.
*1	89	88	88	87	85	84	82	82	83	86	87	89
*2	76	76	76	76	76	75	74	73	74	75	76	76
3	71	73	74	75	76	77	77	77	76	75	71	70
4	15	14	15	9	6	5	4	4	6	5	6	9
5	—	—	—	—	—	—	—	—	—	—	—	—
6	—	—	—	—	—	—	—	—	—	—	—	—

	Jan.	Feb.	Mar.	April	May	June	July	Aug.	Sept.	Oct.	Nov.	Dec.
				Port Said—31°16′N. 32°19′E.								
*1	66	67	70	74	79	85	88	89	87	83	77	69
*2	51	52	56	60	65	70	74	75	73	70	63	54
*3	76	75	74	72	73	74	76	76	73	73	73	76
4	4	4	2	1	1	0	0	0	0	1	2	4
5	—	—	—	—	—	—	—	—	—	—	—	—
6	—	—	—	—	—	—	—	—	—	—	—	—
				Portsmouth—50°48′N. 1°06′W.								
1	45	46	49	55	62	67	70	70	66	58	51	47
2	35	36	37	41	46	52	55	55	52	46	41	38
3	89	87	84	77	74	74	75	77	80	85	87	90
4	15	14	14	12	11	11	12	13	11	16	16	18
5	0.8	0.7	0.7	0.3	0.1	0.2	0.2	0.3	0.6	0.6	0.4	1.0
6	5	2	0.6	0.8	0	0	0	0	0	0.2	2	3
				Prince Rupert—54°18′N. 130°18′W.								
*1	39	42	44	50	55	60	62	64	60	53	46	41
*2	31	31	33	37	41	46	50	51	47	42	37	32
3	84	83	83	81	80	83	85	86	84	85	85	86
4	20	17	20	19	17	14	15	15	17	22	22	21
5	3	3	4	1	0.2	0.4	0.1	0.3	0.5	3	4	4
6	0	0.5	0.2	0.2	0.8	3	3	4	3	2	0.5	0.5
				Puntarenas—53°10′S. 70°54′W.								
*1	59	58	55	49	43	40	38	40	45	50	54	57
*2	45	44	43	39	35	33	33	33	35	38	40	43
3	64	65	69	72	76	76	72	76	69	64	62	63
4	11	9	12	12	13	8	9	8	8	7	9	10
5	1	1	.09	.06	0	0.6	0.4	0.5	0.9	0.7	1.5	0.6
6	0	0	0	0.7	1.0	0.7	5	2	0.3	1.0	0.7	0.3
				Quebec—46°48′N. 71°13′W.								
1	18	20	30	44	61	71	77	73	64	51	35	22
2	2	3	14	29	41	51	57	55	47	37	24	9
3	78	78	82	75	74	76	80	81	83	83	84	82
4	18	10	11	9	9	9	10	8	9	9	12	13
5	9	8	8	7	6	4	2	1	3	4	5	6
6	1	0	1	1	0	0	0	0	1	2	1	1
				Rangoon—16°47′N. 96°13′E.								
*1	89	92	96	98	92	86	85	85	86	88	87	87
*2	65	67	71	76	77	76	76	76	76	76	73	67
3	82	84	85	80	86	91	92	93	92	90	86	82
4	0.3	0.3	0.6	2	14	23	25	24	20	10	3	0
5	—	—	—	—	—	—	—	—	—	—	—	—
6	—	—	—	—	—	—	—	—	—	—	—	—

	Jan.	Feb.	Mar.	April	May	June	July	Aug.	Sept.	Oct.	Nov.	Dec.

Richmond, Va.—37°32′N. 77°26′W.

	Jan.	Feb.	Mar.	April	May	June	July	Aug.	Sept.	Oct.	Nov.	Dec.
1	48	48	58	67	77	83	87	85	80	70	59	46
2	30	30	38	46	55	64	69	67	61	49	39	31
3	71	68	65	63	64	67	69	71	72	68	67	71
4	10	10	11	10	12	11	11	11	11	7	7	10
5	1−	1	2	1−	1−	1−	1−	1−	1−	1−	1−	1−
6	2	1	1	0	0	0	0	0	1	3	2	2

Riga—56°57′N. 24°06′E.

	Jan.	Feb.	Mar.	April	May	June	July	Aug.	Sept.	Oct.	Nov.	Dec.
1	39	39	46	62	78	80	82	79	71	61	47	41
2	20	21	25	34	44	52	56	54	47	39	30	22
3	87	85	82	75	68	69	72	77	81	85	88	89
4	14	12	12	11	13	11	14	15	14	14	16	15
5	4	2	3	1.5	2	1	1	2	3	3	3	4
6	4	4	7	5	1	1	0.4	2	5	6	6	6

Rio de Janeiro—22°54′S. 43°10′W.

	Jan.	Feb.	Mar.	April	May	June	July	Aug.	Sept.	Oct.	Nov.	Dec.
1	82	83	81	78	75	74	73	73	74	75	78	81
2	74	76	75	73	69	67	65	66	66	69	71	73
3	7⁸	78	79	79	79	78	78	76	79	79	78	78
4	13	11	12	10	10	7	6	7	11	12	12	14
5	0.1	0	0.3	0	0.1	0	0	0.1	0.2	0.1	0.1	0.2
6	10	11	14	16	19	19	21	21	18	15	11	8

Rotterdam—51°59′N. 4°29′E.

	Jan.	Feb.	Mar.	April	May	June	July	Aug.	Sept.	Oct.	Nov.	Dec.
1	41	43	47	54	63	68	70	70	65	57	48	43
2	31	31	34	39	45	51	54	54	49	42	36	33
3	88	86	82	74	72	73	75	78	81	85	88	89
4	9	8	10	9	9	8	10	12	10	13	11	11
5	2	2	2	1	0	0	0	1	0	1	2	2
6	—	—	—	—	—	—	—	—	—	—	—	—

St. John's—47°34′N. 52°42′W.

	Jan.	Feb.	Mar.	April	May	June	July	Aug.	Sept.	Oct.	Nov.	Dec.
*1	31	29	34	41	51	61	68	68	61	52	43	35
*2	16	15	21	29	35	42	50	52	46	39	31	23
3	79	79	82	81	78	75	76	75	77	79	83	80
4	15	13	14	13	13	12	12	11	12	15	16	15
5	1	1	1	1	0	0	0	0	0	1	1	1
6	2	2	3	4	6	3	4	4	2	3	2	2

Salonika—40°39′N. 22°57′E.

	Jan.	Feb.	Mar.	April	May	June	July	Aug.	Sept.	Oct.	Nov.	Dec.
*1	48	52	58	66	77	84	90	80	81	71	59	52
*2	35	39	44	60	59	66	70	70	64	57	46	41
3	71	69	67	55	63	59	55	57	61	71	72	74
4	7	8	8	8	8	6	4	3	5	8	8	9
5	4	4	3	3	2	3	3	3	2	2	3	3
6	2	1	1.6	1.3	1.1	0	0	0	1.1	1.6	2	3

	Jan.	Feb.	Mar.	April	May	June	July	Aug.	Sept.	Oct.	Nov.	Dec.
			San Diego, Calif.—32°43′N. 117°10′W.									
*1	63	63	64	66	67	69	73	74	73	71	69	65
*2	47	48	50	53	56	59	63	64	52	67	52	49
*3	66	71	70	73	75	77	78	78	76	72	64	64
4	7	7	7	4	3	1	1	1	1	3	3	6
5	1−	1−	1−	1−	0	0	0	0	0	0	0	1−
6	2	2	1	1	1	1	1	1	2	4	2	1
			San Francisco, Calif.—37°47′N. 122°26′W.									
*1	55	59	61	62	63	66	65	65	69	68	63	51
*2	45	47	48	49	51	52	53	53	55	54	51	46
*3	75	73	70	70	72	74	78	80	73	70	69	74
4	12	11	10	6	4	2	1−	1−	2	4	7	10
5	1	1−	1−	1−	1−	1−	1−	1−	1−	1−	1−	1−
6	2	2	1	1−	1−	1	1	1	1	2	3	2
			San Juan, Puerto Rico—18°28′N. 66°07′W.									
1	80	80	81	82	84	85	85	85	86	86	84	81
2	70	69	70	71	73	74	75	75	75	74	73	71
*3	78	77	75	76	77	78	79	78	79	79	79	79
4	21	15	16	14	16	17	19	20	18	17	20	22
5	1.9	0.5	2.0	0.2	0.2	0.1	0.5	0.5	0.8	0.2	1.0	1.2
6	0	0	0	0	0	0	0	0	0	0	0	0
			Santos—23°56′S. 46°19′W.									
1	83	85	83	81	77	76	74	74	74	75	78	81
2	71	72	71	68	64	61	60	61	63	65	67	70
*3	81	80	83	82	81	82	81	83	84	82	81	80
4	16	14	16	12	11	10	9	10	12	14	14	15
5					Records Not Given							
6	0.6	1	3	5	5	8	8	8	6	4	2	1
			Seattle—47°36′N. 122°20′W.									
*1	44	47	52	58	63	68	73	73	67	59	51	46
*2	36	37	39	42	47	52	55	55	52	47	41	38
3	84	81	81	81	80	81	84	85	86	84	83	84
4	19	16	16	13	12	9	4	5	9	13	17	19
*5	2	1	2	1	0.5	0.5	0	0.5	0.5	1	2	2
6	2	3	2	1	0.5	0.5	0.5	2	4	6	4	3
			Sevastopol—44°37′N. 33°31′E.									
*1	36	37	42	50	61	69	74	73	65	57	47	41
2	30	32	36	42	52	60	65	64	57	50	39	35
3	80	80	75	71	71	70	67	66	68	76	78	80
4	9	10	9	7	6	5	4	4	5	6	8	10
5	2	1.4	2	1.4	0.8	0.7	1.1	1.3	1.5	1.3	1.5	2
6	1	1.2	1.3	1.3	0.4	0.1	0	0	0	0.3	1.1	1

	Jan.	Feb.	Mar.	April	May	June	July	Aug.	Sept.	Oct.	Nov.	Dec.
				Sidi Barani—31°38′N. 25°58′E.								
*1	64	65	67	72	77	81	82	84	83	80	73	66
*2	44	46	48	52	57	62	67	68	65	61	54	49
3	72	74	72	64	59	68	74	76	68	70	71	77
4	6	4	2	1	0.5	0	0	0	0.5	1	3	5
5	—	—	—	—	—	—	—	—	—	—	—	—
6	—	—	—	—	—	—	—	—	—	—	—	—
				Singapore—1°17′N. 103°51′E.								
*1	86	88	88	88	88	88	88	87	88	88	87	86
*2	73	73	74	75	76	76	76	75	75	75	74	74
3	82	80	79	79	80	80	80	80	80	79	80	82
4	16	12	14	15	13	14	12	14	13	16	18	19
5	1.0	0.5	0.5	0.5	2.2	2.7	1.0	0.3	1.0	2.0	0.7	0.0
6	—	—	—	—	—	—	—	—	—	—	—	—
			Spitzbergen, Green Harbor—78°02′N. 14°14′E.									
1	5	3	6	18	30	39	44	43	35	25	12	10
2	−15	−16	−16	−3	12	31	36	35	27	14	0	−11
*3	82	82	81	78	76	82	84	86	84	81	82	83
4	13	10	13	10	6	9	8	8	11	16	14	13
5	1.0	6	1.0	0.4	0.3	0.3	0	0.3	0.7	2.0	0.6	1.0
6	0.1	0.6	0.1	0.1	0.4	3.0	4.0	3.0	1.0	0.7	0	0
			Stanley, Falkland Islands—51°42′S. 57°51′W.									
*1	56	56	63	49	44	41	40	42	45	48	52	54
*2	42	42	40	37	34	31	31	32	33	35	38	40
3	77	80	81	86	88	84	90	87	85	80	75	76
4	19	16	19	19	21	20	20	19	16	17	17	19
5	2	2	2	3	2	2	2	2	2	2	3	2
6	4	4	4	3	4	4	5	3	4	4	4	4
				Stettin—52°26′N. 14°34′E.								
1	34	37	43	53	64	71	73	71	64	53	43	36
2	25	27	31	38	46	52	56	54	49	42	34	29
3	89	85	81	73	70	69	73	75	79	85	88	89
4	15	13	14	13	13	12	15	15	13	13	14	16
5	2	2	2	1	0.8	1	0.6	0.6	1	2	1	2
6	5	4	4	2	0.7	0.7	0.4	2	5	8	8	7
				Stockholm—59°21′N. 18°03′E.								
1	31	32	36	46	57	67	71	67	59	48	39	33
2	22	21	24	31	40	49	54	52	46	38	31	24
3	85	83	78	71	63	62	67	73	78	82	85	87
4	15	13	14	11	12	12	15	16	14	16	15	17
5	0.4	0.5	0.4	0.2	0.2	0.2	0.1	0.2	0.2	0.4	0.2	0.3
6	5	5	4	4	1	0.7	0.5	1	4	6	6	6

	Jan.	Feb.	Mar.	April	May	June	July	Aug.	Sept.	Oct.	Nov.	Dec.
					Suva, Fiji Islands—18°08′S. 178°26′E.							
*1	86	86	86	84	82	80	79	79	80	81	83	85
*2	74	74	74	73	71	69	68	68	69	70	71	73
3	78	80	81	81	82	81	80	80	78	76	76	77
4	23	22	24	23	21	18	17	19	19	18	16	21
5	0.1	0.1	0.2	0	0	0	0	0	0	0	0	0.1
6	0	0	0	0	0	0	0	0	0	0	0	0
					Sydney—33°51′S. 151°13′E.							
1	78	78	76	71	65	61	59	63	67	71	74	77
2	65	65	63	58	52	48	46	47	51	56	60	63
*3	71	74	72	72	72	70	69	60	64	64	68	70
4	14	14	15	14	15	13	12	11	12	12	12	13
5	0.7	0.2	0	0	0	0.3	0.7	0.7	1	0.7	0.7	0.7
6	0.3	0.7	2	2	3	3	1.5	3	0.8	0.5	0.8	0.5
					Tamatave—18°09′S. 49°26′E.							
1	88	90	87	85	81	78	77	78	80	83	86	87
2	73	74	77	71	68	65	67	64	66	68	70	72
3	84	84	84	84	84	85	84	83	83	82	82	85
4	17	17	19	17	16	17	20	17	14	12	9	13
5	—	—	—	—	—	—	—	—	—	—	—	—
6	—	—	—	—	—	—	—	—	—	—	—	—
					Tampa, Fla.—27°57′N. 82°27′W.							
*1	70	71	76	80	86	87	89	89	88	82	85	70
*2	52	54	58	62	68	72	74	74	72	66	58	53
*3	73	71	68	66	66	71	73	73	74	72	69	73
4	7	7	6	5	7	14	17	17	15	8	5	7
5	1−	1−	1−	1−	1−	1−	1−	1−	1−	1−	1−	1−
6	4	3	2	1	1−	1−	1−	1−	1−	1	2	3
					Tampico—22°13′N. 97°53′W.							
*1	72	75	78	83	86	88	89	89	87	85	77	73
*2	59	61	64	69	74	75	75	75	75	71	64	60
*3	78	78	77	78	78	78	79	78	79	77	77	78
4	9	7	7	6	8	12	14	13	16	11	10	10
*5	1.7	1.3	2.9	1.3	1.7	1.1	0.7	0.2	0.4	0.3	0.4	1.6
					Tokyo—35°41′N. 139°46′E.							
1	47	47	53	63	70	76	83	85	79	69	60	51
2	30	41	36	47	54	63	69	72	66	54	43	33
3	64	62	67	73	76	82	83	82	83	80	74	66
4	7	8	13	14	14	16	15	13	17	14	10	7
*5	4	5	6	6	5	3	2	2	2	1	2	3
6	0.5	0.2	0.5	1.0	1.5	1.5	2.0	2.0	2.0	1.0	0.4	0.4

	Jan.	Feb.	Mar.	April	May	June	July	Aug.	Sept.	Oct.	Nov.	Dec.
	Trinidad, Port-of-Spain—10°39′N. 63°31′W.											
*1	85	86	87	88	88	87	87	87	88	88	87	86
*2	71	71	71	73	74	74	72	73	73	73	73	72
3	76	71	71	68	71	78	77	82	80	78	79	78
4	14	8	8	7	10	17	20	21	18	16	17	16
*5	0	0	0	0.2	0	0	0	0.3	0	0	0.3	0
6	0	0	0	0	0	0	0	0	0	0	0	0
	Tripoli—32°54′N. 13°11′E.											
*1	60	62	66	71	75	81	85	86	85	80	72	64
*2	47	49	53	57	62	68	72	73	71	67	59	51
3	66	66	64	65	67	67	66	65	64	63	63	65
4	11	6	5	3	2	0	0	0	1	4	6	11
5	—	—	—	—	—	—	—	—	—	—	—	—
6	0.5	0.5	2	2	0.9	3	4	3	2	2	1.5	0.9
	Trondheim—63°26′N. 10°22′E.											
1	44	44	48	58	68	76	76	72	64	59	49	45
2	15	7	11	24	33	39	44	42	36	26	19	10
3	71	69	68	71	71	71	74	77	81	79	75	72
4	21	17	17	17	20	18	22	23	24	22	19	19
5	5.3	4.5	4.9	3.3	2.4	1.2	1.6	1.6	3.4	3.5	5.0	6.1
6	3.9	3.6	3.2	2.6	2.3	2.4	1.5	2.5	5.0	5.0	6.1	6.3
	Tunis—36°48′N. 10°10′E.											
1	58	61	66	70	77	85	92	93	86	78	69	61
2	43	43	46	50	56	63	67	67	64	57	50	44
3	76	75	72	69	65	59	55	59	65	72	74	76
4	11	10	9	8	5	3	1	1	4	8	9	9
5	—	—	—	—	—	—	—	—	—	—	—	—
6	—	—	—	—	—	—	—	—	—	—	—	—
	Valparaiso—33°01′S. 71°38′W.											
*1	73	73	71	68	64	61	60	62	63	66	69	72
*2	56	56	54	52	50	48	47	47	48	50	52	54
3	81	83	84	81	82	81	81	82	83	82	77	77
4	0.6	0.4	0.8	3	6	8	7	6	4	3	1	0.8
5	0.6	0.1	0.2	0.1	0.2	0	0	0.1	0.1	0.1	0.6	0.9
6	6	6	8	9	7	4	6	5	4	4	4	4
	Vancouver, B.C.—49°17′N. 123°05′W.											
*1	40	44	49	56	63	68	73	72	65	59	48	42
*2	32	34	36	40	45	50	53	53	48	44	38	34
3	86	86	80	72	73	72	72	76	81	86	88	87
4	20	16	17	13	13	10	6	7	11	16	21	21
*5	0	0	0	0	0	0	0	0	0	0	0	0
6	3	3	1	0	0	0	0	1	2	5	5	4

	Jan.	Feb.	Mar.	April	May	June	July	Aug.	Sept.	Oct.	Nov.	Dec.
					Venice—45°26′N. 12°20′E.							
1	41	46	52	60	70	77	82	81	73	63	51	44
2	32	36	42	49	58	64	68	67	60	52	42	36
3	80	78	75	73	70	68	65	67	72	77	79	79
4	6	7	9	11	9	10	6	7	8	9	8	7
5	1	0.7	0.7	0.8	0.7	0.7	0.3	0.7	0.7	0.9	0.7	0.7
6	9	9	5	0.7	0.5	0	0.1	1	0.7	2	4	8
					Veracruz—19°12′N. 96°08′W.							
*1	74	68	78	81	84	85	85	85	85	84	79	76
*2	67	66	69	72	76	76	75	75	75	74	70	67
3	81	83	83	81	80	81	81	79	80	77	78	80
4	6	5	5	3	7	17	20	19	19	13	11	7
*5	12	7	11.5	7	7	9	7	9	10	13	12	13
6	7	6.8	6.8	6.6	5.2	1.7	2.2	2.8	1.7	4.1	5.0	6.5
					Viberg—60°43′N. 28°44′E.							
1	25	21	32	43	56	69	72	71	58	46	35	31
2	9	3	16	26	37	49	52	52	44	34	25	20
3	90	87	84	76	67	67	69	75	84	87	90	93
4	17	15	14	11	12	12	13	18	18	18	18	17
5	6	2	1	3	4	2	3	0.4	3	3	2	1
6	0.4	0.6	0.6	0.2	0.2	0	0	0.4	3	3	0.8	0.8
					Vladivostok—43°07′N. 131°55′E.							
1	13	23	33	46	54	63	70	76	68	55	36	20
2	0	6	19	34	43	52	60	64	55	42	24	8
3	67	68	70	71	77	86	89	86	79	68	65	66
4	3	3	5	7	10	13	13	13	10	6	4	3
5	2	1	1	1	0.8	0.8	0.5	0.9	1	1	2	2
6	2	2	4	7	12	15	17	12	2	3	2	2
					Wellington—41°17′S. 174°46′E.							
*1	70	69	67	63	58	55	53	54	57	60	63	67
*2	56	56	55	51	47	45	42	43	46	48	51	54
3	72	73	73	75	77	79	78	77	75	75	75	73
4	10	9	12	12	16	16	18	17	15	14	12	11
5	5	4	4	5	4	4	3	5	5	7	6	6
6	0	0	0	1	1	2	3	1	0	0	0	0
					Yokohama—35°27′N. 139°39′E.							
1	48	48	53	63	70	76	82	85	78	69	60	52
2	32	33	39	48	56	64	71	73	67	57	45	36
3	67	65	69	74	76	81	82	81	81	79	74	68
4	8	9	15	14	15	17	15	13	16	15	11	7
*5	10	10	14	13	13	9	9	9	10	9	9	8
6	2.0	0.9	1.0	0.4	0.7	0.8	0.9	0.6	0.5	1.0	1.0	2.0

	Jan.	Feb.	Mar.	April	May	June	July	Aug.	Sept.	Oct.	Nov.	Dec.
					Zanzibar—6°10′S. 39°11′E.							
*1	86	88	88	86	84	83	82	82	83	84	85	86
*2	80	81	80	78	76	75	74	73	74	76	77	79
3	73	72	75	78	78	78	78	77	75	74	75	75
4	7	6	14	15	12	7	4	8	9	10	14	14
5	—	—	—	—	—	—	—	—	—	—	—	—
6	—	—	—	—	—	—	—	—	—	—	—	—

CORRELATED LIST OF VISUAL AIDS

The following list of visual aids can be used to supplement some of the material in this book. These films and filmstrips can be secured from the producer or distributor listed with each title. In many cases, these films and filmstrips can also be secured from your local film library or local film distributor. (The addresses of these producers or distributors are listed at the end of this bibliography.)

The running time (min), whether it is silent (si) or sound (sd), motion picture (MP), filmstrip (FS), or color (C) are listed with each title. All those not listed as color are black and white. All of the motion pictures are 16 mm; filmstrips are 35 mm.

Each film has been listed only once, usually in the first chapter to which it is applicable. However, in many cases, it can be used advantageously in several of the other chapters.

The films produced by the Navy are from the Walt Disney Aerology Series. Some of these have already been released; others, when available, will be released by the U.S. Office of Education through Castle Films, Incorporated.

CHAPTER 5. CONDENSATION AND PRECIPITATION

Fog (Navy 24 min sd MP C). Explains radiation or ground fog and advection fog, with the necessary conditions for their formation. The important basic humidity properties of air are reviewed and the best flight procedures under fog conditions are also shown.

CHAPTER 6. CLOUDS AND THUNDERSTORMS

Clouds (CCNY 2″ × 2″ color slides). The O'Connell Cloud Collection—a set of colored slides illustrating the International Cloud Code of Cloud Forms and States of the Sky. (These were prepared with the cooperation of the U.S. Weather Bureau.)

Clouds and Weather (B&H 11 min sd MP). Shows the important types of clouds, how they are formed, and the significance of each form.

Clouds (Weather Bureau 11 min sd MP). Various types of clouds and movement of high-pressure and low-pressure areas across the country are described. Weather forecasting as a result of cloud situations is discussed.

Thunderstorms (Navy 38 min sd MP). A description of the types and causes of thunderstorms, giving the time and place of their

454 METEOROLOGY—WITH MARINE APPLICATIONS

appearance over land and sea and their variations with latitude. It also gives a very complete explanation of the cumulonimbus, or thunderhead, and the conditions within it. Numerous examples of actual thunderstorm conditions are shown and the best flight procedure necessary for flying through them is described.

CHAPTER 7. ATMOSPHERIC PRESSURE

Atmospheric Pressure (EBF 11 min si MP). Shows the various units used in measuring atmospheric pressure; the effect of unbalanced air pressure and how atmospheric pressure varies.

CHAPTER 9. PRIMARY OR TERRESTRIAL WIND CIRCULATION

Modern Weather Theory—Primary Circulation (Castle 19 min sd MP). Depicts the theory of convection due to heating and compares convection of air with liquid in a tank. The movement of the atmosphere in equatorial regions and the development of high-pressure areas in polar regions are shown along with the effect of the earth's rotation in producing subtropical high-pressure belts.

Atmosphere and Its Circulation (EBF 11 min sd MP). The nature of air structure, its chemical composition, and its weight and disposition are described by means of animation. The circulation of the air in relation to the earth and how this circulation forms pressure belts is shown. These belts are effected by the earth's rotation, which in turn causes movement of the air or winds.

CHAPTER 13. AIR MASSES AND FRONTS

AND

CHAPTER 14. DEVELOPMENT AND STRUCTURE OF CYCLONES

Air Masses and Fronts (Navy 30 min sd MP C). A general description of the origin, properties, and important types of air masses and fronts.

The Warm Front (Navy 20 min sd MP C). Gives a complete detailed description of the warm-front structures by means of three dimensional diagrams. Shows the associated weather conditions including clouds, types of precipitation under varied conditions, fog, icing, etc. The methods of approaching warm fronts and the recommended flight procedure for flying through them are shown.

Cold Fronts (Navy 19 min sd MP C). A detailed description of the structure and resulting weather conditions of the cold front is shown. Emphasis is placed on the violent storms associated with such fronts and the safe flight procedures necessary.

The Occluded Fronts (Navy 22 min sd MP C). By means of animation the structure of both warm- and cold-front occlusions with the resulting weather conditions are shown; the pattern and weather phenomena of the occluded fronts at the ground and in the upper air are traced; the events leading up to the occlusion are shown and the proper procedure for flying through them is given in detail.

Equatorial Fronts (Navy 10 min sd MP). This shows the structure of equatorial fronts, the seasonal migrations, and the related wind and weather conditions of these fronts.

Modern Weather Theory—Development and Characteristics of Atmospheric Surfaces (Castle 19 min sd MP). Traces the development of a low-pressure area as a wave on the polar front from inception to occlusion; the formation of the associated fronts are explained without emphasis on related weather conditions.

The Air Ocean (Jam Handy si FS). Gives a description of the atmosphere, the various meteorological elements of it, and the meteorological instruments used in weather analysis.

Air Masses (Jam Handy, si, FS). Shows the formation of high- and low-pressure areas; the various winds around them and the precipitations associated with the air masses.

CHAPTER 16. WEATHER ANALYSIS AND INTERPRETATIONS

Flying the Weather Map (Navy 25 min sd MP C). A detailed analysis of the weather situation across the North Atlantic from Europe to North America; interpretation is given for the existing weather conditions as well as for expected changes in the numerous air masses and fronts shown.

CHAPTER 17. THE OCEANS

Birthplace of Icebergs (TFC 11 min sd MP). A study of the largest tidewater glacier in the world and the two theories of iceberg formation.

GENERAL

Prophet without Honor—Matthew Fontaine Maury (TFC 10 min sd MP). An historical picture showing the early work of young Maury and how his activities led to the formation of the U.S. Weather Bureau.

Navigation Weather (Navy 10 min sd MP). This film shows the application of weather knowledge to the tasks of seamanship and navigation such as: the best course, care of and time and place of loading and unloading cargo, etc.

The Weather (EBF 11 min sd MP). The life cycle of a wave cyclone is given. The formation of warm and cold fronts is traced with detailed consideration. A special sequence shows the instruments used in weather observations.

The Weather (Jam Handy si FS). Shows different cloud formations and the storms associated with them. Shows how the weather map is built up from the weather reports and how forecasting is done.

SOURCES OF FILMS LISTED ABOVE

B & H—Bell & Howell Company, 1801 Larchmont Avenue, Chicago, Ill.

Castle Films, Inc., 30 Rockefeller Center, New York 20, N.Y.

CCNY—City College of New York, Div. of Visual Aids, Geology Dept., 139th and Convent Avenues, New York 31, N.Y.

EBF—Encyclopaedia Britannica Films, Inc., 1801 Broadway, New York 17, N.Y.

Jam Handy Organization, 2900 East Grand Boulevard, Detroit 11, Mich.

Navy (Obtainable from Castle Films, Inc.).

TFC—Teaching Film Custodians, Inc., 25 West 43rd Street, New York 18, N.Y.

Weather Bureau—U.S. Weather Bureau, Department of Commerce, Washington 25, D.C.

INDEX

A

Absorption, 13, 15–16
Adiabatic changes, 30–32
Adiabatic rate, 32
  and chinook wind, 177
  compared to lapse rate, 48
  dry, 47
  saturated (moist, retarded), 48
  and stability, 51, 52, 53, 54
Advection fog, 61–63
  arctic smoke, 61
  conditions causing, 61
  over England, 62
  over the Grand Banks, 62
  over the Gulf Stream, 61, 62
  illustrated, 62
  over the Japan Current, 61
Air currents, 125
Air-mass analysis, 332–333
  examples of, 345–346
Air masses, 261–267, 280–284
  classification of, 262–263
  defined, 261
  effect of ocean currents on, 406–408
  equivalent potential temperature of, 266
  isentropic analysis of, 267
  modifications of, 263
  movement of, 262
  nature of, 261
  properties of, 264
  potential temperature of, 265
  source regions of, 262
  specific humidity of, 267
  weather in, 280–284
  of world, 280–284
Air pockets, 125
Aleutian low, 158
Altocumulus (see Cloud types)
Altostratus (see Cloud types)
Amazon River, 57
American Nautical Almanac, 372
Anemometer, 129

Anemometer, illustrated, 130, 131
Aneroid barometer (see Barometers)
Antarctic low, 151
Anticyclone, 161
  permanent (see Azores high; Pacific high)
  storms and gales related to, 163–164
  weather-map examples of, 161–164
  winds, 161
Anvil top, of cumulonimbus, 90
Appleton layer, 8
Arcs of Lowitz (see Refraction features)
Arctic low, 151
Arctic smoke (see Advection fog)
"Ary Larsen," M. V. (ship), 331
Asia, pressure variations over, 157
Atmosphere, the, 4–8
  composition of, 6
  function and importance of, 4
  heat balance of, 16
  optical features of, 362–375
  relation of, to oceans, 376
  structure of, 7
  thickness of, 376
Atoll clouds, 176
Aurora borealis (also aurora australis and polaris), 6, 374
Azores high, 157

B

Baltic Sea, the, 385
Barograph (see Barometers)
Barometers, 108–114
  aneroid, 113
    corrections to, 114
    illustrated, 114
  barograph, 114
    illustrated, 115
    microbarograph, 116
    effect of cyclones on, 170
  mercurial, 108
    correction to, 109–113
    marine type, 109

457

464   METEOROLOGY—WITH MARINE APPLICATIONS

Temperature variations, vertical, 28–32
Terrestrial winds (see Primary winds)
Theodolite, 127
  illustrated, 128, 129
Thermometers, 17
  maximum, 17
  minimum, 18
  reversing, 384
  Six's, 19
  thermograph, 20
Thermometer scales, Fahrenheit and
  Centigrade, 22
Thunder, 89
  with tornadoes, 179
Thunderstorms, 82–86
  advection storms, 83
  air-mass storms, 83
  frontal storms, 83
  roller cloud, 85
  thundercloud, 84
  with waterspouts, 183
Tides, 396–400
  apogee, 398–399
  curves of, 397
  diurnal, 397
  lagin, 397
  lunar, 396
  neap, 398
  perigee, 398–399
  producing force, 397
  semidiurnal, 397
  solar, 398
  spring, 398
"Titanic," S.S., 386
Tornadoes, 179–182
  illustrated, 181
Tropical cyclones, 184–210
  bar of the storm, 188
  clouds in, 188
  conditions within center, 186
  dangerous and navigable semicircles, 193
  examples of, 202–211
  eye of the storm, 188
  indications of approach of, 195–197
  location of center of, 197–202
  nature of, 184–188
  occurrence and frequency of, 193
  origin of, 188–189
  path and recurvature of, 189–192
  waves in, 186
  wind in, 187

Tropics, pressure variations in, 108
Tropopause, 8
Troposphere, 8
Trough, of low pressure, 123
True and apparent wind (see winds)
Turbulence, 125
  above surface, 126
Twilight, civil and astronomical, 372
Typhoons, 184

U

U.S. Coast Guard, ice patrol, 391
U.S. Hydrographic Office, 391
U.S. Weather Bureau, barometer comparisons, 113, 114
  pressure representation on maps, 119
  rules of wind-cyclone relationship, 171
  ship's weather forms, 213, 217–219
  station model, 247

V

Vertical air motion, 29–30, 47
  effect of, in cloud formation, 80
  in keeping clouds aloft, 59
Visibility, 64

W

Warm fronts, 272
  in cyclones, 293, 295, 296
  weather conditions at, 296
  weather conditions preceding, 295
Warm sector, 292
  isobars in, 292
  weather in, 296
Water vapor, 6, 7, 33
  and condensation, 58
  effect of, on air temperatures, 44
  (See also Humidity)
Waterspouts, 182
Waves, 391–396
  calculations of size and velocity of, 392–394
  effect of oil on, 394–395
  nomenclature of, 391
  tidal, 399
  in tropical cyclones, 186
Wave theory of cyclones, 286–298
Weather, analysis and interpretation of, 316–361
  elements of, 8